"If the words 'life, liber
don't include the right to exp
then the *Declaration of Independe*

~ Terenc

In an age of evolutionary exigencies begotten by uninhibited consumerism, *Cannabis sativa* affords humanity a regenerative source of fuel, food, and fiber produced with organic methods, as well as a realistic tactic for climate change mitigation via sequestration of carbonaceous biomass in cropland, whereby it can yield four times as much paper as the same area of trees. Favorable climes and essentially limitless market notwithstanding, this plant is listed among the most rigorously persecuted psychoactive substances on Schedule 1 of the 'Controlled Substances Act' in the United States of America, the world's leading user thereof; hence hemp cultivation is prohibited here at the present time, despite its 12,000+ year partnership with our specie. To exemplify the message printed upon them, the pages of this First Edition of ENTHEOGENESIS were manufactured from 25% Canadian cannabis and 75% post-consumer recycled waste, making it the first such book in the past American century. This unique textstock, from Greenfield Paper Company, was milled in the USA by a facility that purchases wind energy offsets and reclaims its wastewater. Because the egregious laws of this country place ecological consideration at odds with fiscal efficiency, these materials are provided at the author's expense, and the design of this publication is thus predicated to a large extent upon their efficient usage. Its coverstock is of New Leaf Primavera Silk, whose 60% post-consumer recycled content is the highest of any coated sheet available today, whilst the remainder comprises 20% industrial waste & 20% Forest Stewardship Council certified pulpwood. Currently based off-the-grid at Earthaven Ecovillage, beLove's headquarters are both built of and powered with renewable resources; as the author's tour for meme dissemination is fueled by biodiesel. This volume was domestically printed with nontoxic ink by McNaughton & Gunn, whose EarthCare initiative has reduced its landfill waste per bound book by 95% in the past ten years. We believe that if our culture should achieve sustainability, its new paradigm will not come from atop a pyramid scheme. Although some would protest the status quo or demand solar energy, beLove aspires to a solution-oriented model of artiSunal vertical integration and ecological enterprise, with an eye toward the ultimate obsolescence of government and freedom from our reliance upon petroleum energy. Thanks for your participation in this endeavor, where ethics will prevail over economics.

AEGAIA
Cable Area

RHODESIAN
SOUND

1.00   .75   .50   .25   0
NAUTICAL MILES
Soundings in feet at mean low tide

MESOGAIAN
SEA

DELOS
North
Sentinel
133 B.T.

Cattle Drive Cove
Settlers' Rock
339 B.T.

Logwood Cove

Sourcerer's
Pond

Humbaba
Coppice

Mystal
Pool Pond

Brython's
Rock

KRITI

LAKEDAIMON

Baal's
North Point

Baal's
South Point

Cobblestone
Cove

Swampscot
Islet

Old Breach
cut 111 B.T.

Phalaris
Flats

O.T.Oss
Ponds

Rock of
Aegis

Herakleion
Sentinel

Dead
Man's
Cove

Cormorant
Point Cove

AEGAIAN
Salt Pond

Cunning
Ham's
Point

PYLOS

Durden's
Landing

Goat Boy
Point

Elysion Fields

ITHAKA

KORINTH

Old
Harbor

Delphinion
Theatron

New
Shoreham
Cemetery

Qabalah
Pond

Doe's
Cove

ELIS

Peat
Pools

Pamassos
Telesterion

Tarot
Pond

Levant

Metatron
Marsh

Eleusive
Point

Olympos
Lykaion

ARGOS

ARK

ARKADIA

Old Town
Road

Textile
Mill

ROPEWALK

ATTIKA

Rakhoonimus
Swamp

Dodge
Cemetery

Kerameikos

Airmed &
Aeiolus

Manisses
Point

Protean
Point

Way

Berry Boggy
Bottoms

Fresh
Fish
Pond

Cherry

Blossom

Southwest
Sentinel

Nemo's
Hollow

AEIOLIA

Thousand
Fathom
Wampum
Swamp

Golden
Ram Rock

Nereus
Point

Kemp's
Swamp

Palatine
Graves

Horn
Pout
Pond

Wading
Ewe Cove

AKHAIA

Mohegan

Nehantik

Prajna
Cove

Southeast
Sentinel
126 B.T.

Poseidon
Point

Blackwater
Boulders

Titanomakhia
Cove

AstiSun
Point

Veil Beach

Hydra
Hole

Karma
Point

Bluffs
Thermopylai

Black Rock
Obstn.rep

ATLANTIK OKEANOS

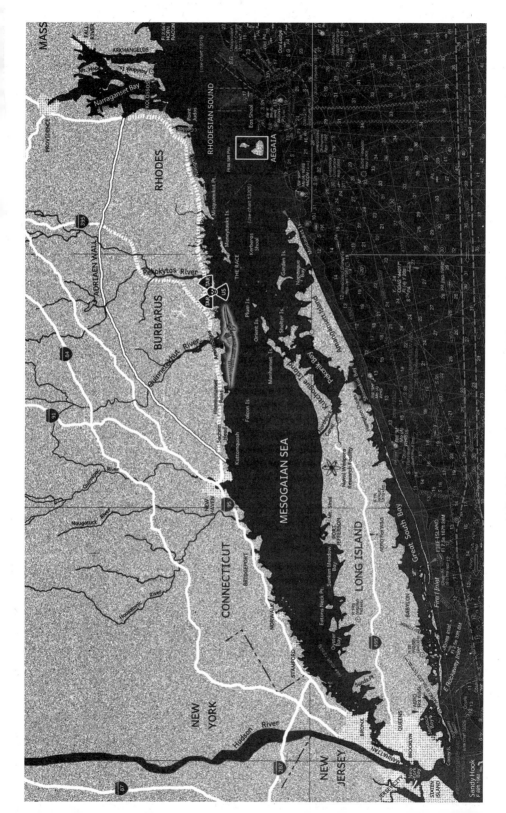

ENTHEOGENESIS

Origin of the Divinity within Us

A novel future from

BRIAN LOVE

Please return this book to:

Jay Driscoll

LOANER

AEGAIA: Volume Two

ENTHEOGENESIS
Origin of the Divinity within Us

A novel future from BRIAN LOVE

Distribution by:

ATLAS BOOKS
30 Amberwood Parkway
Ashland, OH 44805

Mail correspondence:

BRIAN LOVE
9 Full Circle Trail
Black Mountain, NC 28711

FIRST EDITION rev. 6.21.13
isbn: 978-09882354-0-3

Printed in the United States of America on paper comprising 25% Canadian hemp and 75% post-consumer recycled waste. Illustration, graphics, and web platform by Stephanie Usery Text, design, typesetting, and artistic direction by Brian Love

MAY THE SOURCE BE WITH YOU

AEGAIA: Volume Two

ENTHEOGENESIS
Origin of the Divinity within Us

TRIPTYKHO

NEOPSYKHIKOS TOMOS

PALEOPSYKHIKOS TOMOS

METAPSYKHIKOS TOMOS

Dedicated to the shaman at the end of hisstory:
This is my mind, given in your memory,
so you will be here with us
on this day and always.
You are the truth,
the life, and the way;
May your resurrection
concresce upon the eschaton.
Please guide us to embrace our singularity,
as we give thanks for the ingression of novelty.

"I'll try to be around and about.
But if I'm not, then you know
that I'm behind your eyelids,
and I'll meet you there."

~ Terence Kemp McKenna ~
November 16, 1946
April 3, 2000

ADMONITION

Dear reader, be forewarned; ENTHEOGENESIS may require
the use of a dictionary andor encyclopedia, not to mention
a working knowledge of Greek and Roman mythology...
You might want to reread the ILIAD and
ODYSSEY, just to make sure.
Too hard for you?
Too much work?
Then I warn you again:
Walk away, choose another title.
However, you heroes who seek new lands,
who are unafraid of new ideas or education,
those of you who pursue cerebral adventure,
who desire a challenge worthy of your intellect:
Well then, step right up and open this book.
You may not agree, you will very likely be offended,
but you will NOT be bored, I promise you that...and
you will be moved. You will be moved, I say, by the skill
of a storyteller who brings an entire dysfunctional world
into clear focus. You will be moved by the sharp examination
of a brand new way of life. And you will be moved, again,
by the description of the travels and travails of a young man
thrown by fear and horrible mistakes into a brave new world.
This is more than just a dystopia, more than sci-fi adventure,
though it is both of those things. In the great tradition of
NINETEEN EIGHTY-FOUR, THE MAN IN THE HIGH CASTLE,
MEMOIRS FOUND IN A BATHTUB, A CLOCKWORK ORANGE,
MOCKINGBIRD, and FAHRENHEIT 451, this novel, through
its characters, through its epic plot, through its made
up story will bring you to the place all good books will
bring us - to moments of clear vision and real emotion.
Finally, if you have any sense, you will move on to the
wisdom of Terence McKenna, and you will begin to
question the flowery food of the Lotus-eaters.
The song of the Sirens, enchanters of humanity,
will be replaced by music from a new Orpheus.
You might begin to really think for yourself,
to see behind the curtain our culture
uses to hide the truth of things,
and question what you
think you know.
READ.

Patrick LoBrutto,
editor of ENTHEOGENESIS
Astraia, 2012

A novel future from BRIAN LOVE

"The syntactical nature of reality,
the real secret of magic,
is that the world is made of words;
and if you know the words
that the world is made of,
you can make of it
whatever you wish."

~ Terence McKenna ~

INVOCATION

"We the unwilling, led by the unknowing,
are doing the impossible for the ungrateful.

We have been doing so much, for so long, with so little,
that we are now qualified to do anything with nothing."

~ Anonymous ~
from graffiti in a truck stop restroom

Based on future events.

All characters appearing
in this work are mythical.

Any resemblance to real persons,
living andor as yet unborn,
is potentially intentional.

"If you believe, as the Greeks did, that man is at the mercy of the gods, then you write tragedy; the end is inevitable from the beginning. But if you believe that man can solve his own problems and is at nobody's mercy, then you will probably write melodrama."

~ Lillian Hellman ~

"Human history becomes more and more a race between education and catastrophe."

~ H. G. Wells ~

PROLOGUE

A.T. 67, Skorpios 23

I write within
a labyrinth of my own creation.
I know not who you are, but can tell who I am:
the curator of a genetic library, whose myriad plant
varieties comprise hundreds of domesticated species.
Although now alone, I am also part of an island community;
my responsibility is to harbor our horticultural biodiversity,
while my tribe serves as seed bank of a sustainable culture.
Our collective endeavor is to protect the treasures of our
human heritage for the possibility of future emergence.
The forthcoming pages will describe the experiential
arc that transformed my horizons, offered with
the intention of helping in the navigation of
your own evolution. Whether you might
believe their contents is not for me
to decide; yet they comprise
nothing less than a true
scripture of my time
as I remember it,
unabridged and
unadulterated.
This is my story.

NEOPSYKHIKOS TOMOS

A novel future from BRIAN LOVE

"Isn't there any way—" He broke off.
Can't the past be altered? He asked himself. Evidently not.
Cause and effect work in only one direction, and change is real.
So what's gone is gone and I might as well get out of here.
He rose to his feet. "I must be out of my mind,"
he said to both her and Richard Hnatt.
"I'm sorry; I'm only half awake—
this morning I'm disoriented.
It started when I woke up."

~ Philip Kindred Dick, The Three Stigmata of Palmer Eldritch ~

"When I let go of what I am, I become what I might be."

~ Lao Tzu, 2600-2531 B.T. ~

ONE

Despite extensive contemplation of where and when this journey began,
irreconcilable discrepancies remain between logical chronology and my
own memory. In all honesty, I took so much and so many drugs that I
must admit the likelihood of events being rearranged by my mind to
suit its subconscious preferences; for now, there is nothing to do
but tell of the ensuing events as I believe they may have occurred.
I remember skateboarding with Beamer on what grew to a strong troll,
during the break which would precede our senior year. We were dipping
determinedly into a mystery bag of what I had previously identified as X,
until he suggested that perhaps the dopey sensation we could not
overcome was, in fact, coming from the gram in question.
"Maybe laced with opiates," he mumbled, and prepared to roll a joint.
"I don't think so," I said skeptically, fiending for another taste; but when
I laboriously extricated it from my kit at last, found that the contents had
inexplicably disappeared. I split and licked the inside of the bag as if I
could thus judge their composition while my friend mocked my affectations.
"You spaced your shit, methinks," I heard, half cough and half laugh.
"Never," I protested. "Woulda been the wholesaler. Maybe we got the
Drone or Zombie instead." My declaration was of optimistic apprehension;
I had heard of but never knowingly encountered such early precursors of
the synthetic phenethylamine series, and due to the vast range of active
dosages within the family, labeling errors were often involved in fatalities.
"It's aight, 'cause I forgive you," he replied, passing the spliff;
I inhaled gratefully in the face of my trembling doubt and rising heart rate.
"I'm gonna get a burger; want anything?" he asked whilst floundering on
the concrete; gagging, I said, "I don't want anything from a dispensary."
"You think I do?" he scoffed. "Nah bro, only real meats for me."

ENTHEOGENESIS · Origin of the Divinity within Us

"Yeah, maybe tomorrow."

"Fuckin A, tonight; right now!"

"How, exactly, do you think you're gonna get it?"

"From the world's leader in real 'gredients," he said. "How else?"

"Dude, you're the one who's spaced his shit; the McOlosseum is miles away, and hours from opening. It's just a fuckin certification, anyway."

"Don't they...don't...deliver...? Fuck...fuck it...I'm going...going right now."

I watched him stand hesitantly, stumble, and crumple; then get as far as all fours on the second attempt, where he remained, panting heavily.

"I'm just gonna smoke this cig first."

When I looked back, he had lain down again to light it, and his ears emitted the hum of a trance app. I examined my own forearms, which undulated as if with living tattoos – the illustrated man, I thought, without knowing what it meant. I felt decidedly unimpressed by the cartoonish quality of the images when they disintegrated at last into a repetitive pattern of McOlossus clown heads laughing at me.

"Fuckin A, I'm gonna hit that BakonBBQ like nobody's bidness, bro."

He leered lasciviously. "Yo, whatcha want? Big Victory with cheeze?"

The notion was repulsive, pulling me out of the zone.

"I'm not hungry..." I mumbled; then, demanded incredulously,

"What in the hell time do you think it is?"

"Nine thirty-five," he replied in unblinking confidence.

I laughed. "You've really fucked yourself up -- it's gotta be past three."

"No sir; I've got my Tab right here," he declared, waving his intelligent prosthesis in my face. Convinced it was malfunctioning, I reached for my own, but realized after a circuitous search and with mute dismay that I could not ascertain the location thereof.

"You, on the other hand, are wacked out of your drome," Beamer said, watching me pat myself down. "And I will prove it. Your brain may be fried, but have no fear - Beamer's coming back with burgers and beers and then everything is gonna make sense again."

"Get some water instead," I suggested.

"Why? Beer's cheaper!" he protested, laughing.

"Don't you think that's kinda...wrong? Besides, where you gonna get it?"

He sat up and pointed west. "Look bro, the golden arches is right there."

In the direction he gestured, I saw a luminescent wall of high-rise luxury condos dominating Hoboken's waterfront, and beyond them, the endless dance of cranes, barges, trains, and drones by the freight terminal.

"Whatever," I growled, annoyed with his insistence upon a seemingly absurd fantasy. "You don't even know what we took, or when."

His confused frown suddenly gave way to a broad grin.

"Neither do you! But that's the point, right...else, where's the fun?"

"You're hallucinating," I argued forcefully. "The Parkade is that way. You've gotta cross town, and go up for miles."

He rolled over, looked in the opposite direction, staring at me with bloody rivulets where pupils should have been on his iNterface.

"I'm sorry, but you're dead wrong, and I'm gonna prove it," Beamer said.

I rested my head on the pavement for a moment to muse on this quandary, considering for the first time the possibility our so-called real life was

a mutually-reinforcing perception that might just be shared delusion.
Although Beamer and I both grew up in Manhattan, we could not reach
consensus on the nature of our common environs, without which any
reference to objective reality became far less meaningful because it had
ceased to exist. Moreover, the notion of an agreement that defined 'real'
assumed there was actually another person with whom I could compare
my perception, as opposed to a projection of my imagination –
and this corollary struck my mind with chilling gravity.
"We need to clean up. I think we've entered the realm of 'too fucked up'."
He looked at me blankly whilst taking what seemed like an eternal drag;
I expected it was as likely that he thought about my statement as he was to
be reading messages on his iNterface instead, but eventually he furrowed
his brows, spluttering with an eerie mix of laughter and disbelief.
"Cool," he said in a plume of smoke, whereby he rose to his feet
successfully. "I've been waiting for the realm of 'too fucked up'!"
As he departed, I called after him, "You're sadly mistaken, my friend."
"After you've eliminated the impossible, the alternative,
no matter how implausible, must be the truth."
Cold panic possessed me. "What did you just say?"
He turned, flashing a toothy grin. "I said I'll bet you a gram of that shit,
whatever it is, I'm gonna be back here with the goods in ten minutes."
He managed to gain a stance on his skateboard, and pushed off unsteadily.
I noted, once he left, that without my own iTab, I had no means to measure
his endeavor; uncertainty about my assertion of the time began gnawing
at me then. I walked a lap around the skatepark whilst smoking a spliff
to assure myself it was, in fact, on the pier, thus feeling marginally more
confident in my estimate. If correct, and I waited for Beamer's return,
I would not see him there before sunrise. An undulating blanket of flames,
conjured from the combined effects of whatever we were on, covered the
Hudson, as though its oil slick had passed the flash point again; otherwise,
I did not feel nearly high enough to completely mistake my surroundings,
and by the same token, my hardheaded friend would not have been, either.
His appetite implied that we took Nexus, but I wanted to know what else.
As I turned to catch up with him, the matrix of ads and graphics on my
iNterface flickered unmistakably. I ascribed this ripple to an overloaded
municipal power grid; such enigmas tended to become more common
during summer, which was the season of temporary energy shortages.

The next logical memory I can conjure is of waking next to Varian
on my bed. I briefly wondered whether the incident at the skatepark -
or not, as the case may have been - was a dream, but post-troll cobwebs
still entangled my brain. Whilst I fumbled on the nightstand, her iTab
came to life, revealing a mound of X sitting on the screen; I split it
and set myself straight with a sizable line in each nostril.
"What the hell is going on?" she groaned.
"Nothing," I grumbled as the drip burned on its way down my throat.
"Your shit sucks, like some doucher cut it with caffeine, methinks...
these fuckin idiots dunno you gotta take a half to even get an effect.
Whatever happened to professional reputation, or basic fuckin courtesy?"

"Fuckin A, I dunno," she whined, more alert. "I got it from you anyway. Just leave some for me, and leave me the fuck alone; I gotta work today."

"Sorry babe," I whispered meekly. "I think I might have had a dream, and I needed a little something to fix my head for remembering."

She did not answer this invitation to reconcile, so I stared silently at the countless layers paint that peeled off the ceiling whilst wondering whether I had eaten with Beamer the evening prior. Amidst the visceral sensation of coming up, my attempted recollection only brought confusion, interrupted at last when I received a message from him asking to meet.

I found my pants, withdrew my Tab, and sent him a manual reply –
'U GT BRGR @ MCOLSEUM LST NYT?'

He responded with, 'WHR R U NOW? XTNG ZION & NEED RX!!!'

This unnerved me because any view of the situation indicated I had lost my grip. Beamer evidently thought we were not even together the previous evening; I wondered whether he forgot our disagreement, or if I missed a whole day without noticing. The X was working by then, but stimulation did little to help my logic, whilst there was a weird blurriness to the high, as though tainted by a trace of dissociative narcotic. I rubbed my nose, frustrated with my delirium, but since my accounts were in the black and, for all intents and purposes, I had no obligations aside from my customers, mental functionality hardly mattered, except to me. Nevertheless, I could not shake the uneasy sense of being trapped in an invisible puzzle; or to put it more precisely, that there was more to reality than what met my eyes.

I put on some clothes in the dark and left the apartment with minimal disturbance, stopping by the door of a neighbor on my way down the hall. Mrs. Jefferson lived alone, except for a pathetic three-legged dog, part Chihuahua, part neurotic, simultaneously tiny in stature and obese.

She rescued the miniature mutt when he was hit by a car as a puppy; afterward, she even paid to amputate his ruined hind leg. Over subsequent years, his pelvis rotated to bring the remaining hip under the center of his body; the twisted spine morphed into a domed hunchback; and he received the name Kerberos, which connoted a tripod, yet was otherwise mystifying. Given his physical abnormalities and small size, the canine managed to get around with remarkable speed, albeit via gyrations that were disturbing to behold. He was almost as old as me, and going blind, like his owner; she, on the other hand, had been confined to a wheelchair for as long as I could remember. When I entered middle school, the elevator in our building began malfunctioning and the absentee landlord never bothered to have it repaired. I wondered for a time why Mrs. Jefferson chose to continue living on the fifth floor, but suppose now that the enterprise of moving was deemed too logistically difficult by default. She had already implemented a system for navigating the unit and meeting her subsistence needs without leaving, thanks partially to assistances provided by my mother or me.

My contribution included walking Kerberos up and down the stairwell before and after school, so he could frenetically explore the same curbs each day whilst leaving furtive deposits in the back alley. I also delivered weed to Mrs. Jefferson, for her glaucoma; she often used such opportunities to make disparaging comments about her mandatory health insurance policy, which drove her to illegal drugs on the paradoxical

grounds that hers was an undiagnosed preexisting condition.
"You're late," she barked as I knocked. "I nearly entered the iNterface
to send a message; it's not like you to flake out. Is everything all right?"
"I think so." I rubbed my plasticine face, devoid of sensation
beyond my nostrils. "I woke up from this dream a little confused
about what day it is. School's out, and I...well...I've been celebrating."
She always kept the door on a chain, communicating through the gap it
permitted, whence she passed the leash. Her dog jammed at the hips
for once and squirmed frantically, whilst his rattish tail wagged
as if it might propel him to the other side, hypnotizing me.
"I can tell," she replied.
"Beg your pardon?"
"That you've been celebrating - a bit too much, I might add."
Using her grapple for leverage, she pushed on the stile to liberate Kerberos,
issuing an exaggerated cough in the process, which restored my attention
to the present. I glanced between the slab and jamb as I turned to go,
whence her lingering eye fixed upon me in apparent disapproval.
"You have the look of someone who accepts what he sees
because he still expects to wake up."
Despite her nonchalant tone, the words rang with grave familiarity,
seeming to hang on the air for a rare lapse wherein the dog was becalmed.
"Come again?" I asked, breaking the uncomfortable silence.
"Are there, by any chance, any herbs in my future?"
It took me a dissonant moment of confusion to get my act together;
Kerberos strained against the leash I held in one hand, whilst I fumbled
indiscreetly through my pockets until I found a bag with the other.
"This one's on the house...and don't worry about me...I'm careful."
"Thank you, dear, though I am far from consoled. You, as well as I, know
that you have no idea what you're getting in those powders you blow."
"Yes ma'am," I agreed insincerely. "And maybe the dog eats too much."

A few blocks down the breezeway we met Beamer, who looked like hell;
his face lit up nonetheless when he saw me, joyful upon expectation of a fix.
By all normal indicators he had indeed attended a show the evening before,
and this observation augmented my anxiety considerably. He was grabbing
for the bag prior to even rounding the corner; after taking a decadent dose,
he crouched on his haunches, leaning back on the crumbling stucco veneer.
"I'm glad you were home, bro." He patted my shoulder in camaraderie,
sniffed loudly, and tipped his head forward, sighing with relief.
"I was coming down so fuckin hard."
"You know, maybe you should come down more often," I suggested
reluctantly. "That way it might not hurt so much if I'm not around."
"Sounds bad for bidness," he said, laughing as if it was a joke; and added
an afterthought for his own consolation; "Besides, I'd just call Minus."
Unable to remember whether I had my breakfast, I took a scoop myself.
Per custom, we burned a joint in the alley; Beamer was wealthy enough
to smoke compulsively, and focused fixedly on blowing prodigious rips at
Kerberos. I remained distracted by the apparent displacement of time,
while he ignored my halfhearted protests that Mrs. Jefferson would know

he got her pet stoned. Upon finishing the session, we rolled aimlessly along the tunnelwalks; though streets would have afforded us more room, it was already pushing a hundred degrees and not yet noon. I had almost given up on skating the city's cracked, decaying thoroughfares anyhow; hindered by the dog scampering behind, we kept a pace of leisure sufficient to catch scornful pedestrian expressions in the breezeway. I watched the iNterface signals change at its far end from atop an incline midtown, and picked him up so I could accelerate uninhibited, weaving through the crowd toward sliding glass panes as they parted; but when I emerged in broad daylight the autoshade on my lenses malfunctioned. Beamer called, whilst blazing rays blinded me amidst the intersection; yet shading my brow, I discerned his waving arm, silhouetted at the dark threshold. Turning back whereto he pointed, I could only see advertising animations across the block until my iNterface flickered, darkening at last as it should have from the start. In the opening opposite stood a man that did not belong there; albeit a mere glimpse, the figure became etched in my memory like my friend's antithesis, wearing light colored, tautly-tailored clothes with leather accoutrements, evidently handmade, from an ancient or alien setting whose people had skill and space for such elegant crafts. I was intrigued by the sight of his upraised hand because it had five fingers beyond the thumb; then his clear, powerful voice, which said, "Pay attention," as he gestured skyward. My iNterface flashed and failed again; I raised my hand to block the sun as an automated cab swerved wildly from behind me, clipping my hip. I dropped the dog and time stopped whilst my death flew past, trapping me betwixt the twin doorways by destiny or disorientation. Through a cacophony of brakes, tires, and horns I heard a crack when the taxi ran over my skateboard, driving off without hesitation; yet my reaction to the impact seemed strangely delayed. Once finally spun around, I saw Kerberos run into the shadow of a brick facade that was plummeting to the ground. Moving my hands instinctively to cover the back of my head, I dove away from the collapsing wall as it tore down towers of scaffold. Bits of masonry battered me; the clatter of steel, concrete, and shattered glass deafened me; but nothing life-threatening came at me from the cloud engulfing the scene. I recognized Beamer's voice, as well as alarms, above the ring in my eardrums, though it sounded distant; crawling toward him, I choked on panic and crystalline silica until he pulled me out of the fog, thrusting a shirt soaked with Electrolite over my face.

"You aight, bro?"

"The dog..." is all I could manage between wheezes.

Laughing, he passed me my deck, broken and covered in powdered mortar. "Yeah, you can forget about the dog...he's done...but for real, that was the most fucked up shit I've seen since the show at Zion. Did you get hit?"

Examining myself for permanent injuries, I grunted that I was fine; as if for proof, I shakily arose to begin digging in the debris field. Whilst the dust settled, bystanders flocked to jabber at the obvious, gesticulating from the exposed sheathing to the pile of bricks. Beamer joined me, perhaps sensing my frustration, and thence went through the motions of searching also.

"We outta go, you know; cops are gonna be here soon," he noted, after a few ineffectual moments wherein their sirens grew louder.

"You can do what you like." I coughed, "but I'm not going back without knowing for sure if Kerberos is dead or alive."
"Come on bro, I saw it; he's a goner."
I glimpsed a tiny paw beneath a twisted aluminum walkboard and clawed at the pile of bricks covering it; subsequently struggling to lift an edge, I withdrew the lifeless canine to whom the leg belonged. His mangled carcass provided my first direct contact with death, whereas I had felt the shadow over my shoulder for more than a year. I felt morbidly fascinated by the blank, glassy eyes, and a shiver ran down my spine, as if the cold wind blew at my back to affirm something I intuitively knew.
"Can we go now?" Beamer asked, impatient; I remained quiet. "What the fuck, eh?" he added, chuckling, but his callousness suddenly irritated me.
"This is fucked up," I snapped. "I told you to not smoke out the dog, and now I gotta tell my neighbor that we killed him."
"Whatever," he said dismissively. "You stayed in the street; you dropped his leash. Besides, that damned dog saved your ass by running away."
I stalked to a trash can at the corner, grabbing a pizza carton from on top to awkwardly scrape up bits of gravelly viscera with the flap of its lid. Although the plastic package was floppy, I managed to collect and discard the majority of his body without getting any on me.
"What the hell were you doing out there, anyway?"
"Nothing...a fucking glitch with the traffic signals, plus my autoshade wasn't working," I growled, as shock faded and pain rose in its place.
"You didn't see the bricks come off?"
I could scarcely distinguish the naked wall from its previous appearance beneath the graphics projected by my browser, accepting a lit cigarette.
"Nah, bro, just the ads; guess I was too high."
"Ads?" Beamer raised a solicitous eyebrow; with a mix of pity and astonishment he confessed, "Fuck, I didn't know you still had them."
"I'd rather go to shows than pay for my programming each month."
I shrugged indifference to conceal a trace of shame from the wealth gap underscored by his concern. In my life prior, surfaces surrounding me had always been festooned with marketing promotions, which were projected by the optical iWare of anyone using the free iNterface operating system; however, my perspective on the world changed abruptly that day.
"What do you think?" Beamer wondered.
I first registered a feeling of expansiveness and relief in my mind; making the subsequent observation of profound dilapidation. Absent embellishments of my lenses, the city changed to a sepia monoculture of decrepit buildings, corroded metal, and plastic trash dancing in the breezes of traffic, punctuated occasionally by a flashy new vehicle or aristocrat in designer apparel. All apparent life took the form of human bodies, organized within the confines of a digitized, utterly mechanized environment whose unveiled ambience reminded me of incarceration.
"Thanks bro," I muttered apprehensively. "I'll get you back."
He waved with the nonchalance of his inheritance. "Forget about it; your ID's on my autopay, so you just gotta take care of my needs."
Given a father in politics, the risk of disgracing his party begged Beamer to avoid holding or handling the illicit drugs he consumed whenever possible.

If we were together, he treated me as a sort of personal pharmacist;
I tolerated my obsequious role, despite the annoyance of this patronizing
demeanor, since his bulging accounts could easily afford all our drinks,
rides, and rolling papers, thus elevating my own standard of living.
"So what happened to that man?" I inquired.
"Who do you mean?"
"On the other side," I clarified; he still looked at me blankly. "There was
only one...in the door across from you, with the strange clothes..."
"Everyone else saw that shit coming and got outta the way."
"Stop fucking around," I exclaimed in agitation. "He stood right there,
he had six fingers, and he told me to pay attention."
"Ummm...can you say...hallucination?"
"I don't think so," I argued. "He was real, as real as you or me."
"I dunno, bro," Beamer replied, glancing dubiously. "Sure you
didn't get hit? Maybe you should have your skull checked."
My intravenous cocktail of stimulants, adrenaline, and the previous
evening's residue left little question of whether I was awake by then;
I gave my head a shake to make sure, releasing a dust plume in its wake.
"Forget it," I groaned. "I've gotta tell Mrs. Jefferson about Kerberos.
Thanks again for the upgrade...I'll catch up with you later."

Varian had already left when I returned home, which was a relief because
I felt very weird. Cleaning up improved my sense of equilibrium slightly;
afterward, I went to see Mrs. Jefferson, and explained some of what
occurred, omitting the figure that I may or may not have encountered.
"You look like you've seen a ghost." She let an eerie moment of silence
pass, then merely asked, "The body?" with a silver eyebrow raised.
"Oh." Disguising a frown, I cast my gaze upon the floor.
"I guess I didn't think you'd want me to bring him back,
so I put him in a box and threw it away downtown."
"Well, your 'guess you didn't think' is correct," she reprimanded,
imparting emphasis to my words with air quotes, "yet you should
remember that there is no 'away'. I'm glad, for your sake, you had the
decency at least to get him out of the road. Did he feel much pain?"
"Doubtful...he was pretty much turned inside out," I mumbled,
regretting the tactless expression as it escaped my lips.
"That's fine," she sighed, though my guilt kept me obliged.
"I'm truly sorry...I dunno what happened."
Her eyes squinted ominously; she waited to speak again until I faced them.
"Someday you might, but in the meantime, please don't blame yourself.
Kerberos cheated death once before; now he has gone where he belongs."

""The fear of death follows from the fear of life.
A man who lives fully is prepared to die at any time."

~ Mark Twain ~

"I would not that death should take me asleep.
I would not have him merely seize me, and only declare me to be dead,
but win me and overcome me. When I must shipwreck I would do it in a sea,
where mine impotency might have some excuse; not in a sullen weedy lake,
where I could not have so much as exercise for my swimming."

~ John Donne ~

TWO⊙

I went to visit Mrs. Jefferson a few days later with buds in my pocket and
the weight of remorse on my shoulders. Unable to shake the feeling that
her dog would still be alive if he had not been stoned at the time, and
convinced she knew the truth by a nightmarish troll, my heart fluttered
with anxiety at the sound of my own knock. Whilst waiting for a response,
I remembered how he ran toward the wraith; although Beamer claimed it
was a figment of my imagination, I felt a surge of hope since what I had
seen might be definably real; but a voice inside reminded me that, like the
six-fingered man, Kerberos could also be an invention of my own mind;
and in fact, his three legs added to a disconcertingly consistent theme.
No answer came at first, so I rapped again more vigorously; she could not
be reached via her iTab, as one of the few without an iNterface. Assuming
she was in the bathroom, I lit a cigarette to settle my nerves and waited,
realizing at its end that I had not heard any water running. Crouching
down, I called into the illuminated gap above the floor where a sweep
belonged. Struck by the smell there, I reflexively grabbed the handle,
which yielded a turn; thrusting it open, I expected the chain that she
always kept engaged to arrest my momentum, but the door swung freely,
as I tumbled inside instead. Her domicile was a studio, with a galley
kitchenette on the right side of the entrance, which gave no view of the
living space because a small hall bent around a bathroom and closet along
the way. I called out again, proceeding hesitantly down the corridor like
an intruder more fearful of receiving a response than not. When I turned
my head around the blind corner into her main room, why she never let
me in became immediately evident; besides two greasy glazed openings,
the exterior-facing wall of the apartment was covered from floor to ceiling
by bookcases. Mrs. Jefferson sat in her wheelchair, back to the shelving
between the windows, with her head thrown to the side at a contorted
angle and mouth open wide as if about to sneeze. Although flies crowded
on the glass, only a few had gotten through the photodegraded gaskets,

indicating a recent death. There were external speakers jammed in her ears, connected by wires running down to her lap, where cold fingers clutched an ancient sort of Tab with a battery that had also expired. Empty canisters from tranquilizers, sleeping pills, and painkillers sat on the small table, next to an ancient vintage of liquor in a bottle made of glass, as was a flat-bottomed bubbler, meticulously clean for the occasion except for her half-burned final bowl. Rather than let it go to waste, I smoked the remains, partially for sake of my desire to commune with her as we never did before she died, despite me being her supplier. At that time I knew several people who had gone to the other side, and my life seemed saturated with its influence, from virtualities to Tablogs, from body bags carted out of buildings at night to subway ads, whose celebrity sponsors warned me of a hidden threat to my life expectancy with one side of their mouths whilst heralding the newest pharmaceutical treatment with the other. Nonetheless, death had been at arms length - sanitized or abstracted through my iNterface - prior to the experience with Kerberos. Mrs. Jefferson provided my first encounter with a human corpse, in the biological sense, and standing before her, I was sobered by a strange mixture of grief, reverence, and nausea. Possessed by my ambivalence about finishing the dead woman's weed, I saw a pile of books atop her bed; she left a note written on a blank page cut from one of the larger formats.

I pray I don't give you too bad a scare in my current state and regret you must find me like this; yet the fact remains I've tasted better times, and the present day has become unsavory to me. This is not a world I care to inhabit longer than necessary, while I've grown old, older than most dare hope. I have no money and use to nobody alive now; therefore, I've chosen not to stay. If power goes out this summer, I'm not sure I'll survive the heat; but in any case, suicide seems to me the more dignified escape. My greatest regret is the squander of my library. If you are a good citizen, you will leave everything as is, call the police, and let them confiscate it all; but if you have the curiosity I suspect, or if you've ever yearned to know more of the world than what our cultural control systems have told, you should read the books I've selected on the bed. I am comforted in my final hours before departure by the thought that you might do so; just please don't get caught! I go to join Kerberos. You won't be far behind us, by the way, unless you lay off those drugs. Remember Homer: 'They die an equal death, the idler and the man of mighty deeds.' Take care, and may the source be with you. ARIADNE P.S. No need to worry about the accident; it freed me to leave.

I had previously seen such artifacts in reality at Beamer's flat, where encyclopedias and works of literature bore titles stamped in gold on their spines. The volumes so enchanted me that I pulled them from the shelves, thus attracting the indignant wrath of his father, who indulged in alcohol and vociferously informed me his books were for display, not for reading. "Do you have any idea how much those are worth, you ignorant shit?"

Afterward I went there less often, and only ever would with my friend's assurance that his family was not at home. They lived in the Park Towers, which my kind did not enter except by request. Ironically, my social status, or rather lack thereof, worked to his advantage, insofar as I could perform criminal chores of keeping him supplied. He may have enjoyed my company, at least to the degree he had capacity for such feelings; regardless, given my skate-worn shoes, iWare verging on obsolescence, and a conspicuous dearth of cosmetic enhancements, I remained inadmissible to the inner sanctum. Beamer's propensity for drugs his dad seemed able to ignore, so long as he never brought the unsavory society he kept therefor in their penthouse to disrupt its carefully arranged rows of casebound antiques. Mrs. Jefferson's books, conversely, were mostly paperback, with colorful covers cracked and faded from age. Fifty or sixty lay in disarray beneath her message, whose script had been so perfectly composed that I did not recognize it as handwriting until I saw her sweeping signature. The effort she invested in this last living act impressed me, especially since I was still unable to write back then. Because tampering with evidence, even absent criminal intent, could lead cops to my pharmacy, I regretted sharing her bubbler and feared touching anything else besides the note. Grabbing both, I left abruptly; but at her threshold something impelled me to turn around - perhaps the maverick inside, or a subconscious sense of my duty to redeem the dog's death by fulfilling his owner's last wish. With the corners of an afghan upon her mattress, I gathered her books together in an unwieldy bundle too heavy for me to lift solo and dragged it home against my better judgment. Fortunately my mom had not yet returned; I hid the collection, took a bit of X, then flushed the message. Glancing at Mrs. Jefferson's door on my way out, I decided to leave it ajar and reported her suicide whilst waiting for the subway. The automated system's voice sounded bored, without inquiring beyond perfunctory data; 'self-inflicted injury' ranked third amongst Americans' leading causes of death, behind heart disease and cancer, although demographers suppressed this fact by classifying most drug-related suicides as accidents, which I regarded as fallacy. The serious narcotics user, regardless of education, knows opiates or tranquilizers taken on alcohol to be potentially fatal; and flirtation with this combination implies a disregard for one's own life that is definitively suicidal, albeit by inattention rather than intention.

I was spawned by New York City, the densest and most populous metropolis in the United States of America. Despite a degree in civil engineering, my father could only obtain work as a concrete installer. I imagine that he struggled to maintain what he considered acceptable standards of living for his family in an overpriced corner apartment on the east side of Manhattan, until he was killed on the job during construction of a new seawall; I have no memories of him. My mother sought recompense from the Port Authority, the contractor, and their associated insurance companies, securing for her efforts the equivalent of six months' salary. As a single parent without any professional credentials, I suspect she felt hard-pressed to find work, let alone sustain the lifestyle they once enjoyed. Following a variety of temp jobs she capitalized on her natural endowments by providing escort services through an agency that counted Wall Street barons and media moguls among its patrons. Pursuant to the nocturnal dictates of her occupation, she relied on our neighbor, the sympathetic and also-widowed Mrs. Jefferson, to monitor me when she worked nights until I attended grade school. While I was thus deprived of nurturing influence, the silver lining in my mother's obsession with appearance led necessarily to fitness. She brought me to the gym from a young age, perhaps as much to discourage predatory male advances as for convenience, and later she enrolled me in a variety of team sports. Whereas I never excelled at any in particular, athletics did reduce the amount of time I would otherwise have spent in virtuality or watching television. Thanks to these, and her diet, I escaped the obesity and diabetes that afflicted so many of my fellow students, though addictive substances challenged my health eventually. Because of my test scores, or perhaps strings pulled on my behalf, I gained entrance to a competitive public high school, one of very few still funding extracurricular activities at the time. As a freshman, I enrolled in football, wrestling, and track, but due to the fiscal crisis, that was the last year for such programs. In the absence of these outlets, and their associated social connections, I spent much of the idle time in my first sophomore semester collecting habits I am not proud of, which tended to involve sitting alone on the couch or at my console. In a feedback loop of plummeting self-esteem, I lost interest in real life, isolated myself, behaved destructively, put on weight, and was ultimately diagnosed with depression, like so many peers. Initially, my neurochemistry seemed insensitive to standard prescription drugs, individually and in various combinations. As the school psychiatrist tested courses of therapy on me, the effects ranged from numb apathy to excruciating bursts of pain, which I can only equate with electric shocks in my brain. After exhausting the available SSRIs, SNRIs, and even older TCAs, the doctor prescribed a restricted-use monoamine oxidase inhibitor that lacked the detrimental effects of the other pharmaceuticals, because according to her, we had to be trying something, given my diagnosis. The remark she made where phenylzine was indicated on my script said 'major depressive disorder with nonendogenous symptomology.' Whilst deciphering its meaning, I encountered what I thought an apt definition: 'nonendogenous: a factor that arises or is produced outside the organism.' My psychic chaos shifted during the spring when, on a whim, and in defiance of contraindications, she added ethylphenidate to the regime. I accepted the risk of hypertensive crisis gladly, since it was accompanied by the exhilaration of legal speed; then I made the acquaintance of Beamer, who introduced me to skateboarding. Soon we were spending all of our free time together, pushing each other to hone our skills against unforgiving steel and concrete, as if by masochism we meant to confront mortality. My career as a drug dealer began at age sixteen, though I considered myself an apothecary. Upon learning that I had uppers, my new friend wanted to buy them, and showed me how to bypass their delayed-release formulation with basic chemistry. He was blowing lines off his skateboard at the park one day, brazen with the privilege of social position, when a group of older hoodlums mistook the white powder for something illegal. After resolving their confusion, we engaged in animated conversation about drugs, and I left with my first bag of cannabis, Manhattan's only agricultural product of any significance. From there, I became a scholar of the psychiatric interview process; giving correct responses hence increased my prescription, helping me to ply my new trade. I reported anxiety next, then insomnia, treatable via Alprazolam and Zolpidem respectively, which the gang would also trade for nuggets. Their leader, named Minus, took Beamer and me as protégés, providing alcohol, cigarettes, and entrance to our first 18+ show, where he baptized us with doses of X. We spent the night swooning amidst kaleidoscopic holograms and synthetic beats, enamored of stimulant-induced energy, replete with bodily sensations of ecstasy, babbling excitedly about our unconditional bond of friendship. When the house lights shone at the night's end, we had barely peaked, but security guards drove the crowd to the street relentlessly, whilst migrant janitors with push brooms followed close behind, consolidating the cups and bottles that littered the floor. A young man stumbling around its periphery caught my eye; his black hair was stringy and matted, starkly framing a face that shone so pale with sweat it verged on green. I watched in pity and fascination as he approached the small affinity groups coalescing by the exits; they consistently recoiled from his presence, and he moved on, undeterred, with the same dejection but no less determination. The others had met some girls, who were festooned in the usual ornaments and luminescent cosmetics; as the outlier advanced toward our crew, I saw the dark, cavernous flesh encircling his eyes before I could hear his words.

"Who's got my downers? Do you? Barbs or benzos? Do you got my downers? I just need a little help; I gotta go to sleep..."
Although he swiveled to face me when I called, his cavernous, mydriatic pupils seemed to stare through my waving arm.
"What are you doing?" Beamer hissed.
"He needs help," I replied. "What do I care? Pharmies are free to me."
"Fuck, that guy is coming over here..."
Minus postured for the giggling females, saying, "Yeah, it's great, but you see some nasty shit like this sometimes," and my friend moved to my side, taut in anticipation, as the insomniac came near. He compensated for an obvious lack of balance with constant bouncing motions; up close, I noticed his bare feet amid the trash and furrows of worry engraved over his brows. Spectators had gathered for our exchange, beginning with his incoherent blithering; in response, I simply held out a bottle of pills. He lifted it to one eye, yet was apparently unable to read; the void consuming his iris could as easily have been observing anything or nothing at all.
"Xanax," I told him, asking how many he desired, whereupon his mute mouth writhed and he stared at his hands for a time, then hesitantly held up six outstretched fingers. I quoted a price and he searched his pockets, visibly dismayed in the end to find he had only a vial of his own to offer.
"Exchange," was all I heard.
"What is it?"
"You're not cops?" He scanned our posse with a jittery gaze that fell and focused on Minus, who laughed with scornful amusement.
"Check this etard - he's been trying so hard to score, he forgot to worry about the law until he found his meds!"

Our barter became an ordeal when the outlier dropped his open canister; white tablets showered upon the floor, and he crawled through debris in a frantic hunt leading him far beyond the geographic realm of possibility. Spotting them more readily, I helped reconstitute his stash; even my efforts were far from discreet; yet at least I waited for Beamer and the crew to form a blind hiding me from public view. With a handful, I recovered his inconstant attention for just long enough to complete the deal, which seemed like it must have been skewed heavily in my favor.

"Are you sure you want to give me all of these?" I asked.

He stopped, stood, grabbed the capsules, and gulped them all, neither looking at me nor bothering to count. Whilst shuffling off, his head hung down, glancing back at us periodically with paranoiac suspicion.

"That guy had no shoes," Beamer announced.

"That guy is wacked," someone else added.

"What's wrong with him?" I wondered.

"Toxidrome," Minus replied. "Happens to people who can't handle their shit. Let that be a lesson, kids, or the robotroll's gonna get you."

"You think he's gonna be aight?"

A few guys around me shrugged noncommittally; by then, our group's focus was reverting to the females, who were finished iNterfacing the party and busily planning social engagements of their coming day. Whereas life continued almost unruffled, the sensations of a shadow behind me and a foreboding feeling in my gut remained long after the insomniac had gone.

"I didn't think he would take six Xanax at once..."

"Forget him," Minus said. "Not your problem. What'd you get, anyway?"

"I dunno." A dozen blank white pills rested in my palm, evidently homemade, though much smaller than trolls. Minus grabbed two, held them to the light, and swallowed without further delay.

"You may have hit the jackpot, my friend."

"I thought you told me not to take the pressies."

"Yeah...this is different. 'Cause they're so small, its gotta be something good if they work. I'll know for sure in an hour, but I suspect you've got the Nexus - which would be a real treat." He laughed heartily. "And don't worry about the cost of test kits; this one's on the house."

During our investigation of substituted phenethylamines, Beamer and I discovered that my prescription antidepressant, if taken with Nexus, would approximately double its potency. Since we both sought risk as an integral part of peak experience, the warnings we encountered of adverse reactions in his father's annals of psychiatry only enhanced our excitement about the prospective combination. Minus had casually taken two at the outset, so we aimed to achieve the same effect more efficiently, thus extending our limited supply. To this end, I saved my Nardil for a week, and we ate them together without precautions. I later learned that proper dosage of such substances had a narrow range of tolerance between the desirable and dangerous; but the gods showed mercy on us, insofar as we each only took one of the tiny tablets, because we were totally unprepared and misguided for our first psychedelic experience. If smoking weed or taking X compared with putting on different iWare, then our MAOi-catalyzed Nexus was like a

new operating system. The body load came faster than we had been led to expect, and we barely made it to my building's roof for the launch, a fitting setting for a trip much like the stimuli of iNterface spaceflight, intensified. At first we smoked with fixed determination, as though more substances could anchor us to the world we knew, but our resistance proved futile. Overwhelmed, I either blocked or blacked out the peak, and after returning from separate transpersonal journeys, we spent the hours before dawn transfixed by towers of the Central Parkade, flying through a coexistent alien skyline without need for a roleplay app; the perceptions via Nexus suspended disbelief due to their seamless blending with our environment. To me, the entire world seemed made of energy, or a throbbing emulsion of fluids that changed in color, texture, and speed with electronic beats; a matrix I shaped by merely changing my point of view. Soon other people appeared along the parapet, causing me a hallucinogenic panic attack, as I saw that we were immersed in a war zone where armored mercenaries chatted amongst themselves casually, unperturbed by the spray of ammunition, blood, and shrapnel. I witnessed the scene, rendered in keen detail, whilst carrying on what sounded like a coherent conversation with Beamer, though he had been drawn into the fray as an animated commander who wore a frightening cyborgesque mask. My vision of the roof did not vanish immediately once I closed my eyes, and I gradually became aware that the projections of my cultural subconsciousness lurked at the edges of the impression left behind, mocking me. With no place to hide from them, I was afraid and lost control of the illusion, entering the crowd at the show a week prior, firmly convinced I had gone back in time. When the performance ended again, I turned toward my companion and found the outlier instead, staring at me through eyeballs of solid black. He attacked too fast for me to get away, restraining my efforts to escape. A splash of Electrolite brought me face to face with Beamer at last, still attired as a soldier-drone, but readily identifiable as himself. The cause of my concert reminiscence was a recording of the set, which issued from his iTab, and he grabbed my shoulder firmly, in earnest concern.
"Yo, bro, you gotta calm the fuck down," he urged. "We're on drugs, and on the roof. You can't be attracting attention like this or falling off on me."
I finally returned to a state of awareness that permitted me to differentiate between open and closed eye images. We smoked some weed whilst reality stabilized, laughing hysterically upon eye contact at the revelation of all we would be missing if not for the perseverance of organized crime.
"You know what would be good?" he asked, as if prompted by the roar of a corporate jet passing above our heads.
"Lay it on me."
"Doing this shit with some X next weekend."
I savored another rip, and relaxed on my back.
"Yeah," I intoned, drawing the sound out agreeably. "I bet it would."

Armed by the knowledge that security guards typically accepted buds as bribes, I never had difficulty getting into clubs, where I familiarized myself with an array of psychoactive substances larger even than the pharmacy at the disposal of my psychiatrist. We took weed for granted; considered alcohol a diversion or cushion for coming down, when there was nothing better around; while exotics like cocaine, if you could find them, were little more than toys to pass the time, which never lasted long amidst the fiends they made. Per Minus' suggestion, I avoided homemade tablets because of their justifiably dubious contents – often a mixture of dirty crank and prescription opiates, or caffeine laced with a bathtub brew of substituted phenethylamines. The rip-off sector was sustained by anonymous cons who thus profited, as well as the steady flow of amateurs who would be taken for a ride on their ignorance of differences between drugs. This facade provided a screening process, to prevent neophytes from accidentally crossing the membrane of the psychonauticon prematurely; although as Beamer and I demonstrated, it did not always work that way. Once inside, anyone who knew anything about the filter they had passed wanted to go trolling, and beneath superficialities of the performance scene lay a hedonistic capitalist economy, in which X predominated. Given the appropriate connections, one chose from various flavors for an admix - G for ghettotroll, P for psychotroll, K for holytroll, or Dex for robotroll - the latter reputedly being the most interesting, but also most hazardous, of synthemex formulations because it led so easily to the serotoxidrome. Via self-experimentation, with subsequent corroboration from Beamer as a test subject, I achieved proficiency in my judgment of dosage, timing, and substance interactions amongst the trolls. I inevitably discovered that I could guarantee the purity of my own drugs, whilst profiting from my expertise, by acquiring the ingredients in quantity, breaking them up, and selling doses. Minus was good enough to front me sufficient supply for building operational liquidity; as a merchant, I added value by my willingness to defy legislative prohibitions of the American police state. After our first experience, Beamer and I combined the Nexus with X for a high whose intensity surpassed all of the others at first, permitting us to travel throughout alien realms where boundaries between life, technology, and information disappeared; but when we came to the last pair of pills, the mere titillation of kaleidoscopic visuals was no longer satisfactory. By adding Nardil, we extended the effects of both troll ingredients all night without need for the compulsive redosing to which methedrone usually made us prone; then we dubbed our triplet blend the cybertroll. Once he suspected Nexus to be available, Minus sniffed out a connection, positioning himself as broker-mule between retailers like me and a chemist whom I never met. Amidst plentiful supply and dealer competition, I kept X in stock for the sake of my own habit, but did not need to mark it up much or to advertise my wares, as some kandikids were apt, vociferously at that. Nexus, on the other hand, was obscure, only familiar to a few among the hardcore, and thus often mixed into pressies along with other oddments, or sold in unidentified capsules by those uninformed of its full potential. True heads called it Mex, semantically derivative from mescaline, an old-school psychedelic to which it was chemically related, though many times more potent, courtesy of advancements in pharmacology motivated by the Federal Analogue Acts. At shows, people with a sense of what they wanted saw me as a likely suspect, since my attitude and attire intentionally exuded an accurate impression to prospective customers; thus an intrepid minority,

sufficiently traveled in forbidden realms to choose their own adventure, or just plain bored with the alternatives, visited my corner for supplies. The McOlosseum was the biggest venue of its kind, located on the ground level of Zion, which conveyors conveniently connected to Beamer's family penthouse in the adjacent Park Towers. When asked, he neither confirmed nor denied urban legends that below the arena lay a maze of panic rooms, bomb shelters, and secret railways, designed to afford the affluent class residing there safe haven, along with direct escape from Manhattan, in the event of emergency or attack. The Parkade's then-current rulers were the bourgeoisie of the American empire, who inherited the accumulated wealth of their predecessors but little of the expansionist ambition whereby they had established dynasties. Prodigal heirs depleted inconceivable fortunes without care for the future of their families, and many of these pedigreed celebrities enjoyed trolling at the same shows as us juvenile proletarians. Even in our stratified culture, the McOlosseum provided a social equalizer; youth of all classes mixed inside, homogenized to a large degree by drug experience and utter lack of personal space. For children of the financial or political elites, their status could be a liability during attempts to score on the arena floor; immersed in gaudy entourages, marked by expensive cosmetology, and heralded with clouds of engineered fragrance, they were easily identified from a distance. I typically restricted my interactions to the peripheral sycophants conducting illicit deals on behalf of these idols; nonetheless, at my third stadium show as a merchant, I was approached by an older businessman who dispensed with liaisons, as well as foreplay. Although modestly dressed, he gave his status away via diamond earrings, perfect teeth, ostentatious shoes, a tan complexion that looked much too natural, and an analog watch worth more than the sum of my vital organs; the sort of client I imagined might seek my mother's escort services.
"Any candyflips in the vicinity, my young friend?"
His question confused me, until I glimpsed his forefinger and thumb outstretched at right angles to one another on his forehead.
"No? Some fungus amongus? If you can help me, I'll pay for yours."
"Sorry sir," I began, acknowledging him whilst staring straight ahead. "I dunno 'bout any L, except I think I still have some N-bombs here..."
"Ugh - thanks, but no thanks." He bowed conspicuously in my direction. "I apologize for presuming to impose on you with such an overt inquiry."
"Not a problem, dude; it's why I'm here," I said amiably as he left.
"Well, you seem like a pro, at least," he replied, turning toward me again.
"That I am." I smiled on anticipation of a sale, albeit from the novelty of crossing our socio-economic schism instead of any potential profit.
"What poison do you pick, then?" he asked, peering into my iWare.
I laughed, confident my lenses did not betray the buzz behind them.
"Let me tell you about the cybertroll," I proposed.
Obviously intrigued, he squirmed through the crowd. "Lay it on me."
When he reached my side, I explained how the synergism of Nardil and Nexus produced a stronger, longer experience than other admixtures, with the disclaimer that only seasoned psychonauts should partake in public.
"I'm out to have to a good time this evening. It's been a while, but I took more than my fair share of acid, molly, and deems

when I was your age, which is what we had back in those days."
Whereas I had not encountered them, I heard of tryptamines or lysergide
in passing as old school psychedelics, ostensibly purged from the scene by
the DEA for their alleged carcinogenicity. I supposed that, beneath the
youthful disguises of surgery accompanying his wealth, there could be
somebody qualified; so I warned him as a simple matter of formality.
"If you're working for cops I'll make sure you beg for death before the end."
He grinned broadly. "Indeed - do you mind if I use that sometime?"
Reassured by this reply, I opened my kit. "Do what you like, dude."
I gave him the X and Nardil first, advising him to wait thirty minutes for
the Nexus, so the MAOi had time to absorb before the phenethylamines hit.
"Since it's slower orally, snort that cap if you really want to kick the night
off with a bang," I added. "It hurts, to be sure, but boy, does it work."
Whilst I conducted this transaction, Beamer had done an admirable job
occupying a spot near a group of attractive girls, whose male companions
only encouraged his smirking presence. "Yo, I'm so fucked up," we heard
one shout over the crowd's din, then took turns imitating him in caricature,
intoxicated by a smug sense of superiority. He was among those who drank,
maybe did a little roids or pharmies, and thought they knew about getting
high, but were still in the preschool of altered consciousness, to my mind
at the time. The businessman had tipped me extravagantly for my wares;
hence, when the show began, I shared our joint with him to set the mood.
His bleached grin gleamed bright in the ultraviolet light, and though out
of practice, he seemed to know the drill. After a few solid rips, one of our
female neighbors noticed the smell, then his status; at my nod, he passed it,
and subsequently amazed me by insinuating himself behind her, grinding
early in the first set, age notwithstanding. Per Beamer's request, I went to
get us drinks at the break; upon return, however, I found the businessman
squatting down and mopping his botoxed brow with obscene frequency.
Uncapping a bottle of Electrolite, I tapped him on the shoulder.
"Here you go, bro. You need it more than me."
As he glanced up, his dilated pupils betrayed a familiar tale; rising
unsteadily, he took the bottle in his hands, slowly turning it over in awe,
as if it held some ancient mystery. Once he realized what I had given him,
he thanked me profusely, tears, quivering lips and all; I persuaded him to
rise from his knees before his companion for the evening saw him in such a
pathetic state. She silently leaned her weight against his chest and never
seemed to observe his grimaces; meanwhile, I glimpsed him pop something
in his mouth, chasing it with Electrolite at the opening of the second act.
Despite the girl's inviting gesticulations, the businessman had no interest
in dancing; his stare meandered randomly, as if unaware of the show.
"It's hot in here, huh?" I said, suggesting he remove his jacket with a tug;
he laboriously did so, splashed bottled water on his face, and regained the
coordination to smoke another joint. The peak of my troll was unusually
fraught with fearful premonitions, even though logic told me that in all
likelihood he would be fine; I played an entirely impersonal role in his
choice, while concerns about his experience only underscored my own.
"My area, my area," he chanted, visibly agitated and swooning
from hallucinatory disorientation. "Just stay out of my area!"

An tall, aggressive jock had begun harassing him. "You might think
you run shit outside, old man, but in here you have NO area!"
Beamer gave a firm shove in response. "Leave him alone, asshole."
"What, poor rich guy buy bad drugs? Not feeling so powerful anymore?"
"You dunno nothing 'bout it, fuckin poser," my friend declared disdainfully,
turning his back with a protective arm upon the hunched businessman.
Watching the insulted ringleader wind up for a punch, I felt enraged by
everything abhorrent in my culture, epitomized by his belligerent attitude
and compensatory machismo. Had human males really degenerated so far,
or been so emasculated, that we would resort to pissing contests in order
to impress women? As he swung at Beamer in apparently slow motion,
the tolerant self-restraint inside of me snapped; surprised by its force,
I dispatched him with a single blow of my fist, a perfect overhand left hook,
which landed flush on his temple before he saw it coming or I registered an
impulse to strike. The crowd retreated from his fall, affording us a small
bubble of open space. As the jocks huddled over their unconscious cohort,
I attended to the businessman, lying curled in a fetal position on the floor;
disturbed by the violent commotion, he had reverted to a childish mentality.
"I don't know where I am," he cried piteously. "I want to go home.
Who are you? I want my mom...I don't know where I am..."
"Listen to me!" I shook him by the shoulders. "Its gonna be OK...you're on
drugs. We're gonna get you out of here...I promise it'll all be over soon."
"I'm...on...drugs?" he repeated, stuttering.
"Yeah, you took some drugs..."
His tantrum went unabated, as he sobbed convulsively, hyperventilating;
I looked for the girl with whom he was dancing, if only for information
but she had vanished. Wrapping his arms around my neck, I lifted him
to stand, assisted by a different female neighbor. Beamer blocked for us,
creating a path, and we worked our way off the floor, his limp legs dragging
behind. Due to his feverish tremors, we laid the businessman down on
cool concrete in the lee of a trash bin near the mouth of the vomitorium,
thus affording him some privacy; yet to me it seemed that he could not have
cared less about where he was, since he had become unresponsive by then,
with his jaw chattering and twitching eyes rolled backwards in his head.
We poured water onto his chest whilst forcing him to drink; he sputtered,
choked, and struggled against us reflexively. Distracted by the light show,
in addition to my own cybertroll, I thought I imagined it at first glance;
eventually the girl who helped carry him confirmed my observation that,
despite his catatonic condition, the dude sported a sizeable erection.
"Fuckin A," I exclaimed, remembering he had taken something just
past the set break; when I put my hand on the side of his scorching,
sweaty neck, the pulse I felt was impossibly fast and arrhythmic.
"You're closer to sober," I told her. "Can you time this?"
She counted two hundred beats per minute, albeit doubtful of her precision.
"What should we do?"
"Get his Tab," Beamer suggested.
In our search, we found more Viagra but no intelligent prosthesis; the girl
let me use hers to call an ambulance; I impatiently waded through a maze
of computerized voices until finally prompted to describe the situation.

I hollered, "serotonin syndrome," and received an automated response; "Result not found: please restate the nature of your emergency...try something like 'automobile accident', 'I need to report a suspicious person', or, 'I want to pay my bill'..." After I said "tachycardia", "hyperthermia", "drug overdose" and "psychotic episode" without success, the system transferred me to a human, or else what passed for one in a Turing test. "I dunno who this guy is, but you should, because he seems important," I shouted. "I think he took Viagra on top of some X and he isn't doing well." I must have been correct about his stature, since the spotlights of medical technicians shone through the holograms before the track was played out; as they entered the arena, I hailed them to our place by the stairs.

"Sir, what is your name?" an EMT asked.

The businessman's eyes flipped open briefly, fixing on me with apparent recognition and a plea in them I will never forget.

"I'm...on...drugs?" he whimpered fearfully; I hid my face and left.

The three of us ran down the vomitorium to escape interrogation or identification; once we had safely exited the McOlosseum, my friend and I introduced ourselves with self-aggrandizing epithets. Varian, as she was named, must have been charmed by our flamboyance, which she rewarded via batted eyelashes, then friend requests on the iNterface. "What's next?" she asked; Beamer recommended my roof, where the cybertroll began.

"Yo, thanks for covering me," he sang as we galloped along a conveyor leading to the train. "Where the hell did that come from, anyhow?"

I clenched my fist and uncurled its digits a few times; although the knuckles were swollen, I did not feel pain.

"I dunno; I guess from doing so in virtuality, it just happened naturally."

I neglected to say that, after I hit him, I wanted merely to know whether my experience was real.

"You decked the fuckhead! I've never seen anything like it in real life."

The word had been haunting me, and there it was again.

"Me neither...but he deserved every bit," Varian added.

"You know him?" I inquired.

We made eye contact through our iNterfaces for a fleeting, almost accidental moment before she looked away. "He was my boyfriend."

"Was?"

"Well, until now."

I awoke beside her the next day, regretting my failure to take the businessman's Viagra for myself. In its absence, I slipped out to get mocha shakes at a vendor on the corner; upon return, I found Varian on her Tablogs, still naked and alluring in my bed.

"Wanna know who that dude was?" she asked.

"The one who lost his shit last night?"

"Andre Geos," she replied, preempting my guess.

"Is that supposed to mean something to me?"

"I dunno," she began. "It says he was the former president of FUC."

"What...you mean the cage fighting show from the old days?"

"Yeah...that's the same guy."

"Wow...holy fuck."

"I know it. He's dead."
I stared at her blankly. "Dead...how do you mean?"
She did not even bother to look up from the screen.
"You know...not living. Done for. Expired. Deceased. Gone."
"I'll be damned; of what, do they say?"
"Incorporated Press calls it 'accidental overdose on a new kind of DMT'."
"Fuckin idiots," I grumbled, knowing little about tryptamines beyond the
fact that they were not closely related to Andre's actual phenethylamines.
"What time?"
"Says here three AM." Not long after we left him.
"Why do you care? Do you think it might be your fault?" she taunted.
I vaguely remembered that in medical history, Nardil was known to be
potentially lethal in combination with such substances, via serotonergic
or hypertensive crises. Beamer and I fancied ourselves resistant;
by that time, we had taken them together on dozens of occasions
without incident, during our pursuit of all-night trolls.
"Hell no," I declared in false bravado. "I am not his doctor!"
"Was not," she corrected.
"Whatever; how could I know that he would be taking Viagra, too?"
"I'm just messing with you," she said, giggling. "Besides, I admired
how you tried to support him in a difficult experience, and that
attracted me to you almost as much as your knockout punch."
I felt a cool breeze behind me, and strode to the window, shivering,
but realized upon pulling back the shade it was already closed.
The panes actually seemed warm to the touch, as they should have
been from the heat of day, whilst I made an anxious inspection.
"What's wrong?"
The answer, which I dared not speak aloud, was nothing – or rather,
that nothing was wrong. My fist showed no bruising or evidence of
physical damage, and I detected no soreness from the prior evening.
"I'm just wondering what happened to Beamer after we left the roof,"
I lied, hoping to leave it alone as I reached through the liquefied glass.
"This is your life, and it's ending one minute at a time."
Startled, I withdrew my arm. "What did you say?"
"I asked if you have any more X."
"Oh, of course." We burned a joint, and by sheer force of will I stopped
my hand from shaking for long enough to lay out our lines on my iTab.
Varian put on some trance; I climbed back into bed; then my attention
shifted to the concerns of circumstances that were much less unsettling.

"Upon further examination, (Timothy Leary's) experience with psychedelics appears superficial, if the facile philosophy thus fostered is any indication of what happened in his mind...the visions that emerged from his LSD, psychology, and enlightenment were megalomaniac fantasies of himself cryogenically suspended until a future of Nazi androids in space, while civilization lays the Earth to waste. He became not a futurist, but an antichrist; and his lack of awareness inevitably provided the empire with ample ammunition for criminalization of humanity's primordial entheogens."

~ Alexander Fremont ~
Commodification of Counterculture & Conspiracy to Corrupt Consciousness

"Then Eli'hu the son of Bar'achel the Buzite, of the family of Ram, became angry...at Job because he justified himself rather than God... Now Eli'hu had waited to speak to Job because they were older than he, and when he saw that there was no answer in the mouth of these three men, he...said 'Days should speak, and many years should teach wisdom; but it is the spirit in a man, the breath of God, that makes him understand. It is not the old that are wise, nor the aged who know what is right.' "

~ The Book of JOB, 32: 2, 4, 5, 7-9 ~

THREE

My trade in trolls brought sufficient profits to support a profligate set of indulgences, if you will, which made me an appealing mate for Varian. As sales swelled, so did my personal habits; thus I began to consider admission to shows a business expense, whilst amassing an expansive collection of music, apps, and accoutrements. When my mother observed aloud that I was squandering my surplus income on branded clothes, I told her that I served drinks during my nights out - an easy ruse to uphold because it was not far from the truth. She declined to investigate, since I contributed to the rent consistently, regardless of conventional employment. At that point in history, consciousness alteration had risen amongst America's fastest-growing industries, simultaneously, though somewhat differently, in its corporate as well as its illicit cartels. My lifestyle, stemming from and revolving around self-medication, proved more effective initially than anything the psychiatrist ever prescribed me. For the first time in memory I acted 'well-adjusted', albeit a result of criminal activity, along with unfettered access to the neurochemistry of happiness. My Nardil just extended the Nexus, whereas the side effects required that I smoke cannabis to calm down enough for trolling in school on their residues; and what started as an interesting occasional diversion to combat my anxious boredom became standard operating procedure, then a regular requirement for me to bear my compulsory education.

Meanwhile, duration of my forays into phenethylamine-induced euphoria diminished, so slowly the trend passed my notice at first; but I eventually went from exhaustion the day after a troll to outright depression anytime I was not high. Rather than living in the present, my mind fixated on the upcoming party, whose frequency had increased to nearly every night. My dosage grew too, though I took Nardil with intentions of extending the X. I quickly habituated to boosting throughout the night, because making its users forget ingestion was one of the drug's signature effects, and I still could never get as far up there as I wanted, admixtures notwithstanding. This process comprised the beginning of the end for me and many of my peers, who found it impossible to re-create those early experiences no matter how much, or how many, drugs we consumed; our determined pursuit of that mythical, original peak only made daily life painfully drab and dull. X may have enticed us with ecstasy, but ended in abject slavery, by a death of the soul completed when doses were necessary in order to achieve a mood resembling normal. While aware of it happening to me, I felt impotent against the inexorable progress of my problems. More often than not, I would awaken beside Varian in a panic, as if I had impulsively hooked up with a stranger carrying disease. The truth offered little consolation, since what seemed like an intimate connection the night prior was actually devoid of substance - a relationship of convenience predicated upon the mutual desire for inebriation and a neurological brew that resembled the chemical profile of love. Tolerance or not, another hit reliably squelched such apprehensions before they could take hold. A world of simultaneous dilapidation and decadence shone in the eyes of people around me, which once marveled in awe and excitement but gave way to blank stares divulging the emptiness behind them. Through mine, I watched my regulars degenerate from excited kandikids to burnt-out etards, whose hair, clothing, and cosmetics remained roughly unchanged, though increasingly disheveled, whereas the organism beneath shriveled, providing me a frightening mirror. Behind luminescent implants and fluorescent ornaments, our faces turned pale and gray, with dark circles under the eyes and hollow cheekbones obscured by a thin layer of paint or permanent makeup. For all our assertion of individuality via gaudy decoration and dress, we were essentially the same; outside of our clubs, I saw that the young adults bearing marks of my subculture had become merely shells of people; criminals by default, yes, but otherwise static and compliant as the rest. My unique possession of a decent memory allowed me to maintain high test scores despite my escapades, and the faculty neither cared nor observed me fraying at the edges. Monday absences occurred commonly as I struggled to recover from reckless weekends, while instead of burning herb to come down, I soon needed to blow lines or smoke rocks just to get up and go. Our society so effectively programmed its citizens for resistance to admitting addiction that most people would not do so until too late; legal or not, the disease is the same. In my case, concern about my own downward spiral of dependence gave way to hopelessly detached acceptance; and I now know that I would have gone all the way to the bottom, if Ariadne Jefferson's library had not saved my life.

Her suicide happened to be one year later than Andre Geos' death by 'accidental self-inflicted injury'; I ventured on a solo cybertroll the night after discovering her body because Varian was working late and Beamer would not answer his iNterface. My original intention had been to launch from the roof, but I never made it there, which turned out for the best. Time seemed inexplicably compressed, as though I pushed off immediately upon blowing the Nexus, and I feebly crawled into bed, where I endured a terrible, jaw-grinding, feverish experience, accompanied by an ache deep in my spine and a toxic aftertaste at the back of my throat. I wanted to vomit, yet could not, and sensed the determined fingers of a phantom grabbing me from below, drawing me down into an emotional cesspool, thereby entering Andre Geos' tortured mind. Through his eyes I watched my past self participating in the reenactment of that final night; felt his panic rotting my own gut whilst being dragged around; and I choked as he did when I poured Electrolite down his throat. The liquid consumed me, black and viscous as heavy crude; then instead of hallucinating I went blind. My mattress felt like a raft of trash I was afraid to leave, floating aimlessly amid a roiling sea of putrid tar, which burned whenever it splashed on me. "They die an equal death, the idler and the man of mighty deeds," decreed a sibylline voice in the darkness; reassured I was at least not yet deceased, the reference from Homer brought me back to Mrs. Jefferson's message and her library. Struggling with nausea, I sat up, regained visual recognition of my surroundings, remembering only after tearing the place apart I had stashed her volumes atop the ceiling tiles over my bed. Steeling myself to confront the phantoms concealed within, I slid one them open and was knocked down by a barrage of books, whence an arm reached to seize me. I lay on the floor, petrified, realizing in the end that my vision had been triggered by a trade-sized paperback sitting atop the pile, whose cover artwork I saw inverted at first glance. After hesitantly rotating the foreign object, I strained through my hazy visual matrix to see lush vegetation, whereupon a six-fingered hand sprouted from the earth, metamorphosing into an interpenetrating root system at the wrist. I deciphered its title with effort - The Life & Death of Alexander Fremont - only recognizing the name by phonetic pronunciation - "Ariadne Jefferson." The familiarity of the sound wracked my brain with frustration whilst I organized my thoughts around the note again; though it was even longer until they connected well enough for me to recollect its fatal toilet flush than I needed to make a frantic search that was futile at inception. Could my neighbor have been old enough to author the artifact I held, or had I been confused? My intuition told me the book might be a key to some mystery, perhaps encompassing anomalies such as the man who called me in the intersection and my own hand, apparently invincible to injury. I rushed back to her apartment, thinking that I would find some piece of identification tying her to the book, but when I grasped the door knob it was locked, presumably by the cops. Despite a visceral fear of stumbling upon another corpse, I did not resist my curiosity; with a trembling grip, I slid my dispensary card between the jamb and strike plate. Before I turned its handle, the door opened, and I confronted the snub bore of a large-caliber handgun, held by a similarly-shaped man of Mesoamerican

complexion, partially attired in the uniform of a construction worker.
"Can I help you?" he asked, displaying metallic fillings in a malevolent
grin and punctuating his question with an ominous click of the safety.
"I'm looking for my neighbor...I live over there," I began,
pointing to my door, which I had meant to leave ajar; yet every one
I saw whilst looking across the hall was fully closed. Beads of sweat
rolled down my forehead, and my eyes darted restlessly, as I counted
them to confirm that I had knocked at the correct apartment.
"You guys are remodeling her place already?"
"This is my house!" The man's eruption took me aback.
"Oh, I'm sorry; you must have moved in quite recently, then." Standing
on tiptoes, I craned my neck to see over his shoulder to the room beyond,
but my vision undulated too much to discern any evidence of unpacking,
and he blocked the view by mirroring my motions with his handgun.
"Yo, you defective, kid?" The barrel was suddenly pressed
to my forehead, and an infant started wailing inside.
"What's going on out there...." asked a female voice between the cries.
"Nothing; shut up," he snapped, without looking back, and then to me –
"It's only when we've lost everything that we're free to do anything."
"Wait a sec...what did you just say?"
"I said, if you come back here again, I'll blow your fuckin brains out!"
"Oh," I said, stepping away. "I see. Umm...I'm sorry, I must be mistaken."
"Yeah," he growled slowly. "Must be, you fuckin etard!"
He remained at the entrance to his apartment, keeping the gun aimed at
me until I returned to the one I thought was mine; because it seemed a
matter of life and death, my relief exceeded comprehension when the door
actually opened. I went in, locked it, and watched through the peephole as
a woman holding a child on her hip joined him, gazing in my direction.
"That guy had no shoes," she announced.
"That guy is fuckin wacked," he replied.
Once he left, I crept stealthily back into the hall's jaundiced illumination,
out of belief that their studio formerly belonged to Ariadne Jefferson.
I decided to concoct an indirect way for my mother to confirm the
location, and to ask whether she knew our neighbor's first name.

I awakened next in the dead of night, but still was too lazy for the walk to a
light switch. Whilst groping on the floor for my iTab, my hand struck a book
instead - The Life and Death of Alexander Fremont, as fate would have it.
Feeling somewhat more sober following a line of X, I held the volume for
a time and even read the back cover, which explained that it contained
the biography of an activist and adventurer who became an independent
candidate for the presidency of the United States over forty years prior.
Due to his untimely and tragic assassination just before the election of
A.T. 25, I had never heard of him before, and cannot do justice to the
man's life herein; for that, you would begin with the aforementioned
scripture, if you could find a copy. Although my explanation may prove
inadequate, I am obliged to include a few excerpts from this unique period
of history - or cultural singularity, if you will - elucidating our progenitors'
proximity to the possibility of an unprecedented paradigm shift.

ENTHEOGENESIS · Origin of the Divinity within Us

As a young adult, Alexander Fremont studied environmental science and sociology at Harvard University, where he wrote an interdisciplinary thesis detailing the mechanisms by which American counterculture, as it were, had been co-opted and transmuted to another brand of consumerism in the wake of the Vietnam War. His introduction focused fittingly on the career of Timothy Leary, an infamous member of his school's own faculty who was dismissed in 37 B.T. at the conclusion of the Psilocybin Project. Fremont judged that intoxication by celebrity, among others, led Leary to heretically abdicate the scientific method and professional ethics; while dabblings with narcotics, womanizing, and espionage only reinforced his self-aggrandizement, though I must omit the last of these for the present. As a demagogue who presumed to preside over the prescription of LSD in pop-culture, he paved the way for desacralization of what the author called "ineffable vo-yages upon the psychonauticon." Propelled by the media on a meteoric rise, the false hierophant was template for Leary's style; hence his personality provided the powers-that-be with both incentive and means to earnestly begin their crusade against medicines that would otherwise guide humanity's pursuit of the numinous. The prerogatives of skilled psychotherapists and mystics consequently fell to those like me - clever criminals who could profit in some small way from the calculated prohibition of consciousness by making merchandise out of it, selling our wares as commodities in dark alleys or even fouler places. Although rumor held that Fremont's personal encounters endowed him with telepathic and apotropaic powers, his graduate research remained unequivocally scholarly in rigor by steering clear of occult realms, thus establishing for academia the truth of the drug war: entheogen persecution had not only spawned the subculture of profane substance abuse the DEA would oppose; but this effect, superficially seen as a deficiency of government, was symptomatic of an elaborate strategy to repress revolution, whereby its masters achieved insidious aims indirectly. In light of his explanation, I readily observed this phenomenon amongst my peer group, whose youthful aspirations toward positive change were neutralized and nullified by a socially-sanctioned, albeit illegal, culture of inebriation before they could be fully expressed. We traded our dreams of a better world for carnival rides, on which the gratifications of altered states took precedence over unrest. Amidst the stimulation of lights, sound, sex, and addictions, our forgotten bases of rebellion yielded to a pandemic apathy wrought by ill-conceived combinations of brain-damaging designer drugs. Identification with the appearance of nonconformity was far more comfortable than actual defection from normality, giving those of insubordinate inclination an alternative track for assimilation into the mainstream; and therefore, regardless of any expressed contempt for America's status quo, the counterculture strengthened its parental system via pathological failure to invoke evolutionary growth.

I brought <u>The Life and Death of Alexander Fremont</u> to Beamer's a few days later with the assurance that his parents would be at their respective offices. Since he was fiending we blew lines when I arrived; afterward I gave him my attention while touring his domains in *Cosmic Conquest,* the newest roleplay app, whose space-based iNterface expanded as users plugged in to test their skill at empire building. The gametrix's premise comprised a contest for universal domination via exponential expansion; its players began by engineering species and technology to extract the resources of their home planets, then moved on to colonize other worlds through slavery or extermination of competitors. Allegiances were forged for waging war, whereby the conquistadors subordinated other members who preferred the position of a local lord to starting over. Beamer would take eth or meth, as well as X, for accelerating his cognition during crucial campaigns, but claimed an experience with Nexus had changed his view of time, thus inspiring a preemptive monopoly of hyperspace, the importance of which he predicted before teleportation existed in the *Cosmic* virtuality.

Trolling in an uninhibitedly ruthless mindset led him to devise perverse innovations that might not occur to other players, like boobytrapping uninhabited planets with poison and disease. His insectile cyborg colonies moved atop the rankings on a strategy exemplifying, as he often said, "not an institution, but an infection." For his mechanistic prion invasions, in addition to his father's considerable share of the company stock, Beamer had been selected as a guest gamemaker, permitting him access to features beyond his console, such as the power to create supernovae or wormholes.

We visited vanquished enemies and recently-acquired territories, all policed by militant armaments. He was aroused with excitement while showing me cybernetic parasites from his biotech division that transformed via permanent rape other organisms into prosthetic genitalia, but I felt nauseous at the sight of his breeding machines and removed my headgear.

"You all right, bro?" he asked, reaching for the freebase.

"It's too sick for me," I groaned. "I can't get into your fantasy."

"That fantasy is our future," he stated gravely, passing the pipe to me. "Come on...you're a smart enough guy...don't you think that reality could benefit from your intelligence and investment more than virtuality?"

"Sorry, but this IS reality, bro; you got left you in the dust, 'cause this planet is done for, and as soon we have the technology to colonize space, who do you think is gonna be hired to design our infrastructure or plan alien wars?" Breathless, he inhaled sharply. "I'm not yet eighteen, but in the Conquest I'm already a god. What 'bout you? Yeah, you got scores, but in the end you're just a fuckin pusher who lives off my money."

"Don't you threaten me, or try to turn this around," I retorted in anger. "While you were busy playing games, those days have come and gone. Besides your consumerist illusions, the exploration of space is no more than a rich person's joyride. We don't have the resources or intelligence necessary to escape this planet – but actually, that's a relief to me. We are a disease, just like your fuckin minions; it's right that we should be quarantined, and I'm glad that we will be."

I had risen to my feet during the tirade, and Beamer stood to confront me.

"You can go fuck yourself, 'cause this is my destiny. Cold fusion is right around the corner, and once we have unlimited energy, we'll be mining asteroids, and when extraction capacity..."

I interrupted amidst flecks of his spittle striking my face.

"You gotta unplug and come back to Earth once in a while, bro!

I dunno how many apps you're running on your fancy iNterface right now, but ever since you wiped the ads off of mine, for which I am thankful, I've been able to see things a little more for how they may really be. Your penthouse view might blind you with your parents' money, but down there, reality as the rest of us know it is falling apart."
Perhaps spurred by the crank, I surprised us both in a vicious attack, whereby I seized my unresponsive friend, tore off his virtuality headset, and threw him face-first against the floor-to-ceiling windows.
"What the hell is wrong with you?!" he screamed; only then did I realize the violence of my impulse and release him.
"This is my house! Get the hell outta here, you fuckin douche!"
"I'm sorry...I dunno what came over me," I said regretfully, moving to the door. My vision flickered; glancing back, I saw Beamer in a different light - weak, sickly, and he momentarily became the stringy-haired etard with whom I had traded for our first Nexus. This glimpse gave me pause in consideration of the theory that I had a malfunction in my optics.
"I'm just trying to show you...the world we see is not the world as it is."
He smoothed his wrinkled clothing restlessly, running over the same seams.
"Well, soon it won't matter anyway, 'cause my iWare'll be implanted."
To make amends, I cut up some fat lines from my stash, and as we pushed off together again, the argument was all but forgotten. I did not remember why I had gone in the first place until turning to depart.
"What about this?" he called, holding up the book; I swallowed nervously.
"Can you do me a favor? Take a look and tell me what you see?"
Although frowning as if I had asked him to examine some grotesque medical condition, he took a look at the image. "A hand sticking outta the ground."
"That's it? You don't see anything strange about it?"
He stared for another moment, whilst my heart pounded in anticipation.
"Come on, man...how many fingers does it have?" I hinted impatiently.
"Huh? Oh...hmm...yeah...sure, there's an extra."
"Don't you think that's sort of weird?"
"Why would I?"
"Because I saw a man who had six fingers last week."
He tossed the volume toward me with a vacant expression.
"Remember, when the brick wall collapsed downtown?"
"Your iNterface was fucked up from ads..." he mumbled disinterestedly, still giving no sign of recognition.
"I said something about it, right after I scraped up Kerberos..."
His disinterested eyeroll paused on me. "What's that...a new synthemex?"
"Kerberos is...was...my neighbor's dog...you should know that...I dunno if I told you yet, but she killed herself and left me this book, which she wrote!"
I emphasized my point by holding up the cover, underlining its title with my forefinger, whereat he turned and put his headgear on once more.
"Ignore him," he said to himself. "Fuckin shit, I can't wait for iNtution..."
"Yo, Beamer...I'm talking to you...what the fuck?...Hello?!"
"They die and equal death, the idler and the man of mighty deeds."
"What did you just say?"
"I'm...on... drugs."
I ran for the bathroom as another wave of nausea overwhelmed me.

Although his research in cultural psychopharmacy sparked acclaim as well as controversy, Fremont vanished from the intelligentsia soon thereafter to reinvent himself via the construction, in secrecy and from scratch, of his own sailboat. The enterprise seemed symbolically befitting since he self-identified as a psychonaut, from the Greek for 'sailor of the soul'. He designed an open trimaran, whose three hulls were inspired by the outrigger canoes of Polynesia and appropriately baptized *The Fates*. A central *vaka* contained the cockpit and tiny cabin; smaller floats on either side provided storage; and wash-through trampolines spanned the framework of struts that connected them. To embody sustainable transportation technology, he built his vessel, on principle, entirely of recycled and reclaimed metal, biomass-based adhesives and paints, FSC engineered wood products, and sawn lumber from his home ecoregion, which he selectively harvested via timber stand improvement methods, then laboriously removed with horses. Like the tall ships of old, sails and rigging were made of organically-grown hemp, as was the flag that flew from the mast shrouds, thus honoring the original star-spangled banner, and paying homage to national tradition in an age of ubiquitous plastic. Aboard this fantastic craft, Fremont captured media attention when he completed an unprecedented solo circumnavigation of the Arctic ice cap under power of sail only, via the Northwest and Northeast passages, recently opened by the thawing of previously perennial pack ice.

His expedition intended to raise awareness of global climate change, thereby deterring oil and natural gas extraction from the Arctic seafloor – endeavors that petroleum corporations eagerly sought to undertake, because peak oil established their potential profitability, while recession of the ice sheets finally afforded technical feasibility. Though hushed at the time, Fremont's creation of *The Fates* and their maiden voyage had been meticulously recorded as part of an eponymous documentary film production, which sought to change the genre, and received accolades, but could not stop the drilling platforms. These rigs were soon joined by floating refineries, permitting commercial vessels to refuel en route; and icebreakers kept the new shipping lanes clear, saving thousands of miles compared to passages through the Panama Canal or, in the case of supertankers, below Cape Horn. Loss of polar ice accelerated, due to traffic prevented their accumulation. In outrage at government machinations, and capitalizing on the film's success, Alexander Fremont proceeded to take *The Fates* around the globe to document anthropogenic effects on its oceans, representing three quarters of the planet's surface of whose condition most people had no cognizance. He retold his odyssey in Sterile Seas, a bestselling elegy for the marine ecologies where systemic collapse came faster than nearly everyone expected. He sailed through bygone coral reefs of the Caribbean, killed by ocean acidification and devoid of biomass. Desperation increased the brutality of commercial fishing techniques, from trawlers that plowed the seafloor to explosives and poison, as the piscatory stocks they relied on disappeared almost overnight. From *The Fates* he watched the disintegration of ice sheets whence sea levels rose worldwide, displacing millions of people and altering essential conveyor currents. He witnessed an oil spill spread unmitigated from India to Madagascar while its executive perpetrators destroyed any evidence of malfeasance that could be brought to bear under subpoena; battled bankrupt poachers in pursuit of the last cetaceans; and became marooned in the Great Pacific Garbage Patch, where floating plastic formed a swirling mass already larger in area than his home country. "What we do to the world, we do to ourselves," he wrote at sail. "Just as we undermine our health and corrupt our humanity, the devastated oceans offer us a mirror, if we can just summon the courage to peer into the psychonauticon."

No one ever knew what happened between Alexander Fremont and the mushroom in their time offshore because he gracefully evaded questions about his sourcery, though the subsequent tour promoting Sterile Seas showed him to be an eloquent and magnetic presenter. His experience seemed beyond his years because it came from infinity, concrescing in an integrated perspective that embraced but did not cater to the mystical predilections of his day. He was, among other roles, an outspoken critic of the Occupy protest in the early 21st century, who reputedly declared, "I find it perfectly American that money would be the source of angst to bring our generation together in this exigent time; and that the manifestation of our collective angst is complacent occupation of space, in the absence of an articulated goal."

At signings and events, he disseminated merchandise with radical messages like 'To be free of the system, you must first leave the cage', 'Civilization or Survival', 'Sustainability Is The Opposite Of Extinction', or 'Those who can, do. Those who can't, protest.' His rallying call to a host of liberals, libertarians, anarchists, and armchair environmentalists said, "Accept the challenge or become obsolete," emphasizing the importance of solutions, as opposed to incessant elaboration upon the data of problems. Insanity is the repetition of the same mistakes, with the expectation of a different outcome, and he contented that protest as a strategy was doomed except in its own perpetuation. No amount of activity about 'sustainability' in the TV media or on the social networks, nor any positive intention or consciousness evolution, amounted to anything without an accompanying shift in lifestyle. By imagining change coming from the top down, the sanitary and legally permissible realms of the 'movement' disempowered its members by relinquishing their power to humanifest, while respect for 'rules of engagement' passively reinforced the dominance of people and establishments that they decried. The modern power structure existed for the purpose of its own enrichment, inherently immune to persuasion of dissent. Wars had been waged, assassinations executed, and regimes entrenched to lay technological, economic, and bureaucratic groundwork for the endgame. After legislating loopholes in environmental regulations, by what impetus might the government suddenly rise against the industries holding its puppet strings? In the case of petroleum energy, change had to come from efforts focused on the energy demand to which those industries were an inevitable reaction; but a culture of conservation and renewable energy was unlikely, at best, to arise within the system standing to lose the most as a consequence. Only when the last profitable barrel of oil and cubic meter of natural gas had been extracted could the machine come to a grinding halt of its own accord. Fremont prophesied that demands to stop the tar sands pipeline, hydraulic fracturing, and mountaintop removal for coal by bureaucratic authorities would be mired in impotency, since such pleas responded to effects, rather than cause. To his regret, in this case and many others, events proved him correct; yet hope still remained when he gave his final recorded speech at a Central Park rally, which reported over a million attendees. In a twist of irony, his time on the political stage concluded with a quote from StEve Jobs, co-founder and chairman of Apple:

"Here's to the crazy ones, the misfits, the rebels,

the troublemakers, the round pegs in the square holes –

the ones who see things differently. They're not fond of rules;

you can quote them, disagree with them, glorify or vilify them

but the only thing you can't do is ignore them because they

CHANGE things. They push the human race forward, and

while some may see them as the crazy ones, we see genius –

because the ones crazy enough to think that they can

change the world are the ones who do."

"It's just a ride, and we can change it anytime we want. It's only a choice...
right now, between fear and love. The eyes of fear want you to put bigger
locks on your doors, buy guns, close yourselves off; the eyes of love, instead,
see all of us as one. Here's what you can do to change the world, right now,
to a better ride. Take all that money that we spend on weapons and defense
each year, and instead spend it feeding, clothing and educating the poor
of the world, which it would many times over, not one human being
excluded, and we could explore space,
together, both inner and outer,
forever, in peace."

~ William Melvin Hicks, REVELATIONS ~

"As war and government prove,
insanity is the most contagious of diseases."

~ Edward Abbey ~

FOUR

Varian and I made a chemical bond of recreational drugs as well as
sensual gratifications that were their own inebriation, to the degree sex
mediated the flow of oxytocin, along with so much else. Later in my life
I would learn about pheromones, a language unto itself of biochemical
messages between lovers, but at seventeen knew of nothing beyond the
physiology between arousal and climax. Though initially addicted to each
other's vices and secretions, we incorporated pain and paraphilia when
necessary as her challenges achieving orgasm grew. The sexual side effects
of X, once evident in my body, embarrassed me during intercourse; whilst
my confidence plummeted, she became more distant, tied to me primarily
by the sheer quantity of pills, powders, and psychoactive shows we shared.
She wanted mechanical stimulation, then porn, rape roleplays, and
eventually, total immersion in orgiastic virtuality apps for satisfaction.
I participated some, so that I could replicate in reality the perversions of
other players, the details of which I will spare you. Looking back on our
involvement, I see the irrefutable power of consensual validation in society,
because Varian's preferences for personal degradation arose not from
some innately twisted sense of fantasy, or even a childhood trauma,
but rather from the roles assigned to women in its advertising, erotic
entertainment, and the sexuality they fostered. Meanwhile, I felt so
emasculated from my inability to perform, especially when coming off a
troll, that I simply lost interest. Following the death of Andre Geos, I was
cautious when it came to erectile medications, though I still messed around
with tadalafil and vardenafil enough to send myself into metabolic crises
on occasion, characterized by simultaneous blue lips and chest pain.

"What the fuck are we doing?" I demanded after an injection of adrenaline for recovery from such an incident. "You're being gangbanged by crazies and I'm gonna have a heart attack over a hard-on...for what? For the idea we should be getting off together? For the appearance of a relationship?"
She shrugged dispassionately and turned to her iTab.
"Varian, are you even listening to me?"
"No, and I don't care whether you get off, and I'm done hearing about it."
"You're kidding..."
"I'm not, and talking 'bout feelings is boring to me. I just wanna get high, but it seems you gotta have a 'relationship' for that to happen..."
"I don't, actually...not at all, if this is the price I pay."
"Whatever..."
"Is this your way of saying that you're only dating me for drugs?"
Though the question was rhetorical, she responded without hesitation.
"Duh, and now that you mention it, Beamer fucks me better anyway."
Thus I learned abruptly of the affair between the person I considered to be a lover and my closest friend. Admittedly, I had willfully ignored what lay in plain sight; her nights at work coincided with his disappearances for months, while they shared a propensity for the virtuality apps that catalyzed our argument. Honed by dancing, her svelte body still appeared desirable according to conventional standards, whereas in hindsight I could see she had deteriorated beneath her cosmetology. The iNterface diverted her attention and the party devoured her soul; X had taken her capacity for empathy while her mental faculties vanished into oblivion.
Impotence was a familiar frustration, albeit never worse than during the hallucinatory amputation of my testes by her words, or lack thereof. Although ashamed of my role in the situation, I felt sorrow for Varian even more. Without knowing, she had already forfeited her emotional life and was not yet a woman; someone who could be my partner for a year, then convincingly claim indifference to me. Where once I thought a connection of substance conjugated lay only the cavernous wound of my own delusion, unveiled at last. I struggled against intoxication whilst putting on my clothes, trying to summon some feeling for her; either hatred or longing would have sufficed, but I remained caught upon my own guilt. At the beginning, we came to each other in order to take; by the end, she had taken too much, and love no longer inhabited her realm of possibility. My brand of degeneracy, on the other hand, invented intimacy from nothing as a shield against the fear that she chose me for what drugs I brought to the table, because I seemed incapable of satisfying her sexually. For all the mutterings of altered states or my webs of fantasy, there was nothing between us besides instant gratification, and I had failed to deliver again.
I thought of an apology, but spared my pride by leaving silently instead.
"This is your life, and it's ending one minute at a time," I heard her call as the door opened, but over its creaking hinges I could not be sure.
"What did you say?"
"I said don't let it hit you on the way out."
She laughed without mirth, like the synthetic sound of television audiences.
"It's just an expression."

Despite uncompromising censure of such movements, Alexander Fremont found several collaborators amidst post-millennial protests; together they spawned the Sustainable Culture Initiative, a network for post-petroleum publication, research, activism, and education, whose vision acknowledged, "Our responsibility is not, as we once thought, a matter of saving the world. Human activity has created mass extinction, but nature does not require our assistance. She is merciless, and if necessary, will save herself from us. Our responsibility is the matter of saving ourselves, and to do so, we must first face the possibility, then the likelihood, that along with so many other species, we will inadvertently squander her investment in our own." SCI's mission was of healing, both personal and planetary, which began with an awakened worldview, to create empowered individuals. By sharing knowledge and resources freely, they would foster resilient communities, human and ecological, equipped to fulfill longterm goals in climate change mitigation, biodiversity conservation, and environmental remediation. In its statement of principles, founders of the organization asserted that, "We possess the ingenuity, creativity, resources, and will required to transform the nature our of relationship with the interdependent world of life from heedless exploitation to loving synergy.
We need only to cast off the chains of consumerism,
embrace the challenge before us with a spirit of adventure,
and learn as we can from the intelligence of our home planet."
In a satire of neoconservative think tanks such as the Project for the New American Century and the American Enterprise Institute, Fremont released a free download, whose link went viral during an underwhelming presidential selection, describing a series of proposals for what he entitled 'The Doctrine of an American Revolution for Evolution'. Noting with irony the homonym that preceded it, America's 20th century Drug Abuse Resistance Education (and hence 'Drugs Are Really Expensive') the author introduced his own DARE with a radical history of mind-altering substances, propaganda, and imperialist legislation, culminating in the War Of Drugs. According to his analysis, genesis of this cultural conflict could be found in the addictive power of alcohol - a poison derived from the surplus grain production characterizing civilization - which served as a convenient cornerstone in the control of human consciousness. Even prior to biblical times in the West, goddess-worshiping societies had been exterminated by militarism, slavery, and the calculated dissolution of tribal heritage via religious institutions. By assimilation, free people were forced to accept poor palliatives offered to them in lieu of indigenous entheogens; and using deliriants to treat the pain of lost identification with the living world inevitably precipitated collective amnesia and spiritual illness.
In clashes of history, from Roman sieges to the American colonies, those who made instruments of warfare from infectious disease tended to emerge victorious; and what better weapon could there be in civilization's need to control human consciousness than an epidemic of the psyche? Fremont submitted that the system's greatest vulnerability was its reliance on continual mass delusion, epitomized in the United States, where 'treatment' for the majority of the population required industries of similarly staggering proportions. After World War II, psychedelics such

as psilocybin, LSD, and ayahoaska enjoyed a brief period of legitimate scientific research; but since their resurgence catalyzed the shamanic revelation of social crises, these substances had to be supplanted by TV and other stultifying narcotics before the diagnosis became widely known. Proceeding in earnest by 34 B.T., legal prohibition of any drug experience with potential to reveal the cultural psychosis coincided with an expansion of the National Institute of Mental Health; and this collusion between the U.S. government and its corporate pushers of pharmaceuticals would masquerade for the next century as 'psychiatry' - from *psyche iatrikos*, Greek for 'healing the soul' - a field of medicine ironically named for the prognosis these prescriptions were expressly meant to prevent. Beginning long before institutional Christian orthodoxy, the system identified its menaces as moral aberrations, quelled by persecution or torture; then the state grew in strength and surveillance, addressing 'deviant behaviors' as a legal issue with fines, police, and incarceration; whereas by Fremont's time, they were becoming a medical problem, treated via allopathic brainwashing. The Weapons of Mass Delusion employed to this end encompassed compulsory education, fluoridated water, synthetic food, mass media, vaccinations, virtuality, and prosthetic intelligence while the pandemic spread. He pointed out simply that mental illness had not been cured, but rather grew in prevalence during medical advancements because its source, like my clinical depression, was 'non-endogenous'. An infection at the cultural level would require a commensurate cure; he called his proposed panacea the Open Source Consciousness project. Decriminalization of the drug experience would foster an environment free from the risk of imprisonment, as well as its associated costs, where citizens could readily access the requisite information. He believed that a revival of plant medicines and psychedelic exploration had the power to replace narcotics, whose competitive advantages lay only in marketing or their addictive potential. Such an ambitious direction demanded a novel approach, founded on visionary research; rigorous documentation; voluntary programs to treat addiction instead of incarceration; and a decentralized network of citizen-educators to disseminate the memes of responsible entheogen administration. Government participation, if any, he restricted to funding, since experimental efforts might warrant subsidies if they could demonstrate merit and need. Revenue would come from the corporations trafficking in traditionally legal drugs of America, such as nicotine, caffeine, alcohol, sugar, or pharmaceuticals, once taxed at last according to their pollution, healthcare costs, and public safety hazards. Fremont himself advocated small-scale production of natural sacraments akin to dimethyltryptamine, a human neurotransmitter. Although released by the pineal gland amid altered states such as birth, death, dreaming, and meditation, DMT was paradoxically listed on Schedule 1 of the 'Controlled Substances Act', along with its orally-active plant brew called ayahoaska, and all phosphorylated molecular relatives from psilocybin mushrooms. These were the tools of autonomy in the War Of Drugs, he said, because human consciousness evolved in their presence for so long that they could reliably transport psychonauts beyond social conditioning and back again, via journeys esteemed for their potential to induce purgative healing.

When a liberal television commentator asked Alexander Fremont about the perceived threats of widespread psychedelic consumption, he replied, "With all due respect, I must reject such a facile question on its premise, because the tryptamine experience is as much a part of our identity as it is of our neurochemistry, There are sacraments for which every human is born equipped, regardless of whether or not they have remembered yet. Intense though the tryp might be, the question is of our willingness to survive this culture afterward; and the only danger I see is of its suicidal mentality, which will not persist in the healing presence of entheogens."

Withdrawal from my relationships with Varian and Beamer led predictably to self-loathing mental loops; my already-prodigal drug abuse exploded; while I spent insomniac nights wandering the streets of Manhattan, respirator absent, grappling with the logic of suicide, personal and cultural. During a hard cybertroll from which I could not come down, I found myself on the roof, looking across a gap to the next building. The distance was about fifteen feet, with a drop of one story, while the depth of the chasm to the alley below was more than ten. "Why not?" I mused aloud. "The world has gone to shit, and it isn't like I have anything more important to do." "You haven't finished the book yet," Alexander Fremont reminded me. "I dunno if the book is even real!" I screamed. "I know you're not, but I'm not so sure about the rest of this anymore. What's the difference between reality, simulation, and hallucination other than opinion? I don't care and I can't even remember the last time I felt comfortable, like I could trust what seems to be happening in the world around me. I'm always unsure, and it's driving me crazy. I'm jumping because afterward I'll know the difference." "Sounds like nonsense, but suit yourself." He stepped back with a bow. "A different reality is always possible, though it must be imagined first." As he faded into the shadows, I heard him ask, almost tauntingly, "In death, what will you wish you did to change the world with your life?" Except to finish reading his biography, which sat at the crux of my confusion, nothing specific came to mind, thereby affirming my choice. I leaned against the cowling of an air conditioner on the opposite corner of the roof, took a few deep breaths, let go of concern for my safety, and shed my fear of the phantom that haunted me. Although it hovered in that moment over my left shoulder, I was relieved to know that I would soon be free. Death comes for us all, no matter how much we fear or anticipate its arrival, so I ran toward the parapet in rebellion; yet my foot slipped when it meant to push off the edge and I ended up pitching forward in midair. As in the intersection with Kerberos, time felt compressed, enough at least for me to contemplate the odds that I would go the distance. My arms flailed, but could not recover my balance as I dove headfirst. 'I had one shot, and fucked it up,' I thought, surprised to feel regret instead of apathy whilst watching a vent pipe hurtle toward my face.

After establishing that the reader was a participant, willing or not, in the War Of Drugs, and describing his prescription for Open Source Consciousness, Alexander Fremont's DARE moved on to a five-pronged political remedy. Inspiration for its first tenet came from the Supreme

Court, whose decision in *Citizens United v. Federal Election Commission* of A.T. 11 entrenched the concept of Corporate Personhood by ruling that the First Amendment protected rights of businesses to spend money on fixing elections. While liberals of the time objected vehemently to the court's opinion, for fear it would unleash the power of special interests in Washington, Fremont welcomed the decision, because it paved the way toward treatment of corporations as people in the criminal justice system as well. If, after all, they were natural persons with constitutional rights, then by logical extension businesses could be tried and convicted in a court of law, along with their executives; hence, the possibility of imposing a Corporate Death Penalty for malefic abuse of ecological or human welfare. The second component of his DARE repudiated the Federal Reserve System, which Fremont referred to as the FRAUD since it was neither Federal nor a Reserve, but rather, America United in Deceit. By an act of 87 B.T., Congress empowered a criminal cartel to create counterfeit money and loan it at interest. Inflation resulted, as every bill in circulation was worth less with the passage of time, while the value thereby lost from national currency flowed to an unelected, parasitic elite who controlled the money supply. Dollars, or Federal Reserves Notes, were not so much means of exchange as evidence of a 'debt', i.e. deception, enabling bankers to engineer financial crises. They used mortgage-backed securities and default swaps as smoke and mirrors, whereby media reinforced the illusion that dire straits, like 'credit squeeze' and 'economic collapse', could only be prevented by government-issued bailouts and stimulus packages, which were actually funded by the taxpayers whom they would allegedly serve. Every depression or recession in history had increased economic inequality between the rich and poor, as devaluation of the base caused wealth to move atop the pyramid, represented by the all-seeing eye of the FRAUD. Its elimination was his first step toward sound monetary policy, comprising currency with stable value based on domestic re-sources; the end of deficit spending; and attenuation of the national disparity in standard of living.

Part Three of the DARE proposed to overturn the 'Patient Protection and Affordable Care Act' of A.T. 11 in favor of a single-payer system, timely due to the coinciding escalation of IRS-enforced penalties for not obtaining health insurance. Corporations selling it necessarily increased the price of treatment while denying coverage whenever possible because their enterprises turned profits; however, the corruption of middlemen in medicine was a simple concept the public seemed strangely slow to realize. At the time, cost per capita of health care in the United States doubled that of other industrialized countries with universal coverage, wherein citizens enjoyed higher life expectancies, lower infant mortality, and more physicians as a proportion of their general population than Americans. Obamacare, on the other hand, was a testament to the lobbying power of U.S. health insurance companies, whose monstrous ability to charge a 100% markup on the actual cost of any 'health care' rendered had not only been allowed, but mandated by Federal law, then punitively enforced. The fourth and perhaps most inflammatory section of the DARE called for disarmament. Here, Fremont's fantasy began dismantling the American nuclear weapons arsenal; followed by its Department of Homeland Security, while reestablishing the Immigration and Naturalization Service it had subsumed; with complete elimination of standing armies intended by the conclusion of his second term. Preempting objections that such forces were necessary for employment, his plan called for existing personnel to receive their salaries until retirement age if they so chose - a small cost, compared to the value of material and military infrastructure which could be recycled or reclaimed. He suggested the money thus saved by restraint against foreign campaigns might most appropriately be paid as reparations to the various nations victimized by American hegemony, and accompanied by civic monuments of apology. Because 'defense' was the United States' largest discretionary expense, such a shift of priorities would have yielded a budget surplus of nearly a trillion dollars, comparable to a then-typical 'stimulus package'. After atoning for sins of its political forebears abroad, he held these funds applicable to reducing the nation's debt, and creation of a new cabinet agency - the Department of Human Sustainability. Alexander Fremont's analysis in the final, and most elaborate, portion of his DARE described how, for less than its annual military spending, the U.S. could lead the world in climate change mitigation and development of distributed renewable energy technology - areas wherein he found his country to be grossly deficient, especially next to modest economies of the European Union. Sustainability, defined for purposes herein as survival of our specie, was the most important challenge facing humanity; and though the solutions would not come, to any large extent, from the American government, they deserved funding commensurate with the scope of the task, instead of the piteous allocation made for its incompetent Environmental Protection Agency - one quarter of 1% of the Federal budget, equal to 1 part in 75 of spending by its Department of Defense. The primary purpose of the DOD appeared to be maintaining access to petroleum reserves; and environmental concerns aside, this was a grossly inefficient approach to national security. Though monumental, the task of repurposing America's infrastructure for a petroleum-free economy could have provided ample employment whilst making a superior investment of its treasury than permanent military bases flung across the planet to control a toxic source of energy in rapid depletion. If the U.S. did not vie with the rest, then it presented neither a threat to, nor a target for, other countries, and required no military. Moreover, if Americans hoped to pass even a second-rate (let alone first-class) country on to their children, this quest would necessarily be undertaken at some point; better in the present than a desperate third-world future, when it was already too late.

"What the hell...?" I whimpered in anguish as my eyelids were pried open, held there with clamps, and blinded by piercing lights.
"What we do in life echoes in eternity," said the nurse.
"Huh?" I asked groggily once the torture ended.
"Your mother would like to see you now," she repeated brusquely.
Soon I felt her brief touch on my shoulder through the fog of anesthesia.
"You listen to me," my mom began, her voice quavering from emotion.
"I'm glad you're still here, but if you survive a stunt like that again, I will kill you myself to avoid going through this, I swear."

I lost my grip whilst composing an apology, slipping back into numb oblivion before my mouth would form the words. The next time I awoke was at the sound of her interrogating a resident about my vitals, who answered with polite evasiveness at first but then became flustered, fleeing in haste as her questions, unanswered, grew louder and more demanding.

"Not a goddamned doctor in this place, just computers and cashiers..." she grumbled, sinking into a chair at my bedside with a distressed sigh.

"Hey..." I groaned, hesitantly testing my powers of speech.

"You're back." She breathed relief. "Sorry you had to hear all that."

"It's fine." My voice barely rose to a whisper. "How long have I been here?"

"About a week in this room, and two in the ICU."

"Whoa," is all I managed aloud, whilst rejoicing inside that I had unwittingly missed the worst of the comedown, despite a headache whose intensity increased from the effort of speech. "Why can't I open my eyes?"

"There's a lot of fluid accumulation; they're gonna drain it again tomorrow...or so they say," she explained with palpable resentment.

"Could you turn off the lights?" I begged. "My fuckin head hurts like hell..."

"Do you need something for the pain?" she offered solicitously, though she was already reaching for the IV before I answered.

"No...no more drugs...just get the lights...please..."

"I'll see what I can do." Even with my eyes closed, the pain felt alleviated when she finally located the switches for overhead fixtures. "I can't do anything about the instruments or exits, but is that better?"

"Much." I relaxed my clenched jaw and asked, "What happened?"

"You didn't come back from anesthesia for twelve days after surgery. They say they need to observe you, because you might have difficulty remembering things from before, but I think they just want more money..." Fortunately for me, 'they' had been wrong, and I now suppose that the coma was partially my brain's defense against the agony of withdrawal.

"What kind of surgery?"

"There were two, actually...a craniectomy at first, then after the swelling went down they reconstructed your skull...if Beamer had not gone up there to look for you...you were unrecognizable and..." The quietude made her meaning evident, ending in 'should be dead'.

"Beamer came, huh?" Probably out of desperation to score, I guessed, and as such, able to overlook how I might feel about Varian when he went to the roof; whereas on second thought, he could have been with me from the start, embodied in my perception by the phantom of Alexander Fremont.

"He thought you were gonna commit suicide, but from how you landed, the medics said it looked more like you wanted to fly." She paused, holding my hand in hers, and squeezed gravely. "What were you doing up there?"

I saw a flash within my head like the autoshade malfunction, which I thought strange since someone at the hospital had taken my iWare. With difficulty I recalled the events preceding my fateful jump as in a compressed television montage. After abating somewhat, my headache came back in brutal waves that built to a new intensity.

"I was...confused. I didn't know if I was...dreaming...and I needed something...something to tell me if I was awake...or not..."

She interjected by issuing a mixture of gasp and sob.

"Next time you're confused, why don't you ask me instead?"
"I didn't know...and I had to...strange things were happening, and there was a man...I couldn't trust what I was seeing..."
While I struggled with a flood of memories, she must have noticed my grimace and pressed the button that increased the flow of analgesics. Perhaps she knew the truth already, or suspected it but did not want to hear confirmation. As the narcotic warmth, then numbness, spread through my extremities, I lost presence of mind to explain, letting the sentence hang. To defuse the subject, she described intricacies of my craniotomy, along with the hardware holding my skull together; the procedure was primitive, cosmetically imperfect, and executed hastily due to my tenuous situation. Lacking the time to model or incubate proper tissue for a true bone graft, surgeons had embedded a titanium skeleton in my head, extending from the bridge of my nose to both crown and right ear. My mom knew of my interest in such technical details, whereby I think she found it helpful to vent the trauma of bearing witness, alone, to the battle of universal forces battled over my fate, which represented her only legacy.
"Sounds expensive." Although I had drifted off, sarcasm still came easily.
"Not to worry; Beamer's father is taking care of it."
"Yeah, right...that fuckin asshole hates me."
"No, he doesn't, and you should thank him when you get out."
"Oh, I see...he must be a client of your agency."
She would have been right to slap me across the face, or worse, but in the given circumstances, chose restraint. "Never mind...I'll do it myself."
"Yeah, you will." I regretted the tactless expression as it escaped my lips. After an uncomfortable silence, my mother sighed poignantly.
"Well, that's enough for today." She sounded subdued by sadness, and I sensed her reaching again for the anesthesia controls.
"No, please...please, no more drugs...I gotta wake up..."
"Shhh...it's all right. There will be time. You need your rest now."
She inhaled deeply, then I felt her lean over to kiss my reconstructed forehead. Though the touch of her lips was imperceptible, I smelled liquor on her breath and heard the impact of a tear upon my bandages before I fell back into unconsciousness.

The roof incident might have been a blessing in disguise, insofar as the coma saved me from the worst of a long-overdue post-X crash while confinement in a hospital bed denied me my usual substances upon waking, but I left with an opiate habit instead. I was on enough painkillers and antipsychotics that rather than getting depressed in my fourth and final week there, I did not think much of what was going on - or much at all, as a matter of course. When the surgical staples were finally removed, a puckered, angular scar remained, running from the bridge of my nose, across my right eyebrow to the temple, then up the hairline to the center of my forehead. Though half of my frontotemporal bone had been removed, the hospital discharged me in traction once my intracranial pressure diminished to a non-critical level, acquiescing to my mom's vehemence. Of all the ways to keep my mind occupied during subsequent isolation in the apartment, I turned fortuitously to the library concealed above my bed.

Ever since my first encounter with <u>The Life and Death of Alexander Fremont</u> he had haunted me in the psychonauticon, thus compelling me to finish. The DARE, included as an appendix to its author's biography, was written in a style meant to mock legalese, and fascinated me with idiosyncrasies as much as it depressed me with dreams from days where the course of history might still have changed if America adopted transitional strategies such as those diagrammed by his fictional Department of Sustainability. Fremont recommended therein, for example, a fundamental redesign of domestic transportation networks, which already dragged decades behind their foreign counterparts in efficiency. He challenged the U.S. to lead the world by phasing out Portland cement, one of largest single sources of greenhouse gases, in favor of magnesium-based materials whose benefits included lower embodied energy, carbon neutrality, superior in-place performance, and the ability to be blended with an equal quantity of fly ash from coal combustion that would otherwise be landfilled. He called for elimination of offset, cap, and trade - the then-current schemes to reduce emissions ostensibly - in favor of a carbon tax. In that time, the federal government issued permits for pollution based on quantity; and if some corporation did not use the entire allowance bestowed upon them, it could be sold unto another. Conversely, if polluters exceeded their quota, they could purchase abstract offsets to compensate, a la indulgences of the Catholic Church. Fremont characterized this system as a death knell, rather than the solution for which it was mistaken in public discourse, because it institutionalized the production of greenhouse gases whilst instilling in American consciousness the view that such pollution, was not only acceptable, but an inalienable right of corporations, so long as they were regulated by the government their campaign funding had selected. "I implore my fellow citizens to remember that even the best system of punitive emissions regulation we can devise is inherently insufficient," he declared in a political rally. "No amount of tax revenue will ever be sufficient to buy extinct species back from the gates of death." According to the scientific consensus of his day, stabilization of an increasingly-erratic global climate would require prodigious removal of carbon dioxide from the atmosphere, instead of merely decreasing the rate whereby human activities added CO_2. What made the emissions trading program so insidious was how it obscured the exigent circumstances by measuring inadequate future goals against peak petroleum availability; while offsets of dubious merit were manipulated with such success in the ensuing years that American pollution actually increased under its auspices. Whenever necessary to protect profits, as allegiance to shareholder interests dictated they must, corporations outsourced their environmental degradation to other countries and commodified nature. They leased the surface of poisoned oceans to trade photosynthetic potential of algae on the stock exchange; and indigenous populations of the tropics suffered forcible eviction from their homelands so American businesses could claim credits for carbon sequestered by their forests, during a process called 'resettlement', albeit tantamount to genocide. Brokers and bankers accrued billions through emissions transactions and precarious speculation, whereas climate change accelerated.

The DARE also described a fundamental restructuring of the USDA to revitalize rural communities, propagating permaculture and farmland restoration in place of the genetically-modified, chemical-dependent, industrialized agribusiness that predominated at the time. There would be no more of the subsidies for cellulosic ethanol that went entirely to the prevailing agricultural regime, and whose production pillaged the soil, requiring as much fuel as it supplied whilst masquerading in advertising and talking points as renewable energy. Instead, Fremont proposed tax credits to be issued for carbon sequestration in cropland, which he viewed as America's most viable carbon sink, encompassing about four hundred million acres, or a fifth of the country's area. This program to regenerate humus stripped by conventional farming methods had been conceived with the ulterior motives of supporting family farms and organic methods; though the prerequisite for such a vision was repudiation of prohibitions on industrial hemp cultivation. *Cannabis sativa*, a renewable source of textiles, paper, food, energy, and so much else, is readily grown without need of biocides; effectively controls weeds in multi-crop rotations; and can rapidly increase soil organic matter content. The commodity crops hemp could supplant, on the other hand, require GMOs to resist the deluge of chemicals required by monoculture, while their collateral damages include cancer, sedimentation, groundwater contamination, and carbon emissions. Given its capacity to produce four times more paper per acre as pulp from trees, hemp might have permitted the restoration of climax ecosystems where they were sacrificed for pine plantations; and via its capacity for liberating habitat to forestall the mass extinction underway, this basic shift of industry drew support from many among wildlife's would-be champions. What began as an obscure piece of irony with a cult audience became a widely-respected, highly-publicized thought experiment; thereby his work with SCI ultimately propelled Alexander Fremont into the spotlight as leading independent candidate for the nation's Presidency, when still scarcely of age eligible for holding the office. Due to a genetic mutation, he had a unique case of postaxial hexadactylism – a perfectly formed, fully functional, supernumerary digit attached to each palm – and the distinctive logo based on his six-fingered handprint greatly enhanced visibility and prominence of his campaign. Ironically, he could not vote, because doing so constituted tacit acceptance of a charade for liberty; to corpocracy's dismay, his condemnation of Federal Government as an "alternation between two brands, where citizens mistake their selection of a demagogue for a flavor of democracy," only increased his popularity. Although its electoral process was allegedly founded on majority rule, the majority of America's electorate typically abstained from participating. Disillusioned by the disappearance of Social Security upon Wall Street, andor stirred by the prospect of a healthier future world, eligible citizens, especially young adults, registered in droves. Fremont's lament that the voting system was inherently flawed spurred them on, as did his refusal to conform with its conventions of decorum. "My goal is to raise awareness, so I am free to speak my truth, rather than what will get me selected," he said, always wearing handmade clothing of natural fiber in public and eschewing neckties, which he judged as anachronistic fashion.

"I cannot imagine why politicians must have a phallus hanging below their mouths, except as a reminder to service their lobbyists," he quipped in an interview with an esteemed journalist that landed him on the cover of a celebrity magazine. Wielding both fluency and charisma, he polled well enough to be included in the traditionally bipartisan presidential debates. Though I do not know what their organizers expected to happen, I found his domination of this forum to be mesmerizing, from the beginning of the first transcript, wherein he asked the Republican incumbent, "Might we discuss something more relevant to the state of the nation than your unconstitutional crusades against abortion and gay marriage?" to its end, when the incensed Democratic nominee gave him the epithet "naïve idealist," and he coolly replied, "Call me what you will, sir, but I still refuse to accept America as it is as the best we can do." During the course of his biography, I felt such admiration for the man and so much resonance with his worldview that I cried myself sore during the book's penultimate chapter, despite already knowing from its title how the tale would end. Just prior to the A.T. 25 election, the leading independent candidate for the American presidency took *The Fates* on a symbolic voyage from New York City to Washington, D.C. at the conclusion of his campaign trail. He sailed as far as the mouth of Chesapeake Bay, where his vessel erupted in flames, vanishing into the night with his body. The Federal Bureau of Investigation, which failed to produce any credible evidence, determined after mere months this had been an accident and issued a public statement presuming Alexander Fremont to be dead. Though it did not hold water, the official line was that if he escaped the burning boat, he would have suffered from hypothermia and drowned long before reaching the shore. In her epilogue, Ariadne Jefferson presented what seemed to me like a far stronger case for assassination by bomb or torpedo. Her conspiracy theory submitted that the only incendiary materials he kept on board were a small amount of ethanol for cooking, and a tank of biodiesel for the inboard motor, neither of which contained adequate energy to cause a fire of such magnitude. Once the boat ignited, there would have been ample time for him to radio for help andor deploy distress beacons. The surface temperature at the site that night was fifty-one Fahrenheit degrees, wherein even an average person could have survived for the time it took the Coast Guard to arrive. As a seasoned explorer who had sailed the Arctic, Fremont possessed both knowledge and endurance to protect himself from hypothermia by treading water. Neither public outcry nor demonstrations within the capital swayed the FBI's peremptory position, and despite suits filed under aegis of the 'Freedom of Information Act', the details of its investigation remain a mystery, as a matter of national security.

"If it is undisputed that such drug has no currently accepted medical use in treatment in the United States and a lack of accepted safety for use under medical supervision; and it is further undisputed that the drug has at least some potential for abuse sufficient to warrant control under the CSA, the drug must remain in Schedule 1..."

~ 'Comprehensive Drug Abuse Prevention and Control Act of 1970' ~

"It is the sense of the Congress that certain drugs are listed on Schedule 1 of the Controlled Substances Act if they have a high potential for abuse, lack any currently accepted medical use in treatment, and are unsafe, even under medical supervision..."

~ Congress of the United States of America, 2 B.T. ~

"I wasted time, and now doth time waste me."

~ William Shakespeare, The Life and Death of Richard the Second ~

FIVE

My time spent in traction was psychically hideous at its outset. Since reading pierced my bubble of illusions, television and virtuality could no longer beguile me, while without the intravenous drip to which the hospital had me hooked, I found nowhere to hide from the deimans inside. In anguished desperation, I feigned the symptoms of virulent influenza and received a few doses of cough syrup and decongestants during the final stages of my comedown, but these were more repulsive than therapeutic. When finally released from restraints to the confinement of a wheelchair, I discovered that Minus seemed to have lost or canceled his iTab; unless calling upon Beamer, I lacked ready access to my preferred substances. Most of my inventory had been confiscated, and I took what remained in an overlooked pocket, only to learn that trolling in bed, at least in a state such as mine, felt decidedly unpleasant. Rather than distracting me from the pain in my head, X exacerbated it; I meant to neutralize the experience via prescription sedatives, and endured the rest of the night in a purgatory of consciousness instead. Wracked by the pressure of uppers but with my will paralyzed, I remained fully aware of my serotonergic seizure as it occurred. The head trauma had taken my sense of balance, leaving me afraid that I would spend my remaining days like Mrs. Jefferson. To my relief, after a month of lethargy, I could make the painstaking trek up and down our stairs with a walker, by efforts trembling from nauseous vertigo. Neuroleptics repressed my suicidal impulses, restoring what psychiatrists might call 'emotional equilibrium' or 'well-adjustedness', but made me feel so spaced out that I weaned myself off voluntarily; the effects of tranquilizers were boring compared to the uppers and hallucinogens I knew and adored. Although we never met, I left my follow-up visit at the cosmetician's office two weeks later with his digital authorization on a script for painkillers. After collecting them from the pharmacy I swallowed a handful impulsively, followed by shots in a bar downtown; then, because I happened to be out, abided my crutches for a wobbly trek to Zion. There was a trance show playing that night, so I lurked around to score some pressies from one of the usual suspects but avoided getting vortexed into the party. I returned home via excruciating effort, took a dose, and collapsed in opioid stupor.

Whereas I had long grappled with neurotransmitter imbalances, the initial sensations of X were a welcome comfort to me. Giddiness seemed as if it extended down to the cellular level, leading to an engaging illusion of myself as one of the white tablets I snorted, which rolled across the tabletop, fell through the abyss beyond, and landed inside my own brain. There I found myself eating a labyrinth of tunnels through the cellular matrix, despite struggling to stop the process once I realized the damage being done, but my vehicle gained momentum from its own consumption. Areas that had been initially illuminated by energetic synapses lost their brilliance until only brittle skeletons of neurons remained, resembling how I imagined the decimated reefs of Sterile Seas whilst I shot through my cerebral cortex with involuntary perforations. I was finally lost in the toxidrome and forced to witness the destruction of my own cognition.

As the opiates wore off, pain brought me back to the land of the living, whereby I rediscovered corporeality with simultaneous agony and relief. Amongst other sensations, I was unable to breathe, sweating profusely, and clenching the sheets in desperation, in order to have a solid handhold for the throes of what might have been my last hour. Deeply unnerved by my vision of a hollowed-out brain, I resolved that if I survived the night, it would be my final troll. Trapped within my poisoned and feverish body, uncertain whether I was in danger of meeting my end, I wanted only to connect with another person again. My mother had gone to work, and I could only think to call Varian; when I did so, her profile redirected me to a memorial wall, indicating that she died recently of an accidental drug overdose. Horrified, but far from surprised, I read the posted comments, in their midst I received a notification of Beamer's relationship status, which had changed to 'single'. Shadows of death surrounded me as my organism sought some semblance of normal metabolism; and I mused upon mortality until he sent a personal message to my iNterface.

'HV XTR TX 4 HYPNTYZ @ ZION – U WNT 2 GO?'

A flood of memories from our escapades, vandalizing and skating all across the city, overcame me. In totality, they told of a friendship that just diminished over time, while drugs became our primary common interest. In the weeks following my leap, I accepted the superficiality of my former relationship to Varian; with her dead, I worried about more than I resented the friend she chose over me. Accepting his invitation, I intended to thank him for saving my life, and warn him against the road leading to toxidrome.

The Tablet arose as the preferred reading format soon after its advent in the early 21st century, at least among U.S. consumers, since bound pages were comparatively cumbersome and unfashionable. More so even than periodicals, promoting iBooks increased profit margins for internet megavendors with neither personnel nor overhead expenses required for warehousing inventory or shipping physical copies. Public officials eventually realized that they could also save volumes of money in schools by switching to computerized curricula, thus tipping the scales of literary media. Rampant deforestation, then desertification, had taken terrible tolls on the raw materials for paper production, while the consequent necessity of recycling only added cost to print publication. By my time, books were considered fossils, with what remained of the written word contained in the Cloud. One of the most recent editions in Mrs. Jefferson's selection was The Freedom To Oppress, which prophesied the censorship that would accompany the decline of printing. Digitization of information allowed an authoritarian regime control over access to the body of human knowledge without risking widespread awareness of their master plan, beginning via the consolidation of data storage in remote servers.

The government imposed its unconstitutional policies on content slowly, first with provisions of the PATRIOT Act and War Of Terror; followed by mandates for fighting the War Of Drugs. Their reach went largely unnoticed until software as a service replaced applications installed on personal computers, rendering hard drives obsolete; although by then their domination was already complete. The nature of information had fundamentally changed, such that instead of possessing the file itself, readers bought the license to view an iBook on their tablets - a permit which could, in turn, be revoked at their government's sole discretion. Once titles vanished down the memory hole, they left behind only the message "error: page not found" in online catalogs; I received similar results when searching for the books in Mrs. Jefferson's collection again and again, which only aggravated my paranoid alienation from society. Her long-protected library, on the other hand, exposed me to realities I never knew existed, and subjects ranging from politics to philosophy, economics to ecology, anthropology to agriculture. The dystopias of a century previous had come to fruition with chilling similarity to my day, while biographies of culture heroes from generations past revealed how effectively the modern masters of American empire suppressed dissent. I felt enthralled and appalled by the history that journalists reported as events occurred because their descriptions contradicted much of what was inculcated in school. I did not previously know, for example, Iraq bore no guilt for 911; or that the ensuing hunt for Weapons of Mass Destruction served as a smokescreen to establish permanent military bases across the Middle East in tactical response to the reality of peak oil. Most fascinating, though, was the evolutionary story of humanity, a subject strangely absent from my compulsory education. I learned that the tenure of hominids on Earth had lasted millions of years, and our specie, hundreds of millennia; but moreover, for the vast majority of our existence, we had lived in tribes - small, decentralized, relatively egalitarian groups whose size, distribution, and livelihood were limited by the carrying capacity of their environment.

When the Pleistocene drew to a close about twelve thousand years ago, an unprecedented chapter of climatic stabilization fostered coincident domestication of staple crops, as well as livestock, thus establishing agrarian societies. Production and storage of surplus enabled population growth; drought, pestilence, and depletion led to territorial expansion; then, where hunter-gatherers were once ubiquitous, an extreme form of sedentary agriculture known as civilization was born. In seven millennia, an eye blink in the story of our species, albeit far less in geological terms, its fields and cities spread to dominate the world, as in the monoculture of invasive species. Unlike innumerable other forms of social organization thus exterminated, the recently-arisen civilized culture was characterized by stratification, with wealth and power concentrated in the hands of an elite few. This ruling class depended on urbanism, specialization of labor, and broadscale grain cultivation to create and sustain the surplus by which they were enriched; laws, police, and a religious caste to protect their supremacy from revolt of the populace; and control of natural resources via military subjugation, in response to the devastation of their own. After living in stasis with the world of life since time immemorial, human population rose from one million to ten billion – multiplied by a factor of ten thousand in as many years – but more importantly, our rate of growth also accelerated. The first increase of human population by an order of magnitude following the advent of agriculture, from one million to ten, happened over approximately sixty centuries; whereas the increase from one billion to ten took only two and half. My exploration uncovered numerous microcosms of this exponential growth throughout recorded history, whose kingdoms and empires expanded whenever presented with favorable conditions, erecting monumental feats of art, architecture, and technology along the way; but once restricted geographically, either by oceans, mountains, or the limitations of their transportation networks – hence, the ability of government to expand its territory – they suddenly collapsed in the face of resource depletion, environmental perturbations, warfare, and/or disease. I realized my society had been so interconnected via trade and technology that it now covered the entire globe, while the necessary abandonment of space travel left no more room for conquest. Furthermore, the climatic stability whereby cereal farming had flourished for its entire existence was over. Atmospheric CO_2 concentration, one of the most significant influences on global temperature, hovered between 260 and 280 parts per million for much of the duration, albeit doubled by fossil fuel consumption in the two hundred fifty years elapsed since the Industrial Revolution. Civilization no longer approached, but had in fact, met and overshot the limits of the world on which it depended. Instead of course-correction, the system resorted to squeezing oil out of tar sands; extracting natural gas from the bottom of oceans; and tearing down mountain ranges to obtain otherwise inaccessible coal or metals. What topsoil had suffered industrial agriculture was barren and blowing away; potable water became unobtainable in many areas; whilst biological capital, from fisheries to forests, disappeared from the world forever. My culture seemed bent on a suicidal trajectory, like a drug addict unwilling to stop ers own self-destruction. Our leaders in education, media, politics, and science, in spite of any alleged intelligence, somehow remained oblivious amidst all this obvious evidence. I disdained their pretensions of human ingenuity and technological salvation; at my recognition of the truth as too horrific or too humbling for most to comfortably contemplate, my intuition said that society as we knew it would end within my lifetime. Still hanging in the balance were the prospects for our species.

My interaction with Beamer seemed incongruous from the start but neither of us dared to remark on the events preceding our time apart. He was chewing his face off, possessed by unsuitably high spirits, whereas I arrived in sober contemplation of the fate that befell Varian and loomed perilously over our generation. He accosted me for a dose prior to entering the venue, totally inconsiderate of my exposure at the security checkpoint; I was not holding, and by my judgment he had indulged too much already. Although I walked without crutches tolerably by then, once inside the McOlosseum I let him to lead the way, making a wedge of his shoulder that shoved into the mob whilst I filled in the negative space of his wake before it collapsed to conserve my energy. Ignoring the annoyed glares of those displaced, we jockeyed our way to a spot at the front, just left of center, which afforded us a little more floor and good lines of sight from behind a group of girls who he guessed might be seeking dance companions. Myriads like us packed the arena, our cumulative chatter amplified by the architecture of steel-reinforced concrete to a roaring resonance. Wherever I glanced, people busily recorded their presence, posting photos, promoting, commenting, tagging and otherwise striving to leave an impression on the digital universe. I did not understand why they chose to cram themselves in a claustrophobic mass, only to escape from whomever they came with via alternate lives on the iNterface. Moreover, and drugs aside, I wondered what effects all the electromagnetic radiation from data transfer had on the audience's mentality; Beamer's, at least, indicated frustration, until he scored a gram off one of our neighbors. I ignored the exchange since my intention was to abstain, but standing alongside, I sensed the ritual of his practiced dip without turning my gaze. In my peripheral vision I saw how he lustfully sucked the residue from his finger, heedless of its taste, and as he reached across his chest, I shuddered at the memory of my experience from the previous week.

"Thanks bro, but I'm good where I'm at."

"No, you're not; you're a fuckin downer, and you're gonna bring me down with you. You need to get high, bro, and I'm here to help; just take it."

Being on the floor next to him, immersed amid a crowd whose intoxication escalated in anticipation of the show, aroused my craving for X as nothing else could. Recreational drug abuse is interpersonally reinforced, validated by social norms, and addictions are thus induced amongst friends by power of suggestion. I felt enticed by the rush in my veins, tingling fingertips, and vibration of my brain that I knew would accompany a good ol' troll. As Fremont said, insanity is repetition of the same mistakes with the expectation of a different outcome; but given access to chemicals, I found it easier to remember the highlights of former doses than their aftermath. Before I was even conscious of extending my arm, the bag sat in my hand.

"Thought so; I know what you want," Beamer said as he passed it to me. I scooped and snorted two bumps, realizing that I would not have been there unless his words were true on some level. My formerly inexorable resolve crumbled when the devil's advocate questioned what harm there be in one more; by then, all of my remorse could never deter destiny.

"Yo, I got your back." He slipped me some pressies with an eyebrow raised.

"Nexus? You sure?"

"Straight from the source."

Without further ado, I knelt to perform my usual rite of cutting up lines.

"So wassup?" I asked aimlessly to distract myself from the nasal burn.

"iNtuition is wassup," he declared as if on cue, whilst from the projectors in his palm a hologrammatic sphere covered in apps appeared whose size and rotation he manipulated with neither his hands nor his voice.

"Upgrade to life beyond the Tab," he announced in the inhuman tone of a hypersonic ad, "because you're only as good as your iNterface." His father's corporation had recently purchased a controlling interest in *Cosmic Conquest* and partially at Beamer's suggestion, the gamemakers decided to take virtuality to the bionic level through a prosthetic CPU, wired for direct communication with the operator's brain. In use already by the military and in China, but not yet available to consumer markets, such technology expressed sensory data via iBorg, a surgically-implanted hardware package; the only visible evidence of his was an inconspicuous dimple that remained from microphone insertion. Although expected to do well enough in the gametrix, by far its most profitable application would be for cybersex, he told me. An adjacent crew of jocks leaned toward us a moment later, jabbering in covetous approval, during his explanation of how the system enabled him to watch television, surf the social network, or 'fuck your mom' whenever and wherever he wanted, without the awareness of anyone else. A natural salesman, he dramatically revealed his 'bling' in conclusion – a strobing array of lights denoting his various embedded sensors, connected to his iNterface by a colorful network of subcutaneous fiberoptics, which glowed brightly courtesy of an implanted power supply. I swooned at the sight as the troll came on faster than I had anticipated.

"Yo, before I forget, I need to thank you," I said at a break in his display.

"No problem." His grin looked threatening. "That's why I'm here."

"Not for that...for what happened on the roof."

"Oh..." He gave me a blank stare. "So...what happened on the roof?"

"When I hit my head, you found me and called the ambulance..."

"Uh-huh," he grunted skeptically. "Ummm...if you say so, bro."

"Come on, be serious for once; I'm trying to thank you for saving my life."

He shrugged. "Whatever...I dunno 'bout all that, but I'll take your word."

"How can you not remember? It was right after school let out..." Suddenly the house lights dimmed, clouds of synthetic smoke rolled off the stage, and at last the ravenous crowd openly blazed. *Hypnotyze* paraded amidst the fog, a dark silhouette except for the embers of two cigarettes that hung like diabolical fangs from either side of his mouth. He marched forward next, arms outstretched, until the front rank could almost grab his ankles; removed a tube from his mouth with each hand; and stood straight, as if crucified, an almighty pretender soaking in the adoration of the crowd.

"New-www Yor-rrkk, putcha motha-fuckin hands in the motha-fuckin SKY and make some motha-fuckin noise for me RIGHT NOW-WWW!" I managed to plug my ears prior to the thunderous howl, which the DJ savored as he made a cavalier nod and high-stepped back to his console. Faustian matrices of translucent tetrahedrons descended from the ceiling, enclosing his minions, followed by a dramatic pause; then the sound began. Admittedly, I found the iNterface light show to be an impressive display of synaesthesia, wherein multitudinous faces of hologrammatic figures grew into computerized patterns that responded to the beats he dropped. By the end of the first set, I was enjoying my troll enough to forget our unfinished conversation, along with thoughts of abstinence from my primary pastime.

"So what the hell happened to Varian?" I asked, recalling part of my original motivation to attend when we went for drinks at the set break.

"I dunno, bro...she just didn't feel good, and wanted to go to the hospital; she was all hot, jerkin' round like that fuckin rich guy...what's his name?"

"Andre Geos WAS his name..." I corrected. "What were you on?"

"Nards and Dex, bro." My jaw dropped. "Robotroll to the next power."

"For fuck's sake...dude, I know I taught you better than that..."

"Yeah, yeah, Dad...but once you dropped off the grid, I couldn't get hold of any Nexus for a stretch. Like they say, make the best of what you have."

"Best of what...since I dropped off...how can you say such things, after you and Varian..." I stammered as Beamer carried on his train of thought, apparently unperturbed, or unaware of why our friendship had ceased.

"...and I'll tell you what, too – with enough X, I can barely tell the difference between a cybertroll and the robo-boost..."

"Dude, didn't you hear anything I said back in the day?!"

He simply shrugged at my dismay. "I dunno...the ol' rob' just wasn't doin' it...if you know what I'm saying ... and I'm pretty sure you do...so I figured you just built up a tolerance...you know, like how you can blow a line during a binge that woulda killed if ya hit it straight outta the gate?"

"No, Beamer, I don't know, 'cause trolling with Dex is not like that... fuckin A, bro, it's not like that at all! You sent Varian to the toxidrome!"

"No sir," he protested, shaking his head adamantly. "And even if...well, you started it...besides, she was just sick, a little twitchy maybe when I left the ambulance, nothing off the wall...it was the medics' fault."

"You left her? The medics' fault? What are you talking about?"

"She's all crying and tears about how the twitching hurt, so they gave her something for pain...it was gonna relax her, but I guess she died instead." This same combination, of analgesics with an already-brewing serotonin storm, had almost killed me the previous week, whilst I witnessed the Nexus eating away my own brain.

"Fuck, man – did you say she was trolling?"

"Course not - that might've gotten her in trouble, duh, maybe even kicked outta school; and can you imagine what my Dad would think?" In face of Varian's imminent death, he had withheld from her physicians information that could have saved her from avoidable contraindications; hence she paid the ultimate price for an EMT's inexperiece coupled with Beamer's fear of the law. "Kicked out of school?! I can't believe you didn't tell them! So, what – I guess you just said that she wasn't feeling well?"

"Yeah, since she wasn't," He made the statement as though a mere matter of fact. "Anyways, they're the doctors. Dad is gonna sponsor a lawsuit for her family; the lab tests clearly showed a mix of ADHD meds, antidepressants, and cough medicine. They really fucked themselves, huh? I just hope their malpractice insurance is worth a damn..."
He gave his attention to the second set, while I could not discern whether his statement had been made out of callous irony, morbid delusion, or both. I wanted to scream, 'No, YOU really fucked up, Beamer', but observed that he was not to blame any more than Varian, for her curiosity; or me, for introducing her to the troll. Ultimately, the fault lay with our culture, whose reigning power system relied upon a monopoly of consciousness, and was so jeopardized by entheogens that its government raced to place all allies with mind-opening, mystical, or entactogenic power on the strictest schedule of the 'Controlled Substances Act'. However, because law is 'nonendogenous', like the cause of my 'depression', it can never stop people from seeking boundary transcendence. In a time of degeneracy such as ours, the most obvious effect was stimulation of criminal ingenuity; the grievous corollaries of the War Of Drugs were drastic degradations in the quality of psychedelic experience and health of its modern participants. Perception alteration is a defining aspiration of our specie; therefore, when narcotics like alcohol and nicotine, religion and television, antidepressants and benzodiazepines would no longer effectively medicate social collapse, designer drugs became inevitable palliatives. The greatest success the DEA may claim is that the natural entheogens with which human neurochemistry and ritual had coevolved for eons were all but stamped out, replaced by a dark world of artificial analogues and potentially lethal recipes. Hastily developed and disseminated to evade the repercussions of prohibition, 'designer drug' was a euphemism whose users were not spiritual seekers, but rather consumers of a carnival ride, driven to substances and situations whence danger or death came for trespasses unto the invisible landscape. We did not ground our ventures in the morphic fields and akashic records that came from millennia of tribal tradition; amidsr the static of mass media and materialist fetishes, we had been left adrift upon the psychonauticon with unfamiliar poisons instead of natural allies. Where humanity once knew shamans, there were chemists, criminals, and salesmen like me, who provided only drugs of suspect composition or unknown purity.
"Yo, see whatcha been missin'?" Beamer jabbed my ribs with a bony elbow. "Fuckin drum n' bass is the shit! This is what the fuck I'm talkin' bout!"
My visuals appeared to have changed for the worse, and I watched in exasperated frustration whilst vague digital shapes exploded repeatedly, disintegrating into chaos as soon as organized images began to emerge.
"You ever wonder about the end?" I asked him, wincing at the volume. He clapped me on the back with a sweaty palm. "What end? The show?"
"No, you know...this...this whole scene, over...no more. No more shows."
Mouth agape in bewilderment, he declared, "Never...I'll never stop."
"But what if..." I paused, formulating my question, pouring through everything I had discovered by reading, imagining what it might look like for someone in his position. "Say the...say the city was flooded, bombed, quarantined for plague...say...or we couldn't get any food...what then?"

He sparked a joint and offered it to me. "Then I gotta have me some weed."
"True 'nuff, bro; I'm serious though...what if some major shit went down?"
The profusion of sweat on his head sprayed me when he shook it resolutely.
"I'm serious, fuckin dead serious. End of the world, disaster-type shit?
Long as I'm fucked up, bring it; I'm gonna party till the end." He took
another hit. "But you shouldn't worry 'bout that shit; bad for your health."
His concern for my well-being seemed genuine, albeit distant; meanwhile,
the beats intensified. Waving his arms from a stance atop a subwoofer, the
DJ seemed possessed, evangelical even, hollering, "New York, you gotta
fuckin gimme every motha-fuckin-thing you got RIGHT NOW-WWW!!!"
The synthetic sound was squeaky clean; too clean actually, for me, insofar
as it reflected a counterculture insulated from the violent, brutal reality
outside our party. Despite the amped ambience, I felt feverish and queasy
from an excess of stimulation. I could not escape anymore; the magic
of trolling was gone; and gazing upon the arms of my peers held aloft in
celebration, the painful truth of the underground hit me like a pile of bricks.
Regardless of apparel, cosmetics, and choice of intoxicants, we were the
mainstream: feeding the inertia of a societally-sanctioned good time with
our mental deterioration; willing to sacrifice the world, freedom, and even
our lives in pursuit of temporary amusement or other meaningless desires.
From the glow cast by his decorative implants, I saw that Beamer trolled
hard; quite beyond domestication, my friend was completely plugged in,
and as such, incapable of behavior beyond the limits of his programming.
He earnestly believed his cybernetic operating system made him the
apotheosis of human evolution, whereas to me his iNtuition embodied its
end. A pang of jealousy came then, at the knowledge that life would never
be the same for me again; I could neither forget what I learned of our past,
nor ignore future portents in blind pursuit of the ultimate high. Patting
his back, I turned to leave with a mixture of compassion and revulsion.
Wriggling out of the mob, my eyes fell on someone I thought I recognized,
head lodged betwixt his knees, squatting off to the side. His black hair was
stringy and matted, starkly framing a face that shone so pale from sweat
it verged on green. He had no shoes, and on approach I figured he must
have been the same guy I met there a year prior, when I took my first X.
"Yo, you aight, bro?" He gave no response, so I uneasily tapped him on the
shoulder with a bottle of Electrolite. The etard who looked up was familiar,
but not for the expected reason; when we met, he had called himself Minus.
"Who's got my downers? Do you? Barbs or benzos? Do you have my
downers? I just need a little help; I gotta go to sleep..."
I jumped back in fright, rubbing my eyes at the sight of the man
that first warned me of the toxidrome, and became precisely what he
disdained; one of those who, in the end, 'couldn't handle their shit'.
"Pay attention," Alexander Fremont instructed, raising a six-fingered
hand in greeting when I glanced back toward the crouching figure.
"You can't be here...now I know this isn't real life, 'cause you're dead."
"Every man dies. Not every man really lives."
"What did you say?"
Then it was Minus staring at me again with big, blank, black eyes.
"I'm...on...drugs?"

"When the masters of media pass this empire down,
they shall pray that their heirs have intelligence enough to ask,
'By what force was such a feat achieved?' To which they will say,
'By no force at all; we only convinced consumers that this was
what they wanted, and in the end they begged us for it.' "

~ Kassandra Deiphoibos, The Freedom to Oppress ~

"He who controls the present, controls the past.
He who controls the past, controls the future."

~ George Orwell, Nineteen Eighty-Four ~

SIX

The disappearance of Alexander Fremont served as impetus for a series
of protests against the subsequent presidential selection lasting until Iran
conducted its first nuclear detonation, beneath the Kavir Desert. With an
estimated yield thirty times greater than the fission weapons that American
planes dropped on Japan in World War II, the Persian test demonstrated
they had developed or otherwise acquired the Holy Grail in Weapons of
Mass Destruction, or hydrogen bomb, despite the Agency-orchestrated
assassination of their top nuclear scientist in the year of the eschaton.
The United States immediately deployed troops to flank both sides of the
Islamic Republic, via permanent military bases in Iraq and Afghanistan,
whilst demanding a worldwide boycott of trade on the grounds that Iran
had violated the terms of the Nuclear Non-Proliferation Treaty. Amongst
the United Nations, officials from Persia asserted their intention to retain
such weapons for the purpose of deterrence, especially in light of Israel's
increasing belligerence. This position underscored the hypocrisy of U.S.
foreign policy; whereas nuclear-equipped Israel also refused to sign the
NPT, American bureaucrats vigorously opposed the Arab League boycott
and all attempts made by the European Union to impose sanctions upon
the Jewish state. In fact, the United States was, at that time, providing
more aid to Israel than any other country, mostly through military grants.
As American forces amassing along its borders, representatives of Iran
declared that, though they did not wish to initiate a conflict, if invaded or
otherwise deprived of sovereignty, they would eradicate Israel without
hesitation and sabotage the Strait of Hormuz, thereby cutting off a full
quarter of the world's oil supply. For a diplomatic alternative, they
offered to dismantle their new weapons and decommission the nuclear
program, submitting to UN inspections in perpetuity - if, and only if, the
State of Israel would accept, and be held accountable to, the same terms.
Thus, the Islamic Republic turned the Great Satan's own greatest weapons,
in the U.S. arsenal as well as its propaganda, into a fulcrum for pacification.

ENTHEOGENESIS · Origin of the Divinity within Us

In response to the charges of NPT violations, Persian officials indicted the five permanent members of the Security Council for bolstering their own stockpiles in recent years, despite the pledge therein to eliminate them. The Islamic Republic even proposed worldwide disarmament, to fulfill stated intention of the treaty, lest the apocalypse of Enoch, Ezekiel, and John come to fruition in Zion. However, the re-selected Washington executives, who were never interested in establishing a nuclear-free Middle East, called instead for Iran's annihilation, based on the doctrine of preemptive counterattack espoused by the Bush II administration after 911. Resistance from Congress and industry deterred the White House because Iran contained a tenth of known petroleum reserves, comprising much of the world's most accessible and highest quality crude. In the end, they deemed such escalation strategically inferior to the mercenary option.

Beamer continued to pay for my subscription to the ad-free iNterface, perhaps out of friendliness or forgetfulness, though neither would have surprised me, making my return to school as a senior unlike any year prior. Where windowless corridors had been smothered by the animations of its corporate sponsors were merely peeling paint and mandatory instructions. Without hypersonic marketing, I heard little more than a humming student hive full of consumer drones shuffling and mumbling along their well-worn pathways to pupation in an apparently alternate but coextant universe. My newfound modicum of mental clarity also transformed my aesthetic perspectives. As a junior, I evaded some of advertising's influence, or allayed boredom, via quests to push my scholastic intoxication to the limit - crossing the line once on a robotroll that had me puking in the infirmary with a heart rate comparable to Andre Geos' - ergo, I became accustomed to the appealing softness of a world overlaid by streaming visuals and rainbows of hallucinogenic afterglow. In their absence I saw a prison whose guards, by blindly upholding the system, subjugated themselves as much as their inmates despite not knowing it; in fact, they could not know, because doing so would be a violation of the very laws of their existence. If blind obedience failed, coercion perpetuated the power structure by necessity, since no actualized person I can imagine would voluntarily submit to moral bankruptcy. My school, hifalutin though it may have been, retained all the guns, security, surveillance, and psychiatry of the bound society for which it prepared me. Other members of my caliber ignored or accepted the cage, focusing on their test scores, academic success, and aspirations to elite job placements; but I had no interest in joining this competition to climb atop a social structure infected with insanity, founded on slavery, and teetering at the brink of catastrophe. The student body, if you will, comprised the sole biomass within a maze of steel-reinforced concrete, making education a microcosm of the general populace in urban culture. Although we might be blind to its wards, our movements were scheduled whilst our behaviors were regulated by a steady stream of entertainment, addiction, propaganda, and materialist fetishes, carefully administered to effect acceptance of the hierarchy. A few classmates who had missed my services that summer asked about the cranioplasty upon approaching me for a hook-up; once they believed at last I was out of business, life went on as usual for them, but not for me. In contrast to my home course of independent study, I found compulsory classes intolerable and distrusted, by irrevocable default, the institutions that postured for education after I learned their true purpose was training faithful servants. The curriculum as well as commercials both seemed to be created for low intelligence because they actually intended this result. Citizens capable of critical thinking were dangerous; thus any who ever grew wise enough to agitate would be neutralized, or mollified by elevation to the nouveau bourgeoisie before they thought to band together in revolt. To keep my books secret, I only read when my mom went out with clients, and compensated for lost sleep by dozing in class if I could. The bloodshot eyes, darkened sockets, and gaunt features of my reflection reminded me of a zombie, but I felt more alive than ever, motivated for once by my own interests, rather than just reacting to my peers, authorities, surroundings, or the effects of drugs, all of which were dead to me. Genuine passion from an inquisitive intellect, welcome as it was in comparison to the numbness and delirium of my past, came with the painful awareness that I remained as much a victim of my culture as those around me. In my judgment, they either did not know or did not care, leading me to profound alienation, then an inability to accept their attitudes at all. I chose solitude over the parties, clubs, and shows I had frequented a year before, when novelties of the psychoactive underworld defined my life, and self-esteem stemmed from the importance of a role therein. Isolation enabled me to wallow in books and disgustipation, whereby I indulged as surrogate for inebriation. Since I could not stop the suicidal charge of my civilization from the cliffs of carrying capacity, I thought to watch from the high horse of ideologies.

Monday of the third week happened to be the anniversary of 911, and a speech broadcast by our illustrious mayor interrupted school's normally-scheduled programming. Citing the horror of that infamous date, she invoked the emotional power of tragedy with an accounting of casualties in her preamble; went on to commend New York City for its responsiveness; and praised the phallic glory of the World Trade Center built in place of the Twin Towers. Reckoning finally how the United States had smitten the evildoers, she assured her viewers their nation's God-given supremacy in ethics, as in global politics, was incontestable and permanent. After reading America's true history all weekend, this eulogy struck me as an unbridled celebration of imperialism; thus, when national anthem began, I could not bear to stand. Because my station sat toward the back of the room, I dreamed at first with lazy, reckless hope of evading detection; but by the rockets' red glare, the monitor on duty noticed my nonconformity and ordered me to my feet. She epitomized the worst of humankind mercilessly merged in a single enormous, ignorant person, who by my admittedly myopic psychoanalysis, abused her magisterial position to compensate for the wounds of personal inadequacy. Although my test scores ranked among the best in her section, by correcting errors I had crossed her before and sensed that she was out to get me ever since. "On principle, I respectfully refuse," I called over the hymn. A girl across the aisle stifled an indiscreet laugh at my reply, while in spite of permanent

cosmetics by which the teacher attempted to conceal her hideous face,
it swelled red from frustration of deimans I expected she would exorcise.
"Get up this instant, or suffer the consequences," she snarled;
"Who do you think you are? People died for this country..."
"And so many more have died, and will die, BECAUSE of this country..."
By then my adrenaline pumped with effectiveness that no non-endogenous
stimulant possessed, priming me for the reflexive retort. Blood buzzing in
my ears blocked out what additional noise she issued, and I watched her
tantrum like a distant projection at low volume. Disturbed interest from
fellow pupils became perceptible once the 'Star Spangled Banner' reached
its crescendo; by the coda I merely stared at the floor, musing on whether I
committed a terrible mistake. The impulse to escape drew my gaze toward
the door, but I knew the damage was done. I had waited long enough, and
after mobilizing my disobedience, the time arrived for me to see it through.
"How dare you dishonor the flag!" she declared, spewing spittle in my
direction. Although I considered restraint momentarily, arrogance took
hold of my articulation, and words rolled off my tongue as if channeled
from some foreign source of intelligence. "I thought that this country's
flag represented freedom from tyranny. Doesn't coerced patriotism
contradict its founding principles? Isn't mandatory allegiance a farce?"
Whereas her mouth opened and shut, no sound came out. Instead of
responding to me, she called security, describing my attitude as insolent
and defiant in hushed tones. Gaining momentum, I shouted over her;
when my rant started heating up, she uttered the fateful words,
"Yes, that's the one," followed by a pause; then, "Thank you, sir."
"Look, it's happening right now!" I screamed at her vindictive grin.
"We are accomplices in our own destruction, so any dissent must be
silenced - but our acceptance of the same illusion doesn't make it real!
They killed Alexander Fremont because he spoke out against this
mass insanity, and presented a workable plan for a better world.
You might be thinking, 'I never heard of him', and it's true; that's what
I'm telling you...he ran for President, and it wasn't enough to kill the man;
since his vision would live on, they erased him completely from history.
Don't bother searching the Cloud; don't ask your teachers who he was;
they also know only what they're told, and are as ignorant as you..."
My classmates were entertained by my animated display, not attentive.
Two uniformed officers entered the classroom whilst I was mid-sentence,
and the monitor pointed at me unnecessarily. One of them nodded to the
other, who raised his remote; I wish I could say that I struggled valiantly,
but the tazer rendered me inert almost instantaneously. Although an ID
chip containing the receiver had been implanted in my neck since birth,
I was never previously subjected to its force. Anyone I ever met who had
could not describe the sensation per se; they told me only that somehow
the device made them want to obey. I felt what they meant immediately;
it stopped just before the guards cuffed and injected me with a sedative,
leaving time for one final thought, which I endeavored to convey aloud.
"You must refuse their ration of compulsory indoctrination, because we
will always be subservient to whoever controls education, until or
unless we take responsibility for our own in...form...ation..."

Relations between America and China had been tense for years preceding the Iranian nuclear test; however, they remained dependent on each other as trading partners, and once melting ice of the Northwest Passage permitted commercial shipping, it benefited the economies of both nations. Canadians insisted initially that use of these waterways for international transit infringed on their sovereignty, but they soon found an ally in the People's Republic through oil drilling contracts, lucrative shipping traffic in new Arctic deepwater ports, and the protection afforded by a larger military than their own. They also granted leases to the Chinese for the harvest of methane from their permafrost, via matrices of polyethylene greenhouses on styrofoam pontoons measuring hundreds of miles in length, which thawed the tundra and captured biogas thereby released for fuel.

Due to methane in Earth's atmosphere causing many times the global warming effect of the equivalent carbon dioxide produced from burning it, anaerobic decomposition in vast bogs of the formerly Great White North comprised a frightening meteorological variable whose positive feedback could lead to the runaway climate change prophesied by meteorologists.

Although hailed as a miracle, the amount of biogas harvested with the Chinese technology paled in comparison to its cost; yet what appeared to be mercantile insanity was vindicated as shrewd enterprise in the end. Because even the most optimistic climate change models anticipated that the permafrost would melt, the value of associated emissions offsets to be collected in the marketplace solidified the Sino-Canadian alliance. Without an ocean separating them, perhaps the American government felt the People's Republic had gotten too close for comfort, and in any case their competition for Arctic petroleum reserves was far from welcome. The fact that China held a third of U.S. foreign debt, equivalent to a tenth of the entire population's annual income, already strained the relationship. American politicians presumed the Chinese could never withdraw support for the dollar, since the majority of their monetary reserves were in USD assets, while their manufacturing relied on the United States as a market; and when China and Russia toppled the FED's hegemony by announcing that oil of the latter would be traded on currency of the former, the shifting balance of power seemed to go over the heads of orthodox economists. Some of them claimed if the People's Republic ceased buying U.S. bonds, dollars would be unaffected, graphing national debt alongside inflation to support their facile declaration of no correlation. By the arrival of the eschaton, American demographics had shifted such that Social Security did not cover expenses; with fewer people paying, and more retirees receiving benefits, the system eroded its own trust fund, whereas domestic security and military expenditures left the Federal budget in perennial deficit. Privatization was recommended as a solution; then the nation's retirement disappeared in a tragic mystery on Wall Street; and upon total confidence in their sophistry, a smug government colluded with the central banking syndicate to print more money. Maybe Chinese leaders resented the new weaponization of space and overpriced Nuclear Missile Defense Shield begat by their investments in U.S. currency; or they saw that the American empire had overreached, affording a clean shot at one of its vulnerabilities;

perhaps they were strictly concerned with longterm dividends. Their reaction to the 'Economic Redemption Act' of 2023 was what its financial engineers had thought unthinkable. Whether deliberate or not is still up for debate; regardless, by dumping U.S. treasury securities, the People's Republic made real at last the credit crisis that had always been a false alarm of the Federal Reserve. China thus took a tremendous loss on the devaluation of the dollar, but got out of the casino with capital to spare. The absence of correlation between foreign debt and domestic inflation promulgated by American economists was not tantamount to a lack of relationship, as events bore out; rather, the FRAUD constituted a Ponzi scheme, artificially propped up from inception, which collapsed of its own bankruptcy faster than most expected once the People's Republic finally decided to withdraw support. China thenceforth began industrious expansions of its previously modest nuclear arsenal, joining with Russia for the promise of an Eastern prosperity, and it became clear that the world's most populous country positioned itself to emerge as the next superpower. When the American proposal for a global boycott of Iran was presented to the UN after the Kavir nuclear test, diplomats from China exercised the veto power bestowed by permanent membership of the Security Council. Their economy depended on Iran as a source of oil, liquefied natural gas, and mineral resources; invested heavily in Iranian power generation, mining, and transportation infrastructure; and found among the Persian populace a market for refined fuels, consumer products, and weapons technology. Although their vote could not have been a surprise, the U.S. government declared it to be support of terrorism - as such, an act of war against the homeland, along with its allies. In response, Chinese officials mocked the quarter-century War On Terror post-911 as a 'War Of Terror'. The only Axis of Evil, by their well-founded assessment, was an invention of the White House propaganda machine to justify invasion and intimidation of foreign countries, thereby establishing military preeminence in areas of strategic importance to the endgame for control of the world's remaining petroleum reserves. The United States' foreign policy, in truth, epitomized the definition of terrorism, both via the indiscriminate violence against noncombatants, as well as coercion through systematic use of fear. Boasting more military spending than the rest of the world combined, 'Department of Defense' was actually a sardonic misnomer for the most aggressive, extensive, and effective terrorist organization of all time.

My vision swam amid tearful disorientation whilst the guards dragged me to the disciplinary office, where I reluctantly assumed the position for a body cavity search, followed by tissue samples. There was no need for restraints once the antipsychotics took effect, but they confined me to a cold concrete cubicle for several hours with harsh lighting and no plumbing. I huddled in a corner, numb except for the urge to piss, which I barely resisted until the impassive receptionist's voice called via intercom, "He will see you now." A burly armed escort opened the door to my cell; after observing my toilet visit, he led me to a warm, carpeted office, where the well-groomed superintendent of security reclined in a massage chair, making it plainly evident that he was perusing my dossier on his iTab.

"Come in, come in; make yourself comfortable," he said with false courtesy, making a production of the hydraulic adjustments required to sit upright. "Well, I must say your case is interesting, and the rare kind that makes me earn my pay grade." His jowls bounced nauseatingly as he chuckled. "Your aptitude scores are high, maybe too high for your own good... at least according to the teacher who filed the report...let's see...she describes you here as haughty and belligerent, while your lab results indicate abuse of almost every illegal substance for which we can test... but you refuse to take your prescription from the school psychiatrist." He scrolled through my photos, iNterface messages, and bank statements, jumping finally to video from that morning. "Take a look," he taunted, gesturing with a leer to my hologrammatic figure before muting the sound. "It seems your father moved here to work on Zion, got laid off, and was accidentally killed on the job as a subcontractor for the Port Authority. Your mother lived in Babylon before marriage, and has employed herself since his death as a prostitute. Although known to carry an unregistered nine-millimeter handgun, and in spite of multiple arrests, she has avoided any prosecution, presumably by the services of her agency...while you are trafficking narcotics, but haven't been caught in a transaction yet." He coughed for effect, glanced at his watch, and drank some Electrolite. "I'd like to get out of here by happy hour, so I'll come straight to the point. Your traitorous behavior this morning would ordinarily be grounds not only for expulsion, but prosecution by Homeland Security. As a minor still, you would probably be sentenced to a Voluntary Service Colony for rehabilitation. However," he crooned, leaning across the desk, "because I hate to see a good mind go to waste, I noticed, in addition to your drug problems, that you've never had a prior infraction like this; you were quite young when your father died; and you suffered some head trauma recently. In consideration of such factors, exceptions can occasionally be made for exceptional students, if and only if they obey the rules. What do you say?" Using my drowsiness as a disguise, I nodded disingenuously at his smile.

"That's what I thought. To this end, you'll be on a prescription for Conformazine and required to provide a urine sample daily...just so we can ensure that you're not forgetting to take your medication. You will have meetings twice a week with the psychiatrist, once a month with me, until we agree you've been reformed; and you're suspended for the rest of this week, but that is where my leniency ends. I won't protect you if there is another offense; you'll be lucky to find yourself chained on an assembly line for the rest of your life. Do I make myself clear?" With effort to appear passive, I silently indicated my assent again.

"It's obvious from your transcript that you are one of the few who have the potential to contribute. Rather than complaining about the world, you could cure cancer, design new bridges, or help implement nuclear fusion. I strongly suggest you use your time away from our prestigious facility to clean yourself up, get your act together, and reflect on how you can best offer your abilities to our country when you graduate...since I expect you to apply yourself to that goal for the term remaining once you return."

In truth, I wished for him and all of his ilk to die of cancer, fall from collapsing bridges, or be electrocuted by their defective consumer goods.

I imagined screaming in his face my hatred of his precious civilization, and that I wanted nothing more than to see it come crashing down. Fantasy notwithstanding, the tranquilizer worked toward his favor instead. "Yes, sir. I will, sir." Avoiding his icy gaze, I meant my lowered eyes to seem contrite, which must have worked as he grunted with satisfaction. "I've explained this to your mother and am releasing you into her custody." Then a call came on his iNterface, ending the recording of my episode. "Anything else?" I rose to my feet lethargically to seize the opportunity. "Hold on a moment," he said, distracted. "Just one more question..." I froze in midreach for the door handle. "Who is Alexander Fremont?" My heart leapt to my throat while I feigned confusion. "Beg your pardon?" "Alexander Fremont," he enunciated. "In your...shall we say...outburst this morning, you claimed that he had been erased from history." "Oh, right..." I composed myself to conceal terror. "He appeared in a hallucination after I hit my head, and I got a little flashback today." "I see." The superintendent squinted his eyes at me. "So he isn't real?" "No, sir." I would not let my Adam's apple move, but he was unconvinced. "Are you sure about that?" he asked slowly, amid a taut silence. "Yeah..." I sighed, intent on seeming casual, "...I'm...on...drugs." "Well," he began, grinning from the victory, "I know this much is true. That's the reason they've sent you, and in the end, you will thank me." Since my act had persuaded him, I allowed a swallow at last. "Yes, sir." "You're sounding better already. There may be hope for you."

At the time of Iran's nuclear test, no nation besides the United States had ever used atomic weapons in warfare, and its policies reserved the right to a nuclear first strike; as opposed to the posture of China, whose strategy for dominance concentrated on economic efficiency, rather than projection of military might. In light of potential blowback from the international community, American politicians declined to exercise the Holy Grail of WMDs against the Islamic Republic, though they offered an encouraging pledge of full support if Israel would do so in their stead. Upon interception of these covert communications, the Chinese navy moved its expanded fleet of ballistic missile submarines into the Persian Gulf and Mediterranean Sea, as protection for Iran, in case the need should arise. Meanwhile, all public evidence of the Agency's conspiracy with Israel was successfully scrubbed from American media, which reported the news thenceforth as if it had never occurred; in relinquishing physical data storage to centralized remote servers, it seemed that people also lost their biological memory. As the rhetoric of preemptive counterattack, foreign internal defense, and preventive war rose to a grotesque pitch, an amnesiac populace readily succumbed to fear, the standard weapon of governmental coercion. Outrage over Alexander Fremont's assassination gave way to astonishment that anyone could support such insanity as disarmament and gratitude for the regime reinstated to protect America. White House jargon, along with hate-mongering pundits, blamed the Chinese for everything from fuel shortages to unemployment, foreclosures to famine; then, on Valentine's Day, the U.S. Navy erroneously reported that their submarines were deploying missiles from the Arabian Sea.

Thus it came to pass that the United States launched an unrestrained nuclear offensive, with neither provocation nor congressional approval. Although this was hardly the first time its masters of government had used an illusory threat as excuse to make war, the unconscionable scale of the attack caught Chinese targets unawares. Despite recent expenditures to bolster its arsenals, the People's Liberation Army Air Force could not deliver bombs by plane adequately for minimal deterrence; while unlike its assailant, China lacked satellite launch capabilities or sophisticated early warning systems. The cumulative explosive power of the thousand-plus American warheads that ultimately reached their marks approached a billion tons of TNT - greater in total magnitude than the eruption of Mount Tambora, the most violent geologic event in recorded history. This decapitation strike effectively took out China's eyes, ears, and most of its retaliatory capacity, leaving only a handful of weapons housed in hardened underground silos or aboard the submarine fleet for a feeble, uncoordinated counterattack that finally tested the United States' legacy of exorbitant military spending. American defensive systems in Romania and the Middle East destroyed all of the Chinese sea-launched ballistic missiles during their boost phase except one, which escaped the Mediterranean carrying eight independently targetable re-entry vehicles, with a trajectory indicating New York. Four of the bombs had been allocated to its metropolitan boroughs, and two for New Haven; high-yield bursts in the upper atmosphere neutralized these upon reentry. However, such countermeasures were acts of desperation whose secondary electromagnetic pulse effects paralyzed the nation's own guidance systems. To the shock and awe of its citizens, a pair of Chinese warheads fell from the sky like supernova stars above the Thames River's mouth in southern Connecticut. Targets of strategic significance there included the United States Naval Submarine Base as well as the shipyard of General Dynamics Electric Boat, where its fleet was built. Incineration wiped New London off the map instantly, along with the U.S. Coast Guard Academy; while in nearby Waterford, the EMP caused a Corium meltdown of Unit Two at the Millstone Nuclear Power Plant. Fallout from the detonations, plus radiation released by the reactors, forced evacuation of vast swaths of Connecticut, Rhode Island, Massachusetts, and Long Island, extending for dozens of miles beyond the zones of initial mortality. Although a handful of Chinese warheads on sub-optimal flight paths made it past missile defenses for the Pacific islands, California and the continental Northwest went unscathed. Before U.S. Air Force bombers had arrived in Asia for a second wave the People's Republic of China surrendered. This thousand-megaton Exchange was considered modest by some, compared to an active stockpile whose combined potential yield worldwide exceeded it by an order of magnitude. The conflict lasted less than four hours, but caused the death of over half of the Chinese population – or a tithe on the entire human race.

"They who can give up essential liberty
to obtain a little temporary safety deserve neither."

~ Benjamin Franklin ~

"The truth will set you free, but first it will piss you off."

~ Gloria Steinem ~

"To believe that one can have infinite growth in a finite system,
one must be either a madman or an economist."

~ Kenneth Boulding ~

"Better to die on one's feet than to live on one's knees."

~ Jean-Paul Sartre & Emiliano Zapata ~

SEVEN

My mother behaved impersonally, refusing to make eye contact with me,
until she had collected my prescription from the pharmacy. Whilst hidden
from the world behind her tinted windows, we were also protected from the
mephitic city fumes by the air conditioning of a car constituting at once the
tool of her vocation, her most valuable possession, and a financial liability,
insofar as it grew ever more expensive to operate with the passage of time.
"I'm not taking that crap," I told her when she handed me the vial.
"After what you did today, I'm afraid you don't have a choice."
"Sure I do; I can drop out of school, and find work in the trades…"
"Yeah, or you can get yourself tazed." A shiver came at her reminder.
"Let me talk to some people," she sighed. "Maybe you can transfer…we'll
get this cleaned up…they can't even show that you've really done anythi…"
"Clean it up? With your agency? With your corrupt clients? For what?"
I found myself shouting in spite of the drugs. "This – world – is – FUCKED!"
She told the car to pull over, staring straight ahead as I caught my breath;
then removed a flask from her purse, took a long pull, and offered it to me.
"Jesus, Mom…you should know better…I'm on tranks, for fucks' sake."
"I'm pretty sure your body has seen far worse," she surmised, savoring
another draft. As for most Americans, alcohol was her escape of choice;
a deliriant of the legal syndicate that predominated, next to the stimuli
of sugar and caffeine, because it reliably induced the prerequisite apathy,
self-indulgence, and stupor for the perpetuation of our society; whereby
my mother held her deimans at bay with one hand, her head with the other.

"You're just like your goddamned dad, and if you're not careful, you'll get yourself killed like he did," she warned, though her words confounded me.
"I thought he died in a construction accident," I objected.
"Yeah, that's what the contractors called it," she replied, laughing ruefully, "but it's no coincidence that he threatened to blow the whistle on them." In profile, the attitude of her elegant jaw attested to grim acceptance.

I knew from photos that she had been born naturally beautiful; and by social norms she was still profoundly attractive, with vestiges of her youth extended by the best cosmetology she could afford; yet beneath aesthetic proportions, the life had left her face, which looked as if she would never smile again. "Although I probably shouldn't tell you, he would be proud." This comment gave more insight into my father's personality than she had ever previously afforded. Marriages typically appeared to me like business partnerships, with neither party capable of, or interested in, real intimacy; ergo, it was no wonder the majority ended in divorce. The story I gathered over the years implied that my parents, on the converse, shared a truly deep love, albeit much too brief. When she answered my questions with silence, I assumed his absence left a wound she could not heal. Exhausted by the struggle, it seemed she had submitted to grief and accepted bitterness; more troubling was my projection that, in the wake of their tragic romance, she became unable to find a satisfactory mate or enjoy such feelings again. Perhaps she excelled at her occupation because she bore it with bleak determination instead of fantasizing about another kind of relationship. Despite her efforts at secrecy, by keeping these sorrows between herself and the bottle, the resentment was evident to me. With the opening she offered, I felt compassion for my mother, terrible regret for the insults I had hurled in the hospital, and closer to her than I had in memory. "I'm sorry he's gone," I said, reaching for her hand, which felt cold and fragile. I suspect that the visible toll taken by alcoholism caused her stress with respect to work prospects, and left death looming over her expectantly. At a sigh, tears welled in her eyes spilled down her face; elsewise, her surgically-enhanced, botoxed features betrayed no emotion. "You have nothing to be sorry about." She wiped her cheeks and sniffled, then wrenching sobs began; I had not seen her so discomposed before. "I'm sorry," she cried, "...sorry you didn't get the chance to meet him."

By the vernal equinox, private contractors in employ of the United States overwhelmed the Islamic Republic of Iran with conventional and biological munitions. Though these operations were subject to media blackout, the White House press secretary issued reports of elite mercenaries whose surgical precision protected oil fields, along with associated infrastructure. Israel remained intact, and the Strait of Hormuz was reopened within months of its sabotage; while particulates thrown into the stratosphere by the Exchange reduced temperatures worldwide, prolonging the attendant winter. American climatologists celebrated this effect as an unintended benefit at first since it apparently counteracted global warming, which had by then become intractable; but when the last planting dates for corn and soy elapsed, their optimism turned to dismay. Loss of the entire season's grain harvest in Canada was a foregone conclusion, while rice production

throughout Asia suffered terribly from the disruption of its monsoons. The fall gave rise to the most destructive weather event in American history as a maelstrom combining characteristics of a blizzard and hurricane wreaked havoc along the Atlantic seaboard. After months of drought, the quantity of airborne dust that drifted from China provided enough ice nuclei to inundate areas from New York to Boston with ten feet of snow. Roofs not blown away by high winds collapsed, ill-equipped to withstand the weight of such loads; drifts came up to the gutters of commercial buildings; with the power grid crippled, indoor plumbing froze and ruptured. More damaging still was the storm surge, which turned the streets of lower Manhattan into torrents. Flooding pushed ships over the new seawall; automobiles swirled in underground garages or scattered like corks; whilst sudden power outages and pump failures caused untold drownings in the artificially dry labyrinth of its subways. Tides breached the outer barrier of Long Island, washing away the human developments of Montauk, the Hamptons, and beyond. Nantucket, Martha's Vineyard, Aquidneck, and Cape Cod were similarly decimated, as if the gods meant for the shoreline homes of New York and New England's rich and famous to get swept away all at once. Many of these areas were formerly evacuated for radioactive fallout, mercifully reducing the death toll, especially among the upper crust; although without electricity, transportation, or adequate apparel, myriads of those stranded thus died from exposure and famine.
When the Federal Emergency Management Agency finally grasped the Superstorm's significance, the worst-affected region was paralyzed, leaving naught to do but wait; plagued by incompetence, it had already been overtaxed by the initial relocation of residents from critical fallout areas after the Exchange. As the ice thawed, local officials necessarily suppressed the staggering extent of chaostrophe and number of corpses strewn across the coastal northeast. By decree of President Adriaen, FEMA withdrew all of its operations to New York City, which had better weathered the storm, on the pretenses that recovering Manhattan was symbolically essential to national morale, while the branches of its railway system and existing utilities permitted transportation of refugees to a temporary encampment in Central Park, secured by the militarized NYPD. Insurance companies denied claims for property destroyed during the Superstorm, and banks holding the mortgages got bailed out, whereas the indebted homeowners, most of whom paid more for their dwellings than they were worth, lost any accrued equity. With the resources of government stretched thin, the only option available to homeless victims was resettlement in facilities established via eminent domain atop the Marcellus Shale, whose property values and water quality suffered from consequences of hydraulic fracturing for natural gas. Ghettoized evacuees built sprawling permanent slums, enclosed by fencing around inhumane structures of precast concrete, which eerily resembled prisons; these were prototypes for the Voluntary Service Colonies that would receive millions of desperate applicants in years to come. Displaced members of the elite, however, received compensation for destroyed property from Manhattan real estate, via the development of Central Park after FEMA departed. Although inconvenienced by moving to alternate residences between the

Superstorm and completion of apartment towers, their patient endurance was for the common good. As the most expensive residential construction project in history, the new compound gave a moribund economy another breath; but the Central Parkade comprised much more than that, with garages, malls, offices, a power plant, and the McOlosseum at Zion. Vacancies in outer Manhattan and other boroughs were filled by those among the middle class who had escaped destitution, and hence, the VSCs. In response to the eventual announcement that the United States of America would default on its debts, the international community was silent. The Exchange, and its aftermath, had been tremendous expenses, borne to protect the world from the aggression of a sinister nation pursuing its own hegemony above all else. Peacekeeping forces used to service targets in Iran were necessary to ensure stability in the Middle East by neutralizing the threat of defiant tyrants eager to unleash instruments of terror against innocent civilians. Rebuilding the infrastructure of China, to restore the manufacturing industries on which the global economy depended, could cost dearly in years ahead, once radioactivity and nuclear winter abated. As a matter of course, the indefinite presence of American military forces was required to establish freedom and democracy for a population that had suffered terribly beneath an authoritarian regime.

Without other tolerable entertainment, I took to watching people during my suspension with such curiosity as only abstention would bring. My morbid idea that we unknowingly wandered the halls of our own hell already led me to the Plaza. Although run over before the summer and subsequently lost, replacing my skateboard, so I might more healthfully occupy my time, did not occur to me until Friday. There I stalked with ambivalent fascination a specimen whose obesity was veritably disabling. He became lost amidst the balconies due to a GPS error, which had him driving in circles whilst his commands to the iNterface verged on hysterical. I could have shown him the way, but grew more interested in observing the outcome, thus choosing not to intervene. Upon complete depletion of his shopping cart battery, he cried in fear of being stranded, until a security guard finally towed him out of the mall. I watched the incident with mixed feelings of pity and amusement; then a message from Beamer interrupted my sardonic reverie, saying he urgently needed me to meet him at his building. Given the nature of our last exchange, I should have been disinclined to respond, except for the possibility of the call being related to his father cleaning up my transcript. My skating was wobbly and had me wheezing when I met him by the gates of the atrium, an artificial paradise that included valets and cul-de-sac, hidden from public view at the base of the Park Towers. Although our settings emphasized the economic gulf between us, we exchanged courteous daps through the bars, whereby he casually handed me an envelope, as if conducting a reverse drug deal. "My dad asked me to give this to you." Due to his apparent confusion, I knew he had not read the note inside, which was handwritten by my mom and folded around a pair of iNterface lenses. At the time, I did not know how to write; thus, deciphering her childish script required effort:

DHS came here. I had to let them in. They took your books, saying they just want to talk to you, but I have a bad feeling. Please don't come back and don't contact me; destroy this note, lose your tablet, then go as far away as you can. The iWare is cloned from mine, so it should get you on a train if the scanners aren't paying attention. I hope that I'll see you again someday; if not, take care of yourself wherever you may land. Love, MOM

"What's with the covert ops? You in trouble?" Beamer asked.
Stunned, I mumbled something vaguely credible about his Dad pulling strings on my behalf and thanked him for delivering the message.
"Umm...why couldn't he do it on the iNterface?" he pressed.
"He probably doesn't want to be incriminated by surveillance," I replied, covering quickly from the sickly fears my secret provoked.
"Ah-hah!" Beamer grinned at the notion of being an accomplice.
"You see? I told you it's good to have friends in high places; and you thought Dad hated you," he remarked with a wink.
I still wonder whether he was ignorant of, or merely indifferent to, the very likely true nature of the relationship between our parents.
"I need a favor," I added. "Tell him thanks, for me...can you do that?"
"Sure man, whatev." He motioned then for me to lean closer. "Speaking of, where can a dude get a hookup? I tried Minus, but he's outta commission, and I'm coming down hard, I mean HARD bro, you know what I'm saying?"
Up close, I smelled sickness festering on his breath as he spoke and saw spastic twitching around his eyes, both of which heralded the toxidrome.
"Nah, actually...but maybe...you...should...come down for a while."
He leaned back, regarded me quizzically, and affirmed my concern with laughter, since his addictions had convinced him I meant it as a joke.
"It's cool; I'll figure out something..." he said, lighting a cig. "By the way, you going to the show tonight? I'll buy your tix if you wanna do halfers on a bag...they've never played here and word is it's gonna be die-no-might..."
"I don't know..." I began, refusing the money he thrust at me. "I've heard the bass nectar, I've seen the pretty lights...yet, to what end? It's always the same spectacle; another brand wearing a new mask. Don't you think there is more to life than just getting fucked up and being entertained?"
His vacant gaze held no perceptible glint of a soul. "If I can, why should I?"
Conceding that my friend was utterly enslaved by this consumer solipsism, I bit my lip with despair and let go of hope; his fate lay beyond my control.
The sun hid behind an ominous wall of indigo thunderheads looming to my west, whose progress toward the city I marked via shadelines on the towers.
"Yo, I gotta roll right now; we'll catch up later," I lied, skating away from him to swap my optics in a Starbux restroom; although the prescription was wrong, I could make do. Breezeways were clogged by the weekend rush of pedestrians and happy hour, so despite poor vision I threw my board down, taking my chances in the streets. I pushed furiously astride the lanes, at first to beat the rain, then to stave off panic, as my ears rang with an echo of the superintendent's voice: "...if there is another offense you'll be lucky to find yourself chained on an assembly line for the rest of your life."
Thoughts of pursuit by federal agents unnerved me especially due to the

uncertainty of my own guilt, aside from the drug trade, whose prohibitions went well outside of their jurisdiction. If they had either connected me to Andre Geos, or else traced my saliva from Mrs. Jefferson's pipe, it would be NYPD looking for me instead. Dismissing these fears, I wondered whether possession of books previously erased digital archives made me a criminal; though I knew no such laws, the arcane regulations to which I was subject were too numerous for memory. Ultimately it did not matter, because my polemical volumes connoted terrorism; once labeled an enemy combatant, I lost all the rights of my citizenship. If captured, I would have no trial and less recourse; the only ending to that tale was indefinite detention. Past the cartoon cleanliness and glittering ads of Times Square, pavements deteriorated from neglect. After taking a brutal fall, I carried the board, beating my soles on crumbling asphalt leading to the train station instead. The fastest pace I could summon still seemed sluggish, with atrophied muscles impeding my speed as much as the traffic exhaust. Unwilling to slacken, I soon felt the sharpness of cramps in my sides and chest; whilst gasping for breath, the smog I had been habituated to ignore burned my sinuses relentlessly. My dire lack of fitness was evident from the outset; joints rebelled at the strain; my shins ached from the repetitive impact. Sweat droplets stung my eyes until the heavens let loose a pelting deluge of hail; then I squinted harder and hurled myself into the storm, which had just begun to cleanse the noxious air as I arrived at the terminal. My heavy breathing and dripping clothes attracted stares therein, but by focusing resolutely on the task at hand, I found an express line with an imminent departure for New Haven, the farthest destination I could reach directly. I had no plan; just the vague notion that if I got out of the city and across state lines, perhaps I would be left alone for long enough to reorient. Armored NYPD officers swarmed the terminal, in addition to its endemic TSA personnel, and as I approached the security checkpoint my heart pounded audibly from sheer terror rather than exertion. The agent at my scanner proved more interested in the daily Tablogs than her job; relieved when the mismatch passed her notice, I hurried away in the guise of my cloned iWare. At the gates, I slipped through an exit door, moving quickly with the force of adrenaline and my refusal to go back. "Hey, kid!" a cop called, so close there was no doubt he addressed me; I pretended not to hear him, walking briskly in hopes of disappearing, while steeling myself for the likelihood that he would subdue me by tazer. "I'm talking to you," he said as the dismaying weight of a hand fell on my shoulder, stopping me in my tracks. With great reluctance, and against better judgment, I turned to face him, glancing first to his unguarded sidearm, then the dog straining at the end of its leash. "You could catch your death, going out it one of these storms. I don't care how much of a hurry you might be in; the risk isn't worth it. Try the breezeway next time." I found it hard to know in the moment whether I was Raskolnikov reprized, or on the receiving end of a cosmic joke. "Yeah, next time," is all I thought to say, shrugging off his meaty palm. I struggled to remain calm during my careful walk beside the platform, and boarded mere seconds before leaving the station. Surveying the cabin, I tentatively decided that there were no police along for the ride; but even if I might have stolen a few minutes by going through an exit, the ID chip in my neck would alert any person or program paying attention to what train I rode and its destination. I sat amidst lightning bolts on the edge of the front, downpours overtaking my car at each stop, where I anxiously anticipated arrest by watching for cops.

The heat generated by a nuclear explosion is so great that it will cause atmospheric nitrogen, an otherwise unreactive gas, to burn, fusing with oxygen in the process to form nitric oxide. A single nitric oxide molecule can then break down many of ozone, the precious aether protecting our world from ultraviolet radiation, before converting to nitrogen dioxide and coming down from the sky in precipitation. Earth's oceans, already acidified by absorption of anthropogenic CO_2, would not buffer the sudden deposition of nitric acid from the Exchange, whose fallout hence provided nails for the coffin of marine ecology, excepting a few lonely invertebrates. Destruction of the ozone layer increased UV levels at the surface to a degree that made going outside hazardous, while its disruption of plant metabolism extended crop failures for years after nuclear winter ended. As more people emigrated to Voluntary Service Colonies for the promise of reliable rations, the pressure to invent new dispensary foods increased. Efforts at breeding radiation-resistant corn, soy, and other staple crops were encumbered by their seasonal ontogenesis, along with the limited understandings of biotechnologists; but the nation rejoiced once they announced the advent of genetically-modified extremeophile algae that could be profitably grown for primary production in elsewise lifeless waters. The only deficiency seen among industry was of structural carbohydrates necessary to the normal digestion of cattle, which provided in turn the meat and dairy products that Americans preferred. Meanwhile, engineers of experimental medicine had been growing synthetic human organs for years, primarily by grafting stem cells onto biomaterial scaffolds and stimulating them to replicate as the desired tissue types in a controlled environment. Methods for correctly matching recipient and donor cell types to avoid tissue rejection were the province of boutique medical labs, reserved for extending the lives of those who could afford a hefty price tag. Facing famine and potential breakdown of social order, the United States government funded the application of this technology to livestock tissues as well, thus giving an entirely new meaning to factory farming. Though prohibitively energy-intensive at first, artificial animal products became feasible as the scale of production grew, because on commercial bases this machinery made food more efficiently than confinement feeding operations. A synthetic mammary gland, fed intravenously, converted most of its algal nutrients to milk production, without the need to grow and maintain a whole cow; the same held true for cultured muscle tissues marketed as ground beef, finally freed from the restrictions of a bovine rumen, and the costs of processing an entire carcass at a packing plant. Visionary groundwork for this breakthrough in industrial agriculture had been laid in A.T. 7 by an FDA decree that food products from cloned animals were safe for human consumption, and would not be subject to any special identification requirements; whereas Federal law required naturally-bred livestock products bearing the label 'Certified Clone-Free' or 'Real Meat' to also state, 'There is no significant different between meat, eggs, or dairy produced by cloning.' Written before GMO animals entered the human diet, Supreme Court interpretation extended this legislation to encompass synthetic organs that were conceived in genetic laboratories. A decade after the Exchange, the convalescing ozone layer permitted conventional crops to be successfully cultivated again; however, even with corn and soy available as feed again, livestock agriculture was on the way to atavism, except for egg production. Factories could spawn chicken meat, but the genesis of ova still required live birds, which were inconveniently prone to virulent pathogens that had adapted to antibiotics. Despite temporary cooling effects from thermonuclear ash, climate change did not stop in the interim; postwar agriculture thence contended with increasingly variable precipitation patterns, while freshwater aquifers retreated underground. Rising sea levels brought frequent incursions of destructive flooding; millions were displaced from the densely-populated coastal areas of the world, and many more starved due to salinization of arable land by storm events. Nevertheless, private contractors reaped tremendous profits via reconstruction of China, wherein the once-sovereign nation was administered as a protectorate of the United States, effectively eliminating the foreign debt whilst extending its access to petroleum energy and nonrenewable raw materials. The surviving population was cordially invited to join specialized Voluntary Service Colonies, thereby restoring their former country's manufacturing capacity with the aid of robotics. Radiation and pollution at home expedited the rise of cancer as the leading cause of death amongst Americans, whose average mortal age peaked at 80 near the beginning of the 21st century, courtesy of artificial life support, but had plummeted to 60 for people born in my year. In a nation fraught with bankruptcy, this demographic shift eased the Social Security shortfall until the occupation of China paid dividends, which postponed economic collapse. Whereas the majority of U.S. citizens died prior to retirement, the wealthy elite worried about little aside from leukemia and enjoyed generally long lives thanks to the advancements of modern medicine. Although synthetic organ transplants may not have been covered by mandatory health insurance, they were readily available to anyone who could afford them; preventive replacements all but eliminated the risk of cancer developing in an endogenous organ and metastasizing unnoticed. Ariadne Jefferson's library selections, along with the reliability of the historical record, ended here. Conversion of information to electronic formats, remote storage of data, and consequent censorship to protect America from insurgency ended free press, engendering an empire marked by its freedom to oppress, as the thus-entitled text prophesied. Moreover, volumes of knowledge perished in shadows cast by the Cloud revolution. Before reading those books, I understood neither the extent of human influence upon modern ecology, nor the antithetical insignificance of our species in the evolutionary story. I remained unaware of the fascism whereby my nation established its unquestionable supremacy; never considered the fact of my unwitting participation; and lacked any frame of reference for the destruction caused by my unconscious submission. I had been taught, by indoctrination and implication, that the United States was the moral authority; that contemporary culture represented the pinnacle of human achievement; that the Earth existed to satisfy my desires; and that conquering it for that end was our manifest destiny. We put our faith in government, worshiped technology, and thought nothing of tomorrow. Apropos, cancer rose as the leading cause of death amongst Americans, a unique form of parasitism originating within our own bodies in response to toxic changes our society inflicted upon its environment. Beginning via genetic mutation, the disease fittingly causes an organism's cells replicate without regulation until consuming their host, and thus killing themselves. Worldview is the analogue of a genome in society, and it appeared to me like a mutation in perspective as simple as humans being apart from, rather than a part of, the natural order had begotten my malignant culture: a global carcinoma whose unchecked growth was a macrocosm of the same illness that would indifferently take the lives of its own constituents.

When I arrived at Union Station, torrential rain fell from an angry sky with dark clouds glowing red from city lights reflected by their underside. My train passed through the smog-enshrouded incinerator district first, where mined landfill waste was delivered and burned to shore up the failing power grid. From my stance in the front compartment, I glanced backwards as it decelerated along the platform to see a pair of local police officers conversing atop the stairs, just beyond the vestibule. From their hasty drags on cigarettes, I knew they were getting ready to move; my heart leapt to my throat with certainty that they meant to apprehend me. A plan suddenly coalesced to take advantage of their nonchalance and the terrible weather; although my rationality acknowledged the idea as probably insane, it was all I had. Scanning a map of New Haven streets, I committed what I could to memory, whilst passengers pressed against the exits; there I surreptitiously slipped my tablet into the purse of a woman ahead of me. As we stepped over the illuminated threshold, I ducked into the crowd, hidden from view by its movement toward the sliding doors of shelter from the storm. I worked my way to the outside flank, so the cops would be blocked from getting a clear tazer shot; then I dropped to the tracks below, scuttled across slippery railroad ballast, and flattened myself to squirm beneath girders supporting the adjacent platform. Crossing two more lines like this, I came to a chain link fence around the automobile parking lot. Razor wire had been installed at the top, but by using my skateboard as a shield, I climbed over without injury, thoroughly soaked and heedless of puddles as I ran past the station on the shortest route. Uncertain of what equipment my pursuers had, I hoped for them to follow the iTab, since its internal antennae and power supply broadcast a signal that was easy to track, whereas my ID could only be detected by a radio surveillance system of lower range and resolution. I sacrificed my new wheel bearings to corrosion, with the silent admission they would not be used again, gaining a few downhill blocks on strangely empty streets before I heard the sound of sirens. The torrent flowing beside the curb showed me a storm drain inlet; I wrenched on the trash strainer furiously, but it did not yield. Any possibility that my foolish plan might work hinged on me getting into the sewer, and I despaired for want of alternatives, until the father I never knew came to me, as Alexander Fremont had, with a reminder to harness the principle of leverage. There was no time to process any emotions raised by his appearance, so I simply did what he said, forcing the nose of my skateboard into the grate and using its axle as a fulcrum. After prying unsuccessfully, I gave a tentative kick; then a peripheral glimpse of red and blue lights spurred me to jump on the deck, thus emitted a horrific crack. I switched to the tail next, felt the grate give way to the force, lifted it, then threw my skateboard into the stream. Fervently intending for the police not to see me, I attempted to lower my body in swimmingly, but my feet found no purchase and were swept downstream. Left hanging from the underside of the strainer, which had mercifully landed in its proper position, I spent a moment in prayer; upon letting go, I gave thanks for my cranioplasty, because the sluice inlet struck just above my eyebrow as I shot through. The rectangular conduit was scarcely wide enough for my shoulders and half-filled with putrid runoff, whose current permitted me to breathe whilst drifting once I stopped gagging on its stench. My clothes did not last long against the rough concrete bottom, exposing my upper back to abrasion; I bridged off my heels to reduce the scraping, though the impact of my shoulder blades passing across the joints between cast sections felt worse. A reprieve came as the depth increased, but then my face was pressed up to the slimy ceiling, such that I could not get air without also inhaling water. Despite darkness and disorientation, I noticed when the flow changed direction, thus entering a larger, round culvert of corrugated steel, filled completely. I held my breath so long my head seemed ready to burst, saw the pretty lights marking my crossing to the other side, and eventually accepted that the urge to inhale would overpower me, regretting in those final moments, close though I may have came to escape, the system won by my drowning, as it somehow always did. After struggling so hard, anoxia brought feelings of peace, along with the knowledge I had done my best. My mouth opened lazily, as if I meant to savor my long-resisted last breath, and the water flowing in tasted strongly of salt. A burst of will, drawn from awareness that I reached the end, brought me back to my senses just in time to be brutally pummeled upon jagged rocks at the outlet. Somehow I got my mouth above the surface, coughing, vomiting and gasping all at once. My mind spun with oxygen deprivation, my forehead throbbed, my body was battered as never before; but I retained enough consciousness to celebrate life. Planting my feet in the mucilaginous bottom, I sputtered and spewed until I could breathe normally, if not easily. The water was warm, relative to the air, and droplets pounded its surface with such aggression that they might as well have been raining upward. Removing my iWare, I saw the harbor shore wrapping around me through the spray, its piers and petrochemical tanks illuminated by the cityscape. Beyond the gleam of traffic were the blinking beacons atop Adriaen's Wall, then only blackness. The storm had almost passed, and flashes of lightning at its front were etched in my mind like silver nitrate prints whilst I allowed the tide to carry me seaward. Looking behind, I found the dark gap in the coastline whereat water met sky, separated only by my horizon. There was the ocean, along with freedom, and I swam toward them.

ENTHEOGENESIS · Origin of the Divinity within Us

"The sea's only gifts are harsh blows and, occasionally, the chance to feel strong. Now, I don't know much about the sea, but I do know that's the way it is here. And I also know how important it is in life not necessarily to be strong, but to feel strong, to measure yourself at least once, to find yourself in the most ancient of human conditions, facing blind death stone alone, with nothing to help you but your own hands and your own head."

~ Primo Levi, via Alexander Supertramp: INTO THE WILD ~

"He who has overcome his fears will truly be free."

~ Aristoteles, 2384-2322 B.T. ~

EIGHT

When I awoke again, my world was pain; although the rain had ended, torn remains of sodden clothes clung to limbs that were rigid with soreness and hypothermia. My skull seemed split asunder by the rosy glow of what I would otherwise have deemed a beautiful dawn, sparkling brilliantly atop the choppy sea, but I made my first sentient motion to avoid its awful rays. Wounds on my back screamed in protest, as merely turning to my opposite side exceeded the effort I could comfortably endure; then I curled up in the fetal position, shivering on the sand whilst adjusting to my surroundings. Disturbed by the rising tide, I tested my extremities one joint at a time; they responded to my instructions, albeit begrudgingly. Glimpses of my journey came back to me with each of the small waves lapping at my feet; unable to recall the swim, I felt it must have been miles in length as I drew my knees upward, shakily pushing my upper body off the sand with both hands. Sick from rotten salt water, I heaved on all fours until no more would come, and then some, amazed that the taste could be even worse on the way out. After crawling to dry sand just beyond the range of my vomit, I collapsed again, wishing above all I had thought to bring a bag of weed.

As the rising sun warmed me, my headache subsided enough for me to notice my thirst, while the sound of a plane to the west reminded me that danger still lay closer than it seemed. The memory of how I arrived on the beach persuaded my body to move at last; by a feat of volition, I stood unsteadily, and squinted at the piercing dawn in futile frustration, since I did not save the iWare for autoshade. I was alone with the surf, ending in an unbroken ribbon of brown foam running alongside the coast; above me, a windrow of trash like the dump of some third world country stretched as far as I could see in either direction. To the west, New Haven's metropolitan silhouette loomed at the vista's edge, beneath a blanket of brown smog; to the east a narrow crescent of the beach reached out and disappeared into pale mist. I resolved to remain within the intertidal zone, which offered an easy course to navigate, based on the dubious logic that someone tracking me remotely might conclude I had drowned and drifted along the shore. I intended to listen vigilantly for the approach of any vehicles, ready to take refuge in the waves; though this was not much of a strategy, I was comforted by the sight of my footsteps washing away behind me, so my anonymous passage through that place would leave no trace. My shoes were gone, presumably kicked off during the swim, along with my hooded jacket, but I had a longsleeve shirt with holes worn in the back, as well as pants, basically intact except for their rear pockets. Disgusted by my crusty socks, I peeled them off and hesitantly began to walk.

The vertigo I suffered after being discharged from the hospital had returned, forcing me to concentrate on moving one foot at a time for the sake of balance. Looking down, I shaded my swollen brow against solar radiation, which emanated from straight ahead, following the contour of the gradient whose moisture content best supported my weight.

Once I established sufficient coordination to walk on smooth sand, dehydration impelled me to peruse the mountains of debris shoved up the beach. Picking through the mess, I found collections of rainwater at the bottoms of plastic containers and puddles in the depressions of corroded appliances. Some were filthy, or teeming with tiny diptera larvae, but if the liquid appeared and tasted clean, I pushed fear of poisoning aside, pursing my lips together to slurp unabashedly. When my thirst was slaked, I felt alert enough to contemplate my predicament more seriously; it began with just a vague sense of where I was, and none as to how I would survive.

The day prior happened so quickly I did not think past evading capture; in hindsight, however, the odds seemed to be in my favor. Fate had landed me in Burbarus, as some called the fallout zone past Adriaen Wall, and I was walking toward Ground Zero, where Chinese warheads detonated in the Exchange, a destination that struck me as befitting for no intelligible reason. From my grasp of the area's geography, hazy at best, I guessed the Thames River would lay about forty miles away. Even without a useful concept of residual radioactivity there, I expected it to be uninhabited, which felt safe – ironic, I mused, for someone who never previously left one of the world's largest cities. A few books among Mrs. Jefferson's selection included references to the experiments or experiences of contemporary humans with hunting and gathering, so I possessed awareness of these as potential means of subsistence, if only theoretically. Manhattan was nearly devoid of vegetation, aside from the artificiality of planters and ornamental trees; thus my notions of such lifestyles were romanticized by outdated tales of pristine environments, and not necessarily applicable to the toxic wasteland ahead of me; but I learned thence that a surprising number of common weeds could be eaten. Although I had yet to sample them, those I recognized from sidewalk cracks or abandoned lots were lodged in my memory. An intermittent hedge of beach roses ran along the base of the trash dunes, bearing fruits as large as bottlecaps amid their waning blossoms. The mealy outer layer of tart flesh enclosed a ball of seeds, which I scooped out easily with my thumb. For my entire life before that moment, I ate without cognizance of the sources of my sustenance; I never visited a farm or meat factory, and all I knew for sure about the origins of any food I consumed was whence it had been purchased.

Stores, restaurants, and vendors all used the same untraceable commodity ingredients, obtained from wherever they were cheapest; ergo, those rose hips comprised my first meal of real consciousness, whose genesis brought me to epiphany, via recognition of how profoundly disconnected I was from the basis of my existence. After gathering what I could carry, I returned to the water's edge; there I distracted myself from pain by selecting the most distant identifiable object and counting how many steps I took to reach it, with a preference for gulls since their movements kept my game interesting. The rhythmic waves hypnotized me at times, as if cleansing my brain of psychic sewage, while my pace naturally synchronized with their surges.

Eventually I grew ambitious enough to take stock of my surroundings, and despite injuries sought a view atop the refuse. Whilst navigating the precarious pile, I found a barrel that stood stable when upended, whose height provided distant perspectives. The landward side was buried by the accumulation of windblown sediments, its edge demarcated by sparse tufts of grass, whereas the tendrils of enterprising vines climbed over the crest, blurring the boundary between solid ground and garbage. A reedy meadow grew in the lee of trash, crisscrossed by brackish streams, beyond which lay a lush mat of bushes and brambles. Deep green cones of cedars emerged above the shrubbery, until the maze gave way to deciduous trees of magnitude and density that truly stunned me because I had never before seen native forest. Scanning the northern horizon, I was taken further aback by an apparent lack of human settlement and veritable wilderness in what must have been a densely developed region of suburbia less than half a century previous. A few power pylons and cellular antennae protruded through the canopy, former phalluses of American infrastructure networks serving the ecosystem as enormous trellises instead; but housing, roads, and other ruins had become indistinguishable from the jungle. I always imagined modern construction as being permanent, given its emphasis on pavement and maintenance-free materials; yet here was incontrovertible proof that, in absence of a human population, the edifices of civilization would be subsumed by their environment within mere generations.

The beach tapered as I went on, terminated by a pile of granite boulders. Climbing over them cautiously to avert slippage, I came upon the fractured remains of a concrete seawall, whose top edge stood a foot or two out of the surf, offering a narrow but ergonomic walkway. There were occasional gaps in the barrier for cast stairwells, cracked apart and crumbling from decades of weathering, with rusted slashes that seeped like wounds due to the exposed rebar. I could tell from the number of steps that sea level must have risen by several feet since their construction, which retained a flat landscape on my left. Dense turf covered the terrace, punctuated regularly by rectangular bogs filled with tall reeds; I soon recognized these distinct patches as foundations of waterfront homes, swept away long ago. Turning northward, the coastline formed a small bay, alternating between cobbles and decayed abutments, thence passing heavily-vegetated islands close to shore. I came next to another stretch of beach at its protected end and headed south on the opposite side, hunched over from hunger cramps by afternoon. The rose hips, tasty though they were, did little for my hunger; thus my hypoglycemic weakness left me legitimately concerned about finding sustenance. Petrochemical slime, polystyrene packaging, plastic bags, and various pollutants unbeknownst to me filled crevices amongst the rocks, but clumps of seaweed adhered on their wave-beaten outer surfaces had been washed clean. Because I knew it was essential to processed foods, and used whole in the sushi of yesterday, I figured that the marine vegetation contained some nutritional value. Though the fresh version proved rather unappealing, in flavor as well as texture, I ate it anyway by swallowing small chunks since they were too rubbery for me to chew effectively. The slimy pulp hitting the bottom of my gut caused involuntary heaving; when this torment subsided I decided to exercise caution in my diet, with no idea of what better nourishment might be.

Clouds rolled in as I rounded the tip of a peninsula, finding another cove opposite the one I had just circumvented; my feet blistered and the sun set before I observed that it was actually an estuary. A small river's mouth formed its north end, bounded by swamps on both sides, thereby forcing me to either swim or tromp upstream through thickets in search of a place where I could wade. Facing falling temperatures, and loathe to spend the night like my last, I felt disinclined to get wet again. Making camp must have been instinctual, despite the fact that I had never done so; without thought or delay, I knocked down the stalks in a circular area about seven feet across to create a dry bed hidden from view. By folding the shredded remnants of a sail collected from the beach, I improvised my blankets, rigid but with some insulation, and peeled scraps from an old foam buoy to use a pillow. When night cast oily blackness over the sky, I put my socks back on, nibbled at rose hips stowed within, then drank the rest of my rainwater.

Once I stopped moving and closed my eyes, I broke into sickly cold sweat, gripped by panic. To flee in such a feeble state as mine, without equipment or skills, seemed dangerously asinine, if not suicidal. My stomach groaned in revolt, while my feet had worn out in a single day; unless rain came again soon, I would have no water; and if it did, I had no shelter, let alone any means of keeping warm. I thought about turning myself in, and considered the possibility that Voluntary Service Colonies were not be as bad as my imagination, hyperventilating, heart racing, until a voice in my head said, "They die an equal death, the idler and the man of mighty deeds."

I knew not what mighty deeds could be, nor what might lie before me, but the human being I sought to become was not one who gave up. I had been there on a troll, blinded by drugs whilst safe at home in my own bed, and haunted by a book cover when the real threat lay within. Perhaps I feared my end less in the past because I was further from real life; to have it thrust upon me, and with freedom too, made me suddenly feel attached. Reciting Homer as a mantra, I drifted unto uneasy sleep. Presumably due to my phenethylamine abuse, I did not usually have memorable dreams; however, nightmares visited me then, wherein I was chased and tazed by cackling deimans, who described their torture methods as they approached. Howling sirens awakened me; after a terrified moment I realized the sounds surrounding the marsh were not from cops, but instead a pack of coydogs. Although I bolted upright to confront them, their abrupt silence left only the disquieting awareness that I was an intruder there, and far from alone.

In spite of my efforts to seal its edges, and tolerance of the condensation that subsequently formed, mosquitoes found their way beneath my sail before the next morning. The itching sores they caused by feasting on my blood were an unwelcome new experience, as was their constant whine, which kept me woefully awake during the wee hours. My abdominal cramps had subsided to a dull ache, but the abrasions on my back had formed inflexible scabs that cracked as I shifted position, while my skin from neck to shoulders prickled irritation of severe sunburn. Once the moisture and mosquitoes became more than I could endure, I erupted from the cocoon without regard for my soreness, by then among the least of my concerns. Submersion afforded my only escape from being eaten, and although the opposite bank was concealed by shadowy fog, I floundered across the river, towing my bed behind, in hopes of the other side being closer than dimness would allow. After slogging thigh-deep through an interminable stretch of muddy bogs, I clambered onto solid ground and ran directly to the beach. Chilled when I reached it, but relieved to be finally free of biting insects, I washed the muck from my lower body in the sea, even taking a few moments to appreciate the sunrise, mostly on anticipation of its warmth. The observation that I had not yet urinated fed my fears of dehydration; whilst searching for water, I felt floating sensations reminiscent of trolling, except exhaustion from hunger came quickly. Going without drink since the evening prior was a mistake I intended to avoid thenceforth, by filling disposable bottles one mouthful at a time. After accomplishing the task, I rested in the sun; though there were still a few planes visible, they flew at high altitude, giving me some confidence I would not be hunted down or arrested on the desolate frontier. Homeland Security presumably did not care to expend the fuel, personnel, and expense for an extraction from that wasteland, or else expected me to die of my own accord soon enough. My inclination was to head for Boston, still a thriving metropolis, which had been protected from the historic Superstorm by Cape Cod; closing my eyes, I recalled what I could of New England's geography. Beyond Ground Zero lay Rhodes, where the shoreline turned north, and the bridges of Newport would confirm my progress toward Providence; from there I could cross the cape's shoulder by a northeasterly route to the Massachusetts Bay. I did not dare to leave the coast any sooner, since I had neither the navigation skills nor requisite landmarks, not to mention supplies, for weeks of bushwhacking through the reputedly lawless and presumably hostile territory of marauders rumored to inhabit outskirts of Burbarus. Assuming completion of my trek to the opposite shoreline, I would follow it north toward Boston, where I aimed to start a new life. My wager was upon legends I heard of underground surgeons who dealt in black market IDs, typically harvested from junkies and suicides, although people were occasionally murdered for their identities. If a chip recipient ever got arrested, or the donor's body recovered by law enforcement, their crime could be revealed instantly by a simple retinal scan. The default penalty for providing reidentification services was life in prison without parole; while receiving them secured a lifelong stay in a Voluntary Service Colony. If you were outcast from society, or headed to become a volunteer in any case, the procedure might provide your doorway to a new life, for as long as you managed to stay under the radar afterward. Word on the street indicated that many migrants and convicts opted for the surgery in spite of these risks so they could more readily find work in the trades, as I planned to do, because their employers tended to fixate on balance sheets instead of investing in scanners, which were provided to police by the government. Given the appropriate connections, reidentification was available for a reasonable fee to anyone who had sufficient trust in a surgeon's sterility, and the authenticity of an ID – which, if er were lucky, would come without associated warrants, criminal records, or tax obligations. Always a step ahead of features for tamper resistance, this illicit business epitomized evolution's inherent ingenuity; just as parasites and diseases mutate in response to the defenses of their host species, so does the underworld consistently develop tactics to evade every regulatory innovation of law enforcement technology. The War on Crime, thus named, might appear an exercise in futility, except to those who realize its quintessential motive is never to eliminate criminality, but rather to rule by oppression and fear. However, my lack of money required that I either find an able surgeon willing to reidentify me on credit, which was improbable at best, or raise the funds for my chip hastily. In the latter and far more likely case, my most viable option would be to sell a kidney, whose price I estimated high, upon consideration of my health and youth. Synthetic organ replacements in legitimate circulation had their own IDs embedded, were recorded via an international inventory, and could only be transplanted by physicians whom health insurance companies had approved to do so. Ordinarily machines performed these operations, while the role of doctor was reduced to that of a contractor handling the business practice, equipment, and licenses. When people needed transplants not covered by insurance but unaffordable legally, their options were acceptance of what fate decreed, or hiring the sort of practitioner I also meant to seek. They risked having their health care coverage dropped entirely; whereas the greatest danger for a donor candidate like me was that of encountering an unscrupulous surgeon who, presented the opportunity to turn a tidy profit off the disappearance of a dissociated criminal, would ensure I did not wake from anesthesia by removing from my body any organs of value. The master plan, if you will, to trade one of my kidneys for a dead stranger's identity and minimum wage labor, as an outlaw in a strange city, was hazardous to say the least; yet such things were done in those times, and it certainly seemed better than my alternatives. Devising a strategy, insane though it may have been, hence allayed my apprehension, enabling me to dismiss second thoughts about my escape from New York that kept me awake the evening prior. In the meantime, my immediate problem was getting there. I guessed the distance to Providence at about a hundred miles as the crow flies, which meant walking over twice as far as by following crenelations of coastlines; maybe fifty more to the Massachusetts Bay; then, depending where I came out of the woods, at least this much again via yonder shore to Boston - in total, three or four hundred miles on foot, unless I got lost, of course. If I enjoyed good weather and overcame my various handicaps, I figured my pilgrimage might average fifteen miles per day, plus the necessary swimming; requiring, all told, that I find food, water, and shelter for three weeks, by an optimistic outlook, in order to complete my journey. Contrary to popular belief, a person in normal body condition theoretically stores enough fat to walk for six weeks without eating before succumbing to starvation; while Mohandas Gandhi, who had naught to spare, allegedly lived on his reserves for a hunger strike as long a time as my projected trek. His venture was not much of a comparison to mine, since I held no intention of fasting for the duration, whereby I would brave injury, police, poisoning, radiation, hurricanes, and hijackers as well as food deprivation. Still, the Mahatma's story reminded me that the greatest challenge was of my will to persevere; in light of the risk, success appeared possible, albeit improbable.

"Nothing to do but get it done," I said aloud, sitting upright and bathed by morning sun; the corollary I dared not speak was, 'Or die trying.' Although the briny water stung my wounds, surrounding skin felt more flexible after it dried. My dizziness had passed, and I harvested plastic scraps from the top of the beach to protect my feet, cinched at the ankle with dry-rotten rope, planning ahead for a change to save what flesh remained for traction on slippery boulders. I put a few miles behind me, satisfied by my mobility, whilst scouring sands along the way for two technological artifacts that I had deemed most essential to my survival – a cutting edge, and means to make fire. Observing them via detachment, I thought my circumstances a sardonic recapitulation of human phylogeny. The inception of tool use spawned *Homo habilis* from australopithecines, some three million years ago; whereas controlled use of fire coincided with the appearance of *Homo erectus*, some million and half years later. Mine was the *sapiens* specie, most advanced yet amongst hominids, but to be a 'thinking man' seemed overrated when, unlike my primitive predecessors, I could not recreate their inventions, on which my own life utterly relied. Bemused by the notion that my kind would be more appropriately named *Homo sapiens ignoramus*, I found a jagged scrap of steel flashing to use as a crude saw, whose hemmed edge I could comfortably grab. For slicing, I shattered an old cathode ray television display and selected the largest shards; landed there as a constituent of its former home, then exposed by decay, the TV made a strange sight to behold, while the emotional gratification of the throw that broke it made my day, even though no incendiary device materialized. Because the atmosphere was heating rapidly, I spent some time laboriously cutting my sailcloth down to a manageable size, fashioning thence a hooded cape, tied at my neck and arms with twine, draped loosely to protect my peeling back from further damage. The frustration of constant squinting motivated me to fabricate eyewear in the style of Inuit snow goggles from a shard of a broken bucket; I sliced my palm on the glass in the process, and rebuked myself sternly, since I could not afford to lose the function of a hand. For prevention in the future, I lashed a driftwood handle to my blade with wire; the first benefit derived from this neoprimitivist knife was an additional lens of translucent plastic in lieu of the autoshading iWare I had left abaft. Continuing thus attired through static vistas past solar noon, I came to a stretch of coastline running due south, where I opted for an inland route upon my supposition that it was another peninsula. Behind the dunes lay vast marshes of soft grass appreciated by my feet, irrigated by a network of ditches, most of which I could leap. Occasionally I fell short, sinking hip deep into sulfurous-smelling muck, and the mosquitoes were bothersome, but my persistence was rewarded on the far side, where the land began to rise. Birdsong drew me toward broad bushes, sagging under the weight of small scarlet nodules clustered along their branches. Although it was no guideline for diet, I remembered reading that poisonous fruits usually had a disagreeable flavor, and took my chances by tasting the berries; my mouth puckered from sourness at first, but their astringency was relieved, then surpassed, by sweetness, while I swallowed the small woody seeds easily.

Stripping the drooping limbs from fork to tip, I gorged myself without delay, collecting double handfuls of ripe autumn olives as they separated readily from the parent stems and foliage. When my stomach filled, I noticed that their speckled skins were firm and dry, so they might store well if I had a container for them; once more, I sacrificed my socks to the cause, which fortunately I thought to wash, thereby carrying respectable sackfuls of food, whose weight brought with it a real sense of wealth. Thicker vegetation prevailed beyond the shrubbery, which soon shredded the layers of plastic on my feet; their bare blistered soles did not willingly suffer the groundcover of prickly debris. I disentangled myself repeatedly from unavoidable barbs of brambles that caught on my clothes and skin, but by the time I admitted my chosen route was madness, I had gone too far and made too many maneuvers to retrace my path, so any attempt at backtracking was likely as not to be a losing proposition. Clawed at every frantic step along the way toward where I thought water would be, I felt thankful for the ground thus gained when I finally came to old pavement, serving as mulch for larger trees. In their shade, thickets gave way to an open forest floor where I stepped gently, glad for a break from the thorns and sun. On the edge of the woods I disturbed a graceful herd of deer, their white tails flashing between the trunks as they flew away from me. The area they had been browsing was littered with contorted, misshapen fruits covered in dark spots, bruises, and wormholes that I recognized as apples from their odor. The half-wild flavor was sour, and more potent, than the genetically-modified version I knew, but still perfectly palatable.

Thence I could smell salt spray as well; if not for a canopy-high wall of vines standing in the sun I might even have seen the waves; so I hauled the firmest apples in my sailcloth cape until later discovery of a solid bucket.

Leaning against a crumbling jersey barrier upon what was a waterfront sidewalk of yore, I closed my eyes and rested for a spell in an effort to quell my stomach, which did not feel entirely at peace with all of the acidic fruit I had consumed. To replace the abandoned tatters of my trashy footwear, I spent the rest of the afternoon crafting sandals, using nylon strapping that may have been part of someone's luggage to hold soles cut from the same remnant of decayed carpeting I would also employ as a bedroll. Whilst gathering materials, I noticed the deposits of rainwater on which I subsisted were evaporating, and sucked up whatever was available through a bit of tubing, adding more bottles to my reserve; then I indulged a bit of pride in my resourcefulness, new shoes, and the cache of provisions strung from a tumpline across my forehead. Energized by the food as well as my self-preservation instinct, with visions of Boston dancing in my head,

I found a second wind, walking the seawall long past sunset, my steps illuminated by the past-full moon, enormous and brilliant orange as it emerged above the horizon. Given a modest boost of my confidence, the magnificent scope of the sky, lost on me when I cowered amid reeds the night prior, shone with beauty beyond belief. Removed from the light pollution to which I was accustomed, a profusion of stars stood in the void opposite our satellite, exceeding anything I knew to be visible from Earth via my naked eye. Prismatic clouds undulated like translucent tapestries where moonlight shone through, while refraction drew rainbows in the ether between their dimensions. Each had its own characteristics and motions, together composing a visionary symphony that complemented apparently stationary but in fact ever-evolving fabrics of infinity, whose sparkling jewels and alien worlds reflected our own. To my surprise, the heavens impressed me far more than the synaesthetic holograms of any concert I had ever attended, regardless of my state of consciousness. Despite a determined quest for peak experience, the most amazing of my life to date arose in sobriety and circumstances I never expected.

On the third day, I rose again and ascended a rocky mount to watch morning come, where a brilliant eastern star, which was actually Venus, heralded the sun. As I gazed toward my destination in solemn meditation upon myriads of steps lying ahead, a superstitious voice inside me said, 'Do this and you shall live.' Exploration of the summit led me to ruins of a house or temple, hidden from the casual eye by climbing bittersweet vines, with abundant scarlet berries that tasted terrible, regrettably, if not toxic. The roof was gone, replaced by a stand of trees growing from where a had once been, but walls of solid stone still stood strong. A gap in the canopy, left by a fallen locust, allowed a beam of light to reach the former porch, and I wearily leaned against one of the pillars, enjoying its warmth. Unbeknownst to me, a black snake shared the rays, and I jumped instinctively when it uncoiled from the masonry. I can only ascribe divine intervention to my discovery of a lighter in the crevice where the serpent had lain, empty but with a mechanism that was sheltered from weathering. Carrying this seed of hope in my pocket, I scoured the beach assiduously, spotting another near noon; though my delight at the sight soon turned to despair as it did not work either. Undeterred, my search continued through the day; after finally surrendering to twilight, I found a corroded Bic with fuel in the sand whilst I made camp. Using the other for ignition, I kindled a small fire of driftwood, giving thanks for my fortune via heathen dance.
I awoke from dreams of all-you-can-eat buffets the next day with drool running down my face, observing piteously that I was not Gandhi; in order to go the distance, it would take more than seaweed and fruit, since my diet seemed to promote purgative diarrhea. Under a dour sky I rebuilt my fire from coals, noticing that the tree leaves had changed visibly overnight; then strolled into what seemed to be a zone of urban development, judging from the windowless structures of concrete block. Amidst rusted heaps of old cars upon former parking lots, I tested my knowledge of herbalism with lamb's quarters, which were decent, and dandelions so bitter they made me doubt whether whoever designated them as edible ever actually ate any.

Nutritious though they may have been, the greens did not begin to satisfy my hunger, while chewing only intensified my craving for meat. Utterly disturbed by the ghastly scene and my fears of leached toxicity, I returned to the beach, vowing to avoid such graveyards of civilization. In desperation, I threw rocks at increasingly common flocks of gulls, but since I had poor aim the birds flew away before my projectiles hit their targets. The next stretch of coast was relatively straight for a change, with few obstacles, hence allowing me to keep a steady pace despite my weakness, even as I plunged into an altered mental state. From my view atop the seawall, mirages replaced the water's surface, and delirious urges to walk upon it possessed me. I retained sufficient presence of mind to resist until the concrete ended at marshes more extensive than I had yet encountered; my progress thereby dropped to a crawl. Demotivated by several wrong turns, I carelessly slipped off a stream bank, landing in the shallows on all fours, and I stared at the stars dancing across my vision, then pockmarked mud flats above the waterline. Transfixed by bubbles emanating from one of the pores nearest me, I dug without knowing why; after excavating the hard object embedded below, I rejoiced to find it was a quahog, one of the few bivalves whose shell formation proved adaptable to ocean acidification. Although vaguely aware of their existence, I had overlooked, and walked over, an abundant food source for days because I never wondered where clams might live; probing with my feet, I soon had as many as I could carry. I struggled at first to pry open the shells; then bashing them between rocks just made a mess; however, when boiled in a can of seawater, the mollusks yielded their meat easily. I bit into the first one enthusiastically, whilst still hot enough to burn my mouth, and spat it out because the flesh tasted like a salt marsh smells, with the texture of rubber laced by tooth-grinding grit. Ultimately, I crudely hacked the clams into chunks I could swallow whole; the meal was unappetizing, but once I got them down, they stayed there.

I awoke on the fifth day feeling better than I had since leaving New York. My sunburn peeled; scrapes on my back ached; poison ivy festered between my toes; most of my skin itched from scratches, rashes, or insect bites; but I could feel my muscles and feet healing, as if they would be stronger afterward. Invigorated by clams, I went to collect seawater for a breakfast of more, and in so doing, caught a glimpse of myself upon a stagnant tide pool. Shocked at first, I stood to regard the reflection of a person different from the one I remembered. My body was lean, its muscles and tendons clearly defined beneath tanned skin; the dark circles around my eyes were fading; and with a week's growth of hair on my gaunt face, I looked like a genuine peri-apocalyptic forager-vagabond who belonged in the wilderness. As I proceeded, the density of wreckage had been gradually decreasing, while the stretch I traversed that day showed no evidence of human habitation besides the usual washed-up trash, as if it was some sort of preserve in the past. Though I should have thought the place gorgeous, conditions soon turned blustery and overcast, with windblown sediment irritating me instead. The beach stopped at a hummock of granite, which stood above any other feature nearby; gazing ahead I saw a narrow spit of cobbles and shrubs reaching out until it disappeared under the waves.

Without noticing, I had gone southeast on a cape that seemed impossibly long, and the promontory furnished northwesterly views of an apparently endless salt marsh sheltered by the peninsula I just traversed. For all I knew, it might take a whole day slogging inland through mosquitoes and muck to discover I was at the mouth of a river. Amid the sea to my northeast lay a lone islet; beyond it, what could only be a continuation of the mainland. Loathe to go back whence I came or into the reedy abyss, I decided to swim the channel. Though striking for the opposite shore in one shot would be the most direct route, the distance intimidated me and demanded that I swim along formidable swells. The land between looked more reasonable, perhaps half as far, on a small detour whose trajectory went into the crests; easier, I thought, since I could see waves coming as they broke, whilst swimming with less concern for direction. Rather than waiting for them to build higher, I stripped and packed the essentials in haste. One of my buckets had a lid sealed by a rubber gasket; when filled with apparel, tools, and what sundries would fit, I tethered it to my right ankle. Bedroll and bottled water were tied to my left; the rest was expendable. As I waded out, the sky grew dark, and the force of outgoing current gave me pause. Feeling my way across slippery cobbles, the bottom suddenly vanished; I had stepped off the edge of a channel, swept away on a rip tide, leaving me no choice but to swim. Initially the challenge was exhilarating; then exertion turned to exhaustion, and my goal did not appear any closer. I picked marks on shore to judge my position; when I looked again a thousand strokes later, reckoned only that it was a long fetch and the waves had grown taller in the interim. I stopped kicking momentarily to detach the bundled possessions, guessing I should probably have abandoned my bucket as well, though I did not know how to live without its contents. Whilst drifting backwards, I inhaled water and choked, admitting to myself that I could not reach the islet. The mainland still lay about a mile off, on a bearing perpendicular to the current, thereby requiring me to swim the distance and simultaneously hold my position in the tide, which was challenging enough when exerting my efforts straight ahead. Whitecaps smothered me every few seconds; saltwater made its way down my throat, up my sinuses, and once the nausea began, it affirmed that I needed to make land soon, or else drown. From some deeply hidden reserve I drew the power to strive as never before, my attention fixated on synchronizing my motions, breath, and the waves. Whereas the shore grew closer, I was weaker with each passing moment and slowly moving out to sea. After hours of effort, my muscles cramped from lactic acid paralysis, unable to keep me warm. Though glancing behind I could see a majority of the total distance, I simply did not have in me the strength or mobility to achieve my goal. I submitted to the inexorable drift with relief, numbly treading tempestuous water merely to keep my head aloft, and as I bobbed, my foot touched something unmistakably solid – the bottom! Against all odds, I had ridden out of the channel, onto another shoal; I flung my arms out with restored hope, furiously pulling land toward me. My clumsy arms splashed; my palsied legs thrashed; and when my shoulders emerged from the surf at last, I yelled for no one to hear, "I will die, but not today!" Then I waded the rest of the way, falling face first on the opposite bank.

"Comparing the humped herds of whales with the humped herds of buffalo, which, not forty years ago, overspread by tens of thousands the prairies of Illinois and Missouri...an irresistible argument would seem furnished to show that the hunted whale cannot now escape speedy extinction."

~ Herman Melville, Moby Dick ~

"In just a few centuries, the people of Easter Island wiped out their forest, drove their plants and animals to extinction, and saw their complex society spiral into chaos and cannibalism. Are we about to follow their lead? ...We can no more escape into space than the Easter Islanders could flee into the ocean."

~ Jared Diamond, 'Easter's End' ~

"If you are squeamish, don't prod the beach refuse."

~ Psappho, 2620-2570 B.T. ~

NINE

I regained consciousness via the sound of my teeth chattering, half-buried in sand and half-wishing I had drowned instead. My body felt miserably cold, so much that the sand fleas scarcely concerned me; fazed only by thirst, I berated myself for jettisoning the bottled water, which could readily have been separated from the bedroll during my swim. When drizzle began I found cause to move, in hopes of replenishing my supply. Standing reluctantly, I brushed off my bumpy skin, and numbly pried open the bucket with fumbling fingers. Consternation seized me at the sight of leakage, and I gritted my teeth from the sensation of damp, tattered clothing. I rushed to build a fire before rain deprived me of dry fuel as well, but after gathering what was available, I could not produce a spark; my igniter had gotten wet since I failed to wrap it prior to departure. I struggled, prayed, then cursed until my numb fingers would no longer turn the roller, and naught occurred except for waste of priceless fuel from the other lighter. To stay warm, I needed heat generated from inside, while the cape I meant to use for harvesting rainwater was thereby required to keep myself dry. Angry with this turn of events, I trotted along the beach on gelatinous legs, my bucket bouncing off my back by the tumpline and my throat more parched than ever. Mistakes had reduced me from a state of capability to sickness in mere hours. The crude sandals that brought me such satisfaction in preceding days fell apart, once my ankles were chafed raw where already swollen from poison ivy. As I jogged, the sky subjected me to cold mist, clearing at sunset without even leaving a drinkable amount of precipitation. I went to sleep bereft of any padding, tossing and turning on cold, damp sand, plagued by vain regret for the gear I had abandoned. In its absence, I was not just dehydrated but also famished again, and made a wretched banquet for mosquitoes with no fire to keep them at bay. Although my feet were in a horrendous condition, I set off apathetically unshod the next day, whose only mercy seemed to be its cloudlessness. A faint stench like rotten cheese clung to the beach that I assumed came from shellfish and seaweed mingled with garbage at the tideline. I found some autumn olives around midmorning; when removing my shirt to use as a container, I sensed an alarming amount of heat radiating from my back, which had finally ceased hurting. Moisture on the fabric revealed that my sores, scabbed over a few days before, oozed chartreuse pus with the consistency of nasal mucus. This was the source of foul odors hanging over my shoulder and attracting a cloud of pestering flies I could not escape. Frightened by the infection, I dove in the ocean to blindly scratch off as much of the foul-smelling slime as possible. My frantic efforts lessened the odor to a degree, but unleashed in the process an unreachably deep itch; adjacent skin remained hot to the touch, whereas the rest of my body felt dreadfully chilled. I shoved fear's grip aside in hopes some exercise might help and moved on, forgetting about the fruits I had never harvested. Whilst realizing this later, I also observed with concern that I recalled neither my last urination nor my last drink. Between the marsh on one side and surf on the other, water surrounded me, but might as well have been desert since none of it was drinkable. For want of clean alternatives, I resorted to slurping from a pool barely above sea level, which tasted as such, mocked for my efforts by crows watching me from perches amid the reeds. During my respite there I remembered the lighter, whose ignition mechanism had dried sufficiently to work once again, and halfheartedly dug some clams, discovering after the chores of preparing them that chewing rocks was actually worse than nothing. Disconcerted by the lack of hunger, I consoled myself via notions of my stomach shrinking andor metabolism becoming more efficient, then bolted a few mouthfuls, despite cramps I ascribed to the rotten brine. Since amnesia began at sunset, I am not sure whether I passed out, went further, or sought water that evening. The seventh day comes to me only in fragments, as numbness took over and I became detached from my body. Though I knew somehow my fever was high, the delirium it induced had me unable to care, disinterested in food or drink, while regard for safety left with my mind. There are glimpses of memory wherein I indifferently observe my senseless behavior as if from a distance. To start the morning walk I waded straight into a swift channel without hesitation, let alone investigation of current or depth; having been there before, the prospect of drowning did not bother me at all. I was caught on a logjam by sheer grace of the gods; coughing brought me back to my senses, but I remained mentally calm, clawed my way up, and stumbled along. I talked to myself, reasoning gone, asking the same questions: "Who am I? Where am I? What am I doing? Why am I here?" Urged on by death at eternity's edge, I slipped into a trance, incapable of moving forward, climbing over the same boulders, where waves and sands ceased to change with the excruciatingly drawn out passage of time.

During lucid moments I considered the prospect that perhaps I already died and was in my hell; but then if I had, why would my wounds still smell? Near midday, I encountered four buzzards besieged by a mob of gulls as they fed upon one of their dead. Three of the enormous birds fought back, allowing the other unfettered access to the body cavity; following a brief period of gorging, the position rotated. They appeared to all be of the same type, sharing a bald red head, but one had solid white plumage while the rest were darkly feathered. I blundered into their feast without thinking, or perhaps reminded by some survival instinct to investigate the possibility of food. The buzzards retreated, leaving a carcass whose innards pulsated with energy that was not a delusion; at its disturbance, writhing maggots poured out from beneath the feathers to consume the freshly-torn flesh, showing me how far I still had to go even after stopping for an end that could be more grisly and degrading than I had previously imagined.

Living seagulls chased off the darker carrion-eaters, who took flight clumsily but easily surpassed their assailants once aloft. The white one stayed behind, brandishing outstretched wings as wide in span as my open arms, and held its ground by rushing the mob with awkward hops. This strategy threatened the gulls sufficiently for them to grant their nemesis a momentary recess; it looked at me, or the meal of which it had been deprived, a final time prior to joining the fellowship in the sky. For the rest of that day they guided my path, circling far overhead along the coast, whilst I exposed my back to the scorching sun, in hopes that it would serve as antiseptic. The eerie correspondence of our routes led me to wonder if I might not the object of the buzzards' interest, rather than vice versa, and whether their readiness to abandon the previous meal was due to the expectation of far fresher fare from me.

At sunset, I came upon the Earth's terminus at the Connecticut River, its mouth much broader between banks than my longest channel crossing. Bitter wind blew the tops off malevolent short chop atop a current that moved out to sea with ferocious speed. The beach turned north abruptly, punctuated by a breakwater made of granite blocks, enclosing yet another marsh whose edges could not be seen. Unable to stop, and devoid of the will for swimming, I thought to follow the waters upstream in search of a bridge. Embedded in the shoreline ahead there was a colonnade of curved prongs, which looked at first to be part of a shipwreck. It seemed weird to me that the bulkheads would have rotten away, while the frame members remained intact; on approach I saw they were actually bones, pitted by the elements. For a confused moment I thought of finding a dinosaur, based solely on size, then realized my path intersected the rib cage of a whale; male, from the spermaceti type, to be precise, once the largest-brained, loudest-vocalizing animal of our age, and its deepest-diving mammal. Such olympian organisms fertilized the ocean surface with their feces, feeding phytoplankton that hence sequestered carbon by sinking to the bottom; but like so many deracinated natural systems, the importance of this symbiosis in the regulation of global climate went unappreciated by modern civilization until too late for it to be saved. After surviving the depredations of hunters in centuries past, and despite near-perfect adaptation to their environs, the mighty whales are now gone forever.

ENTHEOGENESIS · Origin of the Divinity within Us

Irresistibly drawn toward the bleached skeleton, I crawled with humility
into what may have been among the last of an awesome, mysterious specie,
whose individual life expectancy roaming the seas compared to our own.
His partially-buried ribs left ample space for me to pass between, and
enormous vertebrae that formerly connected them protruded from sand
deposited inside his barren carcass. The grave setting sent chills up my
spine, forcing me to a fetal position where I was overwhelmed by remorse.
Despite any professed interests of the zeitgeist in encountering life upon
alien planets, my society had idly exterminated whatever extraterrestrial
intelligence or non-human culture might have existed here. Wracked by
grievous sobs, I gave an insufficient apology to the dead cachalot on behalf
of my kind, wondering how long there would be until we met the same end.
Beyond his skeleton, a concrete lighthouse on the riverbank had collapsed
due to swift current undercutting its base, which I climbed atop arduously
for a view above the reeds. By the lingering twilight, I saw an interstate
highway and rusted railroad trestle a few miles inland; both edifices were
missing their midsections, leaving abutments and short causeways on each
side that led to nowhere but thin air. I swooned, lost my stance, and fell
down onto a pile of brush, thus heaving from pain; then I curled upon the
ground to cry harder than I ever had, wailing and screaming and bawling
as loud as I could. When exhausted, I gasped for a time, and began anew.
Although delusional, I knew my fortitude alone would take me no further.
I started a fire, never rising from a crawl, and spent my final moments
of consciousness in communion with the extinct leviathan.

"Well, what do you think?"
"We should find out what he's doing here first."
"A waste of time, if you ask me."
"I did not, though waste is in the eye of the beholder."
"Whatever...it's late, and I'd like to behold some dinner."
"This won't take long."
"A familiar story...why even ask if we have no choice?"
"All right, boys, calm yourselves..."
I heard one female and two male voices, as if some gods were debating
my fate. When reminded of where I was by my headache, I figured that
they belonged to burbarians or police; neither would have been surprising.
Besides my feverish shivering, I lay still, in paralytic fear whereby visions
of torture and cannibalism brought the unrequited impulse to purge again.
I cast my gaze about, uncertain whether my blindness was due to organ
failure or darkness because the fire had died. A motionless figure stood
close to my face; although unable to focus without any moonlight, the
shifting feet I sensed were no figment of my imagination, and as such,
so frightening that I would have pissed myself if not for dehydration.
"Good evening," he said ominously. "There is no reason to run."
"I don't think he can," judged the other man, looming over my back,
whose tone sounded nasal and higher pitched. His judgment was right;
the only running I could do went through horrific scenarios in my mind.
"Please," I begged, "whatever you do, just make it quick."
After a pause, the woman spoke next.

"You know why we've come?"

"Well, is it to eat or arrest me?"

The man with a higher voice cackled, while his counterpart remained silent. "You have no need to fear us." Her contralto tone struck me as reassuring, albeit unconvincing. "We're not going to do either. We merely want to ask who you are and what your purpose is here."

Since I lacked a ready explanation, the deeper voice filled the void. "Fires on the beach attract attention, especially where no one else lives." His speech sounded strange, for an agent or hijacker; with its carefully measured pace and impeccable enunciation, he seemed rather educated.

"Water..." I croaked.

"I beg your pardon?"

"He's thirsty," the woman declared, kneeling to slip a straw betwixt my cracked lips. "Try this."

Liquid felt foreign at first; as it dribbled into my phlegm-encrusted mouth, the life of me returned, sucking forcefully; whereas the swallow reflex did not come so quickly to my swollen throat and I choked instead.

"Slow down," she advised. "There is plenty more whence that came."

"You must be far from home," added the man standing before me.

I groaned. "Not far enough..."

"Well, why are you here?"

I evaded his question with one of my own. "You aren't police? DHS?"

Both of the men laughed then, and the tenor said, "No sir, you won't find any cops out this way. We can call them if you'd like, though I doubt they would make the trip for as poor a catch as yourself. No offense."

"Don't call...I escaped...and thought maybe you were them..."

"Escaped from where?" inquired the other with intensity that demanded an answer, and I had not the presence of mind to lie in reply.

"New York...no...well, yes...but I took the train to New Haven first..."

"Why?"

"I don't know...it was the farthest I could go."

"What I mean is, why did you escape?"

"They're after me...Homeland Security...I wouldn't stand for the anthem, and they found my books, plus they might have me for possession..."

"So you're a fugitive from the law."

"Well..." I began, thinking of denial, but saw he was correct. "I guess."

"You 'guess'?"

"Yes...I mean, the answer is yes."

"I understand; take heart, for there is no law out here except the laws of nature...speaking of which, how long ago did you make this escape?"

The stressful situation, as well as my mental state made it difficult to recall.

"Seven days," I responded at last.

"Is that so?" He implied some significance with his rhetorical question, though I could not tell whether it seemed a little or a long duration to him.

"And you say that you walked here from New Haven?"

"Except when I had to swim."

"And the smell...is it you?"

I sighed, chagrined by his reminder. "Uh...yeah...it's on my back..."

"May I take a look?" asked the woman, striking a light that stung my eyes;

I flinched as she reached toward me. "You can relax; this won't hurt."
She peeled back my shirt momentarily and replaced the fabric gently;
her fingertips felt my neck for a pulse, then examined my glands.
"Have another drink," she suggested. "Not too much...we'll return soon."
They walked away for discretion's sake, but I lay downwind and in absence
of eyesight my hearing was amplified, almost as if I could hover over them.
"What's your verdict?" asked the deeper male voice.
"Septicemia," she answered.
"Has it gone gangrene?"
"Not yet, but without treatment, it will."
"Can he be saved?"
She hesitated. "Maybe."
"What do you propose?"
"Well, there is nothing I can do here..."
"Not true," said the man with a pinched tone. "There is one thing..."
"That I cannot, and I will not."
"Yet you are the best qualified."
"His fate still hangs in the balance."
"As you said, not for long...taking him with us is too great a risk."
"Unless we leave his ID behind."
"You can't be serious."
"I am...and why not? It's been done before."
"But he's just some drugged-up city rat who happened to get out."
"Weren't you? Weren't we all?"
"That was different...there is no telling what diseases he might have..."
"Though he is badly infected, I do not believe that he is infectious, and I
thank you in advance for leaving the telling to me. Standard quarantine for
parasites will suffice." While her statement left no room for argument, she
went on to make a jab. "When did you become such a coward, anyway?"
"All right, that's enough," interjected the baritone man; I thought he
intended to sound impartial, but had to stifle a laugh in spite of himself.
"Back me up here...let's put him down and move on with our lives."
"I don't think so," the mediator said, taking a position for the first time,
by which the other man seemed surprised. "What? Why?"
"This one is not yet ready to die."
"As if you can tell."
"Can you? More importantly, ARE you?"
Tension filled the silence that followed.
"There is another way to settle this," the woman said.
"All right," the deep voice agreed. "Well?"
"Fine," his counterpart replied. "Do what you like."
All three walked back up the beach, resuming their positions around me.
"Hey there," grunted the figure in front whilst his shoe nudged
my shoulder deliberately. "What's your name?"
I felt saturated with a sense of bitter irony. "Does it matter?"
The pause told me he knew that I overheard their conversation.
"Let's do this a different way. Can you look at me, please?"
He held a lantern near my face and I cracked open the left eye.
"How many fingers do you see?"

Because multiple images overlapped each other in my blurred view,
I had to count a few times to be sure. "Six," I announced, and then
muttered to myself as an afterthought, "just like Alexander Fremont."
This time his pause was prolonged, and amidst sounds of wind-caressed
vegetation I heard the higher-pitched man take several steps away from
my spine, whereas the woman knelt quietly beside me; the other paced,
completing a few slow orbits around us both prior to speaking again.
"I am going to give you a choice, and I shall only do so once.
You will be required to decide right now, right here;
afterward, there is no second chance. Are we clear?"
"As the night sky," I remarked apprehensively.
"Indeed. You have blood poisoning, and without our help, you won't last
much longer; however, the world does not know we exist. Now that you do,
we can make you forget and leave you alone, in which case life goes on like
we never saw each other, while your fate is in the hands of the gods; we
could call the NYPD, DEA, DHS, or whoever you'd like, but they probably
won't come, and your journey ends here. Alternatively, we can give you a
lethal injection; a brief death, an easy death...a death you won't feel."
He waited to make sure I was paying attention.
"Or we can take you with us, and help if we can. I cannot tell you where,
but you should know that when we got there you would be unable to leave."
As usual at such times, sarcasm came to me readily.
"So you're offering brainwashing, execution, or a life of imprisonment?"
He grunted. "In essence."
"Hmm...a familiar story..."
"I'll simplify - do you trust me?"
"Not really, but it doesn't seem like I have much of choice."
"True enough; perhaps you're not as stupid as circumstances may make
you seem." His tone became solemn. "You understand the consequences?"
"You show me your hideout, and if I escape, you'll hunt me down, right?"
"You won't escape, but yes, that's the basic deal."
"So, you're a fugitive?"
"Well, in a manner of speaking..." he began, trailing off in a rare break
of speech, as though his mind changed abruptly. "The answer is yes."
I smiled a little at this, whilst still suspicious. "What did you do?"
"That is irrelevant to the matter at hand."
"You're asking me to take a leap of faith."
"I'm not asking you for anything; my offer is of generosity,
and an opportunity to take a leap of common sense. Think about it;
if I wanted to kill, abduct, rape, or eat you, there is nothing to stop me."
"Very comforting...then why do anything for me?"
"Let's just say someone gave me refuge when I was in your position,
and this is my chance to repay the kindness. I won't take you there
against your will, and I cannot make any promises about the outcome,
but if you choose to stay here, I'd say you will almost certainly die."
"I'm going to die, that much I know; but I don't think I'm quite ready yet,"
I mused, quoting his own words.
"That remains to be seen." He laughed grimly. "You have spirit, at least."
The woman, who had witnessed our entire interaction, interrupted us then.

ENTHEOGENESIS · Origin of the Divinity within Us

"I'll need to retrieve some supplies."
"Of course; he wants to go, anyway," my inquisitor replied,
whistling to his fellow. "Shall I get them, so you can stay?"
She agreed, issuing instructions; next I heard the men engaged in a heated
debate over life and death, whose noise merged with the surf as they left.
When we were alone, the woman approached to give me another drink.
"Are you still with me?" The sound of her voice was strangely soothing.
"I hope so." My articulation had been exhausted by the prior discussion.
"How old are you?"
"Seventeen," I mumbled, but corrected myself after counting sunrises.
"No, eighteen; I think it might be my birthday."
"Really? A virgoan; imagine that." She cleared her throat.
"I must confess there is a catch embedded in our proposition."
"Ah, always a catch...what is it now?"
"To take you with us, I must first remove the ID from your neck,
and due to your youth, I strongly suspect its chipset has the
new tamper-resistant features...do you know what I mean?"
"Yeah, I was gonna get it out in Boston for reidentification; why?"
"Ethics require me to disclose some unfortunate information in order to
help you, regarding the danger of detection during removal...in which case
the unit will expend its lifetime power supply electrocuting you. This would
be torturous, on a level you don't know, but if you could, you would beg
for death before the end. Do you understand and accept the risk?"
"Have you ever done this before?" I asked   instead of answering.
Although blind, I sensed an optimistic smile in her words.
"I consider it to be one of my specialties."
"Then yes," I decided, "but I want the injection if it goes down like that."
"Thy will be done; providence permeates the omens; the whale is my totem,
and his grave a place of power. Tonight is the equinox; if what you say is
true, the anniversary of your birth as well. Are you ready to be reborn?"
I murmured in acquiescence, asking if she was also a fugitive. In response,
she deflected my question with an oblique joke about 'voluntary service'
and bade me relax. I did as she said until my would-be captor arrived
bearing armfuls of equipment. She went with him for one trip, concluding
upon their return, "Thank you; I believe you brought everything we need."
"It's going to be a long night," he observed.
"Oh, you know you love it."
I dozed off as they set up, and woke to her singing "open wide" in my ear.
"Drugs?" I asked with hesitation.
"Medicine," was her clarification.
She thrust a gloved hand into my mouth, slid a drenching gun to the back
of my tongue, then let loose a spray of revolting tincture with the same
practiced austerity one might use when administering a cure to livestock;
although I wanted to spit it out, her grip clamped shut my nostrils and jaw.
"What the fuck?!" I gasped, once she released me at last.
"I'm sorry, but it would have been worse if I'd warned you." Refusing to
give me any more water as solace, she asked, "Did you ever smoke herb?"
"Are you kidding?" I retorted weakly.
"Do you think you still could?"

"Hell yes; to the bitter end."
"Then you should exhale and take a good rip; you won't cough from this."
She put a glass water pipe to my lips and struck a match, coaching me to
draw slowly. I recognized the sensation of smoke entering my lungs,
albeit oddly smooth, easing the burn with a potent floral aroma.
"Well done; now, again." My trachea felt numb and relaxed for the
voluminous second pull; afterward, she asked, "How do you feel?"
I slurred my words as serenity drifted over me. "Much better, actually."
"That's enough." To the man she said, "Let's put him on the gurney."
I smelled antiseptics and sensed, but did not feel, them lift my limp body.
"So if the extraction is a success, what's next?"
"A miracle," she proclaimed definitively.
"Do you think it will work?"
"I don't know, but it's worth a try."
Following a pause, he gravely asked, "What did you just say?"
"For Christ's sake, you never give up, do you?" she laughed.
"No, but you should know this by now as well as I."
"Indeed; it's no wonder you won't die."
"That remains to be seen." He seemed dissatisfied by her turn of phrase.
"Let's see about our patient first," she suggested,
slapping my face repeatedly. "Hey, are you still awake?"
I uttered a single syllable in acknowledgment.
"He's close; you can prepare the syringe," she instructed her companion;
placing her hands on my head, she said, "We'll meet you on the other side."
The last words I managed were, "Who are you?"
Her response sounded of distortion, like I was in freefall through an abyss.
"We are the new paradigm."
As if from across a vast distance, I heard the straps rustling efficiently and
metallic hardware clinking whilst they restrained me; then nothing more.

PALEOPSYKHIKOS TOMOS

"I live on Earth at present,
and I don't know what I am.
I know that I am not a category.
I am not a thing - a noun.
I seem to be a verb, an evolutionary process;
an integral function of the Universe."

"In order to change an existing paradigm you do not struggle to
try and change the problematic model. You create a new model..."

"Dear reader, traditional human power structures and their
reign of darkness are about to be rendered obsolete."

Cosmography: A Posthumous Scenario For The Future Of Humanity

~ Richard Buckminster Fuller ~

ASTRAIA

In the beginning of a dark and formless world, I heard music.
With all that had elapsed, the sound seemed strange to me initially,
beautiful yet mournful, as if my soul was present for its own funeral,
though absent lyrics. Listening more closely, the melody became familiar,
and I recognized it as a symphony of songbirds. My tongue pushed aside
a tube whence bitter liquid dribbled into my mouth, reminding me of the
woman from the beach with her plant medicines, like a fleeting glimpse of
some nearly-forgotten dream. The void in which I drifted felt warm, safe,
and deep; then awareness of my own weight came, resting atop a mattress.
My body lay between soft sheets of fabric; upon return, I wondered how it
had arrived there. The discovery that I wore a diaper caused me alarm;
this was clean, fortunately, and a tube issuing from my urethra poked
through. As if glued shut by mucus, my eyelids initially refused to open,
but clumsy fingertips massaged the life back into them. Once sensation
had been restored, they quivered; my facial muscles regained coordination;
and at last, I saw light again. An opening above my head was the source
of birdsong, admitting a gentle breeze into the dim room along with dawn,
and a rosy sliver fell on its far wall, below another window still showing the
dark firmament. As night gave way to the burgeoning day, I lethargically
turned upon my side, every movement hindered by a resistance similar to
submersion. With effort, I raised my upper body on an elbow to take stock
of my surroundings; the space was bare, except for my bed, a desk, and an
amorphous shape suspended in a dim corner from the wooden ceiling. My
inability to focus obscured the mystery object's identity until it greeted me.
"Good morning," said the baritone voice from the beach. "How do you feel?"
"Jesus Fuckin Christ!" I exclaimed, suddenly awake and panting
to catch my breath. "You scared me half to death!"

As far as I could tell, he wore only closely-cut charcoal underclothes that concealed his lean figure in the shadows. To my substantial astonishment and curiosity, he spoke in an inverted posture, hanging from a trapeze. "Sorry to disappoint, but you've mistaken me; moreover, should you meet, it would be best to remember that 'fuckin' is not Christ's middle name." Ignorant of what he meant at the time, I deemed his statement to be an awkward attempt at humor and responded with silence. "In fairness, you seem to like it there," he said as an amendment, whilst in my drowsiness I had lost the thread. "Where?" "Halfway to death. The crack between the worlds." His words rang true, although he could not know how much so; I realized many of my experiences, from the collapsing bricks to brushes with the toxidrome, head injury to nearly drowning, had prepared or led me to be nestled in that bed, permeated by a weird sense of déjà vu. "I meant half to life," I clarified. He laughed. "Half-life - that's clever." Whether he knew it or not, the pun was not my intention but his invention; I understood him completely this time, yet still failed to be amused. "You are fortunate, nonetheless; to be torn between them and thence return is a rare opportunity." "Yeah...an opportunity for pain and suffering," I groaned. "I won't tolerate that mentality in my house; there are no victims here." His voice abruptly grew forbidding. "You've created your own reality, and the opportunity you have is for transformation - with the benefit of your life intact, and your ID removed for no extra fee." I had neither energy nor inclination to argue, but found courtesy to say, "Thank you." "You're welcome." He allowed a pause at either end for emphasis. "Tell me, did you bring us anything from the other side?" "What do you mean?" He stayed suspended as the increasing light clarified his features. "You know, the usual: prophesy, pearls of wisdom, messages from aliens..." My memory was of impressions I had only begun to digest, which did not yet yield comprehensible information. "I'm afraid not; it's all just a blur." Illuminated motes of dust swirled around his head. "'Tis' a pity," he said, "but to be expected, I suppose; you have been sick and heavily medicated." "How long?" I asked, embarrassed by the thought of my digestive functions. "Seven days," he replied. "We've known for a while that you would live, though it is important to confirm that you can move and speak as well." His arms unfolded and stretched toward floor whilst he proceeded. "I'll say this - with the weather we've had, be glad you went swimming, since salt is probably what prevented the infestation of maggots that I would otherwise have expected in such conditions. I've seen animals die of flystrike, and believe me, it is not the way you want to go." His suggestion drew my attention to the bandages on my back; albeit numb, I flinched at the sensation of squirming larvae. "So...where am I?" "The answer is complicated, but we'll get to that later; it suffices to say, for now, you are my guest, and you are staying in my guest house." He pointed his toes to the ceiling, balanced his weight on the handgrips,

then gracefully let gravity rotate him to an upright sitting position.
"I'm more interested in discussing what you said on the beach."
The lingering haze confounded me. "I said a lot of things."
"You know what I mean," he declared resolutely.
I could conjure the ambience of the conversation, but it was shrouded
in bleary delirium, where fears and dreams entangled with reality.
Seeing me struggle to discern between them, he held up his hand,
its outstretched digits silhouetted inside the window frame.
"I trust that you can still count?" The fingers finally reminded me.
"Perhaps you will shed some light on how you became aware of
a dead man who was erased from history before you were born."
Averting my eyes from the distraction of his continuing gymnastics,
I told the story of Mrs. Jefferson's library as coherently as I could in the
given circumstances, noticing when finished that the sun had fully risen.
"I wondered if there were any copies out there anymore. If they're true,
your claims of living next door to the author would be quite a portent..."
Rays of the corona reached over the windowsill to elucidate his profile.
The visage belonged to an elder; vigorous in expression, yet marked by
age with a leathery tan, deep creases, and bristly white stubble that
extended from scalp to cheek. "I never liked the ending," he admitted.
Turning toward me then, the old man revealed his right side of his face
for the first time, or what remained of it; there was not much besides a
hideous mat of shiny, glabrous scar tissue, with both the lumpy texture
and angry color of an insufferable rash. I stared at him in horrified awe;
the burned eye had shriveled shut, while the ear was a mere orifice.
"But you can't..." I began, doing the math. "By now he'd be eighty..."
"Indeed; and you even remember arithmetic."
At the sight of my stunned countenance, Alexander Fremont nodded.
"How in the world...?"
"My wife, who saved your life, also saved mine, although that was half a
lifetime ago. She saw *The Fates* explode, and happened to find me whilst
approaching the fire, before the Coast Guard arrived. Despite my shock,
I somehow persuaded her to keep my secret; as the gods would have it,
she possessed the medical expertise to nurse me back to health."
His story strained credibility, and I made this known.
"If you are him, why didn't you go back? Why not tell the truth?"
His anguished sigh resounded with grief, putting my disbelief to rest.
"Because I knew it would do no good. As soon as I recovered,
the United States annihilated China and initiated the invasion of Iran.
I might have been a momentary figurehead at a tipping point in American
consciousness, but the empire won, as it typically does. In such times,
what can we do but follow the path of love? I had finally found mine,
and we decided that one attempted assassination was enough for us."
"But what about justice?...and in politics, think of what you could've done!"
"Yes, now that you mention it..." He laughed with wry condescension,
which left me mortified by my presumption, and then drove his point home.
"It's heartening to see youthful idealism persevere in an age like ours;
yet even now, you are dangerously attached to your cultural programming –
so much that you react in defense of the controlling operating system.

ENTHEOGENESIS · Origin of the Divinity within Us

You will see that its executive is a powerless puppet; a mascot of the leading brand whose existence serves only to pacify those who may clamor for democracy, but accept a choice betwixt two similar products instead. The winner is whichever can more successfully deceive the public whilst collecting bribes, in accordance with the laws of campaign advertising; but if you want the whole truth, then the Washington government itself is a Weapon of Mass Delusion to disguise the dynasty ruling your country. Regardless of what demagogue prevails in a given selection, its real winners lurk in the corridors of financial institutions and cigar-smudged conference rooms of corpocracy. I postured under the appearances of presidential candidacy, but never expected, nor desired, to be selected; and even if I was, who knows what I might have done? The primary ambitions of my campaign were theatrical and cheap; in effect, to harness the attention of the mass media industry for my own agenda. I helped when I could and put up a good fight; maybe won some battles or healed a few of the wounded, but that culture is a cause lost to me now, as is Alexander Fremont. I am no longer him, and prefer not to speak of the matter again."

It took me somewhat more than a moment to absorb all of this.

"What should I call you, then?"

"You may call me Aeiolus," he announced, flipping over backwards to dismount the swing with a practiced somersault. Drawing his spare frame to its full height beside my bed, he cracked the interlocked joints of his fingers and stretched his arms overhead. Turning to go was the only indication he gave that the conversation, or confession, had ended.

"How can you possibly still be alive?" I inquired on impulse as he left. He stopped with the door halfway open, his burned side facing my direction.

"Let me be a lesson to you, in this if nothing else: destruction of the self is a source of power, because if you are willing to do the work, you can become stronger by healing than you ever were before. This is your choice to make, and it is one not given often."

The woman from the beach introduced herself to me as Airmed, and the next interaction I recall began with her checking my temperature.

"Your life force returns," she declared upon examination of my eyes, glands, and vital signs. "I daresay that you will survive. Enjoy your convalescence whilst it lasts, since Aeiolus is impatient, and intends for you to work as soon as you're ready, if not before. The time has come for you to return to the land of the living."

She gave me viscous green juice from raw herbs and vegetables to drink whilst removing my stitches. A pair of incisions made a cross on my neck, whose quadrants had provided flaps just large enough for the surgical extraction of my ID. Once she finished, my hand moved reflexively toward the itching skin, but she caught my wrist in midair.

"Don't scratch, unless you'd rather take care of it yourself."

Airmed was stunningly attractive, at least to my mind, which never thought so about an older woman previously. She had the svelte body of a yogini, with silver hair woven into intricate braids, festooned by feathers, shells, and beads, framing her face. Aside from tiny wrinkles at the corners of broad eyes, like icy pools reflecting a cerulean sky, neither her smooth

complexion nor delicate features betrayed her necessarily advanced age.
"Face down," she ordered, making me self-conscious amid my admiration.
"I need you to lie still whilst I change your poultices."
Submitting to her ministrations, I resisted muscle spasms that came as
she washed and dressed my wounds. "What happened to you, anyhow?"
I told her the tale of my trip down the storm drain, concluded by
battering on riprap at its outlet; then of my time in the wilderness,
with its gauntlet of sunburn, mosquitoes, blisters and thorns.
"You should watch out for poison ivy in the future,
at least until we've built your immunity," she said.
"What's that?" I wondered ignorantly.
"A hairy-stemmed vine bearing leaves in triplets; I'll show you outside,
but its oil causes this rash because you are still allergic." Looking at my
ankles, I shuddered from the memory of how I had pulled hairs out of the
liquefied skin without opposition, its follicles reduced to gooey droplets that
clung to their ends. My week of unconsciousness, along with her healing
prowess, left the oozing mess mercifully subdued to a scabby residue.
"Since your system is now on its way to equilibrium, we can begin building
resistance. Despite an overactive histamine response, the good news is
that you have a robust constitution, especially for a victim of allopathy."
"Well, I did a lot of self-medicating."
Her melodic laughter made me feel rather pleased with myself.
"I'm sorry to say that it doesn't work quite that way, though you've
been blessed by rapid recovery, from the looks of the lashing you took.
How you went on so long without noticing that your back was rotting is to
me unfathomable; it seems you and Aeiolus have a few things in common."
She finished cleaning the area, then spread ointment over it carefully.
"He mentioned you're a reader. What sort of books do you seek?"
"Whatever I can get, but I really haven't read as much I should.
My neighbor left mostly history, philosophy, and anthropology for me."
Whilst applying fresh bandages, she asked, "Do you think you can stand?"
"I'll try, if you'll help me," I replied apprehensively.
"Let's lose the catheter, then; my guess is you're ready to pee normally."
After a moment of embarrassment and discomfort, my penis was finally
relieved of the dreadful tube. She next helped me rise to a seated position;
with my legs down and head up again, I swooned from nauseating vertigo.
"You can wait until you're ready," Airmed suggested. "No need to rush."
As the dizziness passed, my motivation increased; she pulled a robe over
my shoulders and lifted me up. "Lean on me," she said reprehensibly.
"Come on now, don't be afraid; I might be old, but I'm far from frail."
With her support, I walked out of the guest house onto a porch under
metal roofing, connected to a larger building whose walls had been lime-
rendered in the same style. Trellised vines with waning blossoms enclosed
the breezeway on my left side; through the insect screen to my right was
a pond populated by ducks, and a gently sloping meadow dotted by dwarf
trees beyond. The half-glass door gave entrance to a sunbathed kitchen
where a cat welcomed me by weaving between my feet, which were stuck
to the floor because I had never seen the interior of home such as theirs.
Immaculate expanses of glass afforded views over the luxuriant garden,

whose verdant vegetable rows alternated with the withered foliage of crops grown for their seed and lush carpets of young winter covers. They took root upon impeccable terraces that wrapped around the knoll from east to southwest, descending like a staircase of the gods. A motley flock of turkeys scratched in the shade of bramble hedges and berry bushes at its base, while young forests tinged with the fiery colors of autumn or meadows awash in gold bounded other horizons of the manicured scenery. Inside, the windowsills were crowded with potted cacti and cut flowers; dwarf citrus trees grew in barrels sitting on the floor; myriad bundles of herbs hung to cure from the joists. Every place my gaze fell was inhabited with a cultivated sense of purpose, beauty, and vitality.

"Welcome to our humble abode - your new home," Airmed declared as she withdrew a curvaceous walnut stool from the peninsula. "Are you hungry?"

Astounded by my surroundings, I merely nodded and settled into the beckoning seat, below the balustrade of a balcony that cantilevered over the north edge of the kitchen, which had a cathedral ceiling elsewhere. A stainless steel chimney passed through the second floor's opening, enveloped by racks holding trays of dried plants and sliced fruit.

"Where am I, paradise?" I mused aloud.

"Paradise is not a place," she replied; "it's a state of consciousness."

"Well, the house of the lord, then."

"Not heaven either, but getting closer." She smiled at the compliment.

"You're on Block Island, and yes, the mainland is too far to swim."

Leaving was the furthest thought from my mind. "I never heard of it."

"Fortunately for us, most people haven't these days, though it used to be a popular tourist destination, where permanent residents were conservation-oriented, albeit upper class; a quiet and modest seaside community, when compared with Martha's Vineyard or Nantucket."

"What happened to them?"

"They had to evacuate the island due to fallout from the Exchange."

Her explanation sounded dispassionate and matter-of-fact.

"We're that close to Ground Zero?"

"Close enough," she agreed noncommittally. "We call the place Tartarus."

"Aren't you worried about the radioactivity?"

She shook her head. "Not anymore. By the time we came, twenty-odd years ago, radiation levels were certainly above normal, but no higher than what occurs naturally in some parts of the world - just a moment." She set a jar on the blender motor, and after a few seconds of cacophony, handed me an aquamarine concoction with a frothy texture - "Breakfast."

Notwithstanding its unsavory appearance, her emulsion was rich, silky, and delicious; the word *ambrosia* leapt to mind as I drank, crooning approvingly. "What did you put in this?"

"Yogurt, pawpaws, honey, hemp oil, and eggs, plus my supplement blend."

I choked in dismay. "Eggs? Raw? Are you trying to poison me?"

She laughed again. "I'm 'trying' to heal you; I thought that much was clear. Don't worry; raw eggs won't hurt you." My face must have evinced concern, because she continued. "Trust me; I'm a student of epidemics; those diseases are unique to the unsanitary conditions of confinement feeding, where incessant abuse of antibiotics and mandatory irradiation have

spawned the most virulent human pathogens the world has yet seen.
Our free-ranging hens are free of such plagues; I assure you their
eggs are among the cleanest, healthiest foods you can eat."
I still would not drink, and she smiled at me forbearingly.
"You're awfully picky, for someone half-starved and riddled with parasites.
I wouldn't make my patient sick, just after restoring his health, would I?"
"Sure you would," I quipped, gagging a bit on memories of clams, seaweed,
and stagnant brine. "In the health care industry, that's good for business."
"Well played, but somehow I sense that I won't get rich by caring for you."
"Fair enough," I replied, sipping hesitantly; the shake tasted great and
I craved more. To evade my suspicions, I pressed her for information.
"If the island was deserted forty years ago, how is this house here?"
"Aeiolus and I built it, naturally. Many of the original structures were
destroyed by the weather, consumed by wildfires, or overtaken by forest.
Once we decided to dwell here, we salvaged what was left, harvested
what we could from the land, and imported what else we required."
"This is beyond a 'dwelling'...this is...I don't know...art."
"That's his touch. Although he won't admit it, my husband derives great
pleasure from his craftsmanship, whilst refusing to do less than his best."
I derived pleasure from our meandering dialogue and Airmed's beverage,
despite the grotesque color that came from her medicinal cyanobacteria.
"Would you like to see the library?" she asked, once I had finished.
"Seriously?" At her nod, an uninhibited excitement flooded my body.
"Unless you'd rather go back to bed..." she joked, moving to help me stand.
"I've got this," I declared; then she went to rinse my jar, glancing
my direction as I saved my balance on the edge of the counter.
"Suit yourself, tough guy," she said in a tone of detached skepticism.
With uncertain steps, I followed her across the atrium to the hallway of the
west wing, wherein she pointed out the bath, closets, and mechanical room
along our way to its last door. An earthy perfume of paper, ink, and glue
struck me first upon entry to the shadowy chamber. As my pupils dilated,
I saw that it had a roughly circular design, unlike the rest of the house.
A series of hinged fireproof panels wrapped the walls; Airmed opened
them to reveal full-height cedar shelving laden with books of unimaginable
quantity and variety, all illuminated by a parabolic skylight centered
in the domed ceiling, whose glossy burnished plaster encompassed the
whole vault of heaven as an enormous astronomical chart. Mosaic tiles
comprehended the Earth's surface in such detail I could have sworn the
floor had been painted instead; the map was bare except for a pair of
armchairs and endgrain table cut from the cross-section of an ancient
oak tree, which sat beneath the shutters of a southwestern bay window.
"Behold our pride and joy," she called whilst drawing back the blinds.
"Books don't fare well in direct sunlight, so you'll need to train your eyes."
They had already adjusted enough to dumbfound me with the sight.
"Make sure you close the doors when you're done, or else Aeiolus will have
your head; remember to sign everything out, and restore it to the correct
location. You're familiar with the universal decimal classification system?"
Since I was not, she showed me the card catalog - a mind-bogglingly arcane
artifact, given my habituation to predictive googles completed before their

queries were completely entered in the search field of my iNterface.

"You can read anything you like, as long as you're careful; old bindings are brittle, as you should know, and easily damaged. We intend to have a printing press someday, but for now, many of these are our only copies."
I recognized Food of the Gods immediately - *ambrosios*, in Greek - which happened to be the last book I picked up prior to my flight from the city. While I had just begun to read, my brief perusal placed its author among the most prophetic of Mrs. Jefferson's collection. Perhaps this is why the volume got my attention; maybe the bizarre color scheme on its spine and horizontally-displayed title caught my eye; or it could have been a matter of coincidence. Reason notwithstanding, the discovery that my hosts were collectors of everything he published thrilled me, and I gently stroked his 'search for the original tree of knowledge' as if to affirm its physical reality.

"Are these the complete works of Terence McKenna?" I asked.

Airmed wore a prescient grin. "Oh, do you know him?"

"Not really, but I'm eager to learn more."

"Imagine that." She plucked the book from its place and gave it to me.

"We don't have all of what he wrote; no one will, since some was lost to his library curse; but this is most of Terence, which may be more than any other extant collection. Who knows; you might even persuade my husband to dust off the Apple and show you his lectures, if you play your cards right."

"Terence, alive?" She nodded in response. "Such recordings exist?"

"Memory has ever been the key to our success."
I made a few laps around the incredible room with Food of the Gods cradled under my arm, grazing my fingertips over a body of knowledge comprising centuries upon centuries of banned books that had become stuff of legend.

"Who is all of this for?"

"For everyone...or did you think we would keep it to ourselves?"

"How many people live here?"

"Forgive me," she said, putting her hand to her forehead. "I've forgotten how much you don't know; it feels like you've been here some time, when to you it must seem that you've just arrived." She looked to a shadeline cast near the door across a series of arcs I had not noticed before, delineating the seasons on a circumferential sundial. "I beg your pardon since it's time for me to go; you should rest, and we'll continue with Aeiolus this evening."
She closed the lockers, then left the library abruptly, inquiring hospitably over her shoulder as I followed down the hall, "Do you need anything?"

"Well, now that you mention it..." My gaze landed upon the drying racks above the antique kitchen stove that emanated a familiar fragrance.

"I could definitely deal with a little weed," I suggested hopefully, and she laughed at me. "I suppose you could, but technically you're being weaned."
After springing upstairs on legs of enviable agility, she laid a briefcase on the counter and released an eruption of fragrance. The elegant interior compartments kept separate dozens of cannabis varieties, each labeled with description in script so intricate it was indecipherable to me. I would learn during my first week of conscious convalescence that Airmed was a connoisseur of marijuana for medical, ceremonial, and recreational usage, with strains bred specifically to treat pain, relieve nausea, or bring sleep; landraces for special rituals, of which she grew just a plant or two at once;

and a blend of cultivars selected for a perfect palate and the best-smoking spliff, to be enjoyed on the occasion of a philosophical dinner gathering. I had only ever smoked 'weed', usually from the aptly-named City Diesel lineage, always grown strictly for narcotic effect, along with maximum yield in artificial conditions. Aesthetics of the bouquet and health benefits (or detriments, as the case may have been) of its vapor were of no concern to producers of the commodity crop I encountered in my transactions. Instead, they applied the methods of industrial agriculture to individual containers, wherein a sterile environment and mechanical view of living processes were even easier to maintain than in a field; it often seemed that there was only a plant involved because synthetic cannabinoids remained illegal and beyond the technical capacity of most apartment laboratories. Urban marijuana grown as a drug thus reached its consumers laden with the nitrate salts of chemical fertilizers, biocide residues, off-flavors caused by improper curing, and hormonal imbalances due to electric illumination. Conversely, Airmed derived from her plant allies an entire apothecary via intentional cultivation, and selected a resinous indica-dominant variety on my first encounter with the collection, indicated for digestive stimulation. She bade me lie down in the guest house with a mug of tea before giving me the bubbler, which made me cough like a virgin from my overzealous rip.

"Have you ever read the Holy Bible?" she asked when I recovered. Conservative demographic groups of the time still subscribed to Christian institutions, but mine was distinguished by atheism and I shook my head.

"You probably should, in order to understand the culture whence you came and hence its effects on yourself, since more copies were printed than of any other publication aside from the IKEA catalog. Wait, though, until you've finished Food of the Gods; thence you will have a conceptual framework for the truth that lies between the lines of its testaments." I relaxed back in bed, warmed by a wind from the southwest, and flipped open Terence. Above an illustration on the first page I saw, its text said 'Paradise Lost'; and his last sentence on the left-facing complement read, "Now our choice as a planetary culture is a simple one: Go green or die."

Somewhere between 'Hell' and 'Paradise Regained' I fell into a sleep that lasted until the sun touched the horizon. Upon waking, it seemed I would survive the raw eggs; in fact, Airmed's smoothie had treated my body well enough to feel almost healthy again. Rising of my own volition, I dressed in clothes left to replace my robe and knocked on the kitchen door. She yelled for me to enter; in so doing, I met with aromas more appetizing than any I could conceive, making my mouth water and my stomach growl ravenously.

"It smells amazing in here," I proclaimed excitedly.

"Then I hope you're ready for solid food," she replied.

"I can't tell you how ready I am." I watched her swift, skilled motions for an awkward moment, which she allowed to pass, before thinking to ask if I might help in at all. She sent me into the garden to gather greens, but my incompetence required her to perform the task whilst teaching me their identities, along with appropriate harvesting techniques. Despite excruciating inefficiency, I was permitted to grate brilliant burgundy and golden beets, a vegetable new to me that I enjoyed immensely; the task took me as long as she spent preparing the rest of the meal. In addition to salad there were stewed beans, creamed onions, freshly-baked bread with pesto, and a gloriously roasted duck from the solar oven. She carved it once Aeiolus returned, near nightfall; he headed straight for the shower, emerging soon thereafter to embrace and kiss her uninhibitedly, finally acknowledging my uneasy presence as if he had just noticed me.

"I see you've come back from Erebus to join us; now how do you feel?"

"Hungry," I blurted, and blushed from my lack of restraint.

He gave her a lopsided grin. "Well, let's not keep the boy waiting."

As we sat down, the front door opened again; then in walked the most beautiful creature I have ever seen. Her exquisite features and radiant skin were accompanied by large eyes like Airmed's, except that she had irises of emerald green, cradled within long, dramatically curled lashes. Red highlights flashed in the long waves of her lustrous, dark hair when she moved; yet what took my breath away was her figure, simultaneously athletic, slender, and curvaceous. I guessed her to be twenty years of age, but she carried herself with poise, exuding the confidence that properly belonged to an older woman. Although nervous, I did not avert my gaze from hers as she came toward me without hesitation.

"So you must be the sewer rat," she remarked, shaking my hand formally.

"Bridget!" her mother scolded. "He's a guest!"

"What? It's a perfectly accurate epithet, isn't it?" Our eyes remained locked. "Tell me, guest, how is life in the city that never sleeps?"

I swallowed anxiously. "Not nearly as pleasant as it is here," was the best response I could muster, with the intention of sounding urbane.

"Hah! You obviously haven't been to work yet, then."

She nodded to her father, whose face looked expressionless. Bridget had brought a squash pie, which she set on the counter prior to taking the seat across from me. Her blessing asked the gods for a bountiful harvest, a successful breeding season, and protection from hurricanes.

"Above all," she concluded, "may the source be with the engineer."

"Ahem..." Aeiolus interjected, absent subtlety.

"Oh, yes...and we give thanks for the rare opportunity to welcome a guest from outside, as well as his rapid recovery."

"Amen," said her parents in unison.

Whilst serving food, the family members spoke amongst themselves about the concerns of their daily lives. I was reserved, absorbing what I could via observation, because my hosts made no overt effort to include me in the conversation. Aeiolus reported on the crops, noting that the hay, hemp, and grain were prospering, but the leaves of winter squash suffered from a fungal disease. Airmed said a little about Amadeus, the engineer of Bridget's prayer, whom she had visited during the afternoon. I wolfed down my small helping silently, waiting to address Aeiolus at a break in their talk.

"I heard you have some videos of Terence McKenna, and just wanted you to know that I'd be very eager to see them, if it's ever convenient to do so."

With excruciating slowness, he raised his face from his plate and gave me a piercing stare with the left eye. A forkful of succulent duck had stopped halfway to his mouth; he set it down deliberately, glancing at Airmed, who appeared absolutely stoic, while Bridget giggled playfully.

"It's not your fault," she said in response to my apparent confusion.
"He's afraid of the Apple...oh, I'm sorry...I meant 'intelligent prosthesis'."
"You would be as well if you'd seen what I have," Aeiolus declared. "I hope
you'll never know how lucky you are to be free of such toxicity, my dear."
Obviously disappointed, he next asked his wife, "You told him already?"
This was more than she could bear, and a lovely grin crept over her face
as she looked at her daughter, yet still resisted laughter successfully.
"Honey, I'm sorry. He noticed Terence immediately when I showed him
the library, and as it happens, he was reading Food of the Gods prior to
leaving New York. In light of the synchronicity...well, it just slipped out."
Then she leaned my direction, whispering, "I didn't mean to ask tonight."
The oversight embarrassed me, but she gave a wink indicating forgiveness.
I admired the familial affection that made his fear also a source of humor.
"Hmph," Aeiolus grunted, pointing his knife at me. "We saved your life;
you've been unconscious for a week; you wake up in an unknown place
unlike any you've ever experienced; and your first request is to be plugged
into the matrix again. Beware whose prosthesis is whose, my friend."
"Go easy on him," Airmed said. "He's doing great for an egg and could seek
far worse in media. Besides, his first request was actually to smoke herb."
This joke relieved the tension at my expense, and their trialogue shifted
next to technical problems of what Bridget kept calling "that damned mill"
with evident frustration. After serving the pie, which I scarcely tasted
because I was busy ogling, she excused herself to work on the malfunction.
"Well, I expect to see you later, and hope we can keep you entertained until
then without television," she quipped facetiously, and Airmed interceded.
"It's the new moon; a time for change, beginnings, and personal growth."
She glared at her daughter. "Everyone deserves the benefit of the doubt."
"That's okay; I haven't seen any TV in quite a while," I remarked, "and it's a
pleasure to meet you, too," I told Bridget with a modicum of dignity intact.
"Believe me, the pleasure is mine," she retorted, wished her parents good
night, and left abruptly, flipping her gorgeous, unruly mane on the way out.
Her father invited me to help do the dishwashing, which went from right
to left in accordance with the layout of kitchen fixtures. He stood at the
larger basin to wash, presumably so I would not need to look, or avoid
looking, at the burned side of his face; as my side of the sink filled,
he was quick to criticize my wasteful, unpracticed rinsing.
"Haven't you ever cleaned a pot before?"
I had not; in fact, almost all I previously ate came from a vendor package,
restaurant, or prepared dispensary ration, except for a chance piece of
fresh fruit; while my admission thereof seemed to cause him exasperation.
"Those are bleak circumstances; how did you endure such an existence?"
I told him I knew nothing else; hence, I thought naught of it at the time.
"Well, I'm sorry for that, but you need to begin thinking about what you're
doing now. Not only are you slow, but your water consumption is appalling.
If we were sailing I'd have to throw you overboard to avoid dying of thirst."
I realized his harsh critique had no lasting anger behind it and he was more
frustrated with the culture whence I came than my clumsy inefficiency.
Although still ashamed of my fecklessness, I felt some solace as well,
since the occasion for him to reproach me occurred after Bridget's exit.

"You can forget about that." Out of context, it seemed like a non sequitur.
"Huh?" I replied in mock surprise, knowing fully to what he referred.
"Don't play games with me; I wasn't born yesterday."
"Oh, Bridget?!" Somewhere betwixt evasion and intimidation, I fumbled.
"She's very intelligent and attractive, but I would never..."
"Ahem." His interruption saved me from digging the hole any deeper.
"You're drooling," Aeiolus added, and I wiped my mouth self-consciously.
"It's just a figure of speech," he told me, chuckling.
"Our guest has some questions regarding the village," Airmed said,
intervening on my behalf as she stowed the leftovers.
"Ah, yes...of course he does."
He glanced to a panel at the base of the stairs, where an array of gauges
displayed meteorological data alongside the status of household utilities
systems. An analog clock was mounted on top, though I did not recognize
it as such from the esoteric symbols inscribed within its golden bezel.
"I'd be glad to talk more, but must leave for the evening. Tomorrow I'll
answer what I can, and as soon as you're up to it, we'll take a full tour."

During the Wisconsin glaciation, sheets of ice grew to miles
in thickness and covered much of the terrestrial northern latitudes.
By accumulating water they reduced ocean depth, thus permitting a host
of Asian mammals, including human beings, entrance to North America via
the modern-day Bering Strait. The glaciers reached their maximum extent
a thousand generations in the past, scraping the earth as they progressed;
then retreated north, leaving behind the ridge of debris they had plowed
ahead. As ice melted, sea levels rose, while wind, rain, runoff, and waves
eroded the deposited glacial till of Block Island's nativity to create ten
square miles of tenuous terra firma amidst the waters separating the
similarly-formed fingers of Long Island from the elbow of Cape Cod.
Indigenous Americans inhabited this land for more than three millennia,
harvesting its fish and mollusks, hunting deer, and growing crops for their
sustenance, thereby living in equilibrium with the isle's carrying capacity
prior to the arrival of settlers from Massachusetts four hundred years ago.
Within a century white immigrants displaced the native tribe, razing its
forests for lumber and farmland in order to establish the colony that they
named New Shoreham. Their demolition was restrained, compared with
the rest of manifest destiny; thanks to an economy supported by tourism,
modern residents managed to protect much of the land from development.
Declared a national historic district, their small town successfully resisted
encroachment of corporate franchises with prosperous local businesses -
until the Exchange necessitated its total evacuation and abandonment.
Twenty years of subsequent human desertion afforded Block Island
an unprecedented chance to regrow some semblance of forest cover.
Meanwhile, Airmed and Aeiolus conceived a prototype for sustainable
settlement, or rather a living laboratory to blaze pathways for cultural
evolution that would boldly go beyond civilization, where the recently-
exterminated intentional communities' movement before them had not.
They dropped off the grid to sail the high seas in pursuit of this dream,
seeking an appropriate site for its fruition, and meeting souls of similar

vision in the wake of Alexander Fremont's assassination. Their original intention had been to stay out of the country; and over the course of an international search, they found many suitable locations; but realized along the way that nowhere would such an experiment be more germane, or more important, than in the home of humanity's most unsustainable society. "I love America; I only hate the institution known as its United States." Perhaps it was the allure of challenges posed by flying under the radar, or Aeiolus' fond memories of time spent in New Shoreham during his youth; in any case, the place chose itself as a chrysalis of tribal metamorphosis.

Exercising great discretion, they joined with fifty other willing pioneers from their network of contacts for the mission to re-inhabit Block Island. This exclusive congregation engaged in years of negotiation, research, and radiation monitoring before making excursions to shamanize or survey the land, water, and ruins. The team then proceeded to design a village based on what resources the place could readily provide, as well as an analysis of logistical obstacles to its assembly, not least of which was the overgrown state of former farm fields. Impenetrable thickets of brambles, barberries, shrubbery, honeysuckle, and assorted small trees were laboriously cleared during the prolonged Northeastern drought with a slash-and-burn variant that made charcoal of their organic matter. Such methods sequestered carbon in the relatively poor ground, where it bound with soluble nutrients to form a type of supercharged humus known as *terra preta* whenever left by prehistoric Americans in the likewise-deficient soils of tropical jungles. The pioneers carefully preserved a forested buffer along their coastline for erosion control, windbreak, and security; all village development occurred inside this perimeter, ensuring invisibility to any passersby. Although apparently wild, the margin of trees was hardly without human intervention; foresters managed its ecosystem for desirable attributes, such as high density of visual screening on the outside, saw timber value elsewhere, and diversity of wild habitat, food, and medicine throughout. For example, they exercised particular diligence to select, then release, young locust trees, which produce the same strong, rot-resistant lumber Alexander Fremont used as decking for his construction of *The Fates*. A fast-growing pioneer itself, the *pseudo-acacia* specie has the additional benefits of casting little shade, fixing nitrogen, and aggressive reproduction by rhizomatous sprouts once harvested, not unlike the Lernaean Hydra. According to Aeiolus, twenty-three of the original founders still survived at the time I arrived; nearly five hundred total souls resided on the island, including a hundred or so children, whom he defined as anyone that had not yet been through 'initiation'. This mysterious, new, gender-specific ritual customarily occurred between sixteen and eighteen years of age, depending on an individual's precociousness and inclination. After the rite of passage, young adults were encouraged but not required to leave their parents' homes, choose mates, and raise children; but as my host candidly volunteered, the watersheds of life may not always happen as planned. He mentioned I would join the next group if I 'proved myself', warning me against feeling ashamed of being the oldest, because in many ways I was the least mature, albeit for reasons beyond my control.

In the first week of my awakening, I never left Aeiolia and barely ventured past the bounds of the family compound. Despite Bridget's feigned concerns, entertainment was the furthest thought from my mind; I occupied it by learning instead. Airmed taught me to work in her garden, care for the animals, and listen to my body, so that I could better nourish myself whilst rebuilding lost mass. I retired each evening with scripture from the library, exhausted by recuperation; yet the time I spent reading and sleeping diminished with each passing day, until I adapted to the same schedule as my hosts. Although it had seemed Aeiolus avoided me, he was actually just busy; if I arose before dawn I might see him in the house or share a pot of his adaptogenic tea. He loathed talking during these dark hours, doing so only to convey that they belonged to the gods; my job was to listen, rather than contaminate the sanctity of dreamscapes. I began to make sense of foreign concepts like 'psychic space' by pretending to understand them, then questioning his wife, who spoke freely whilst we harvested her winter inventory, a daily chore lasting from as soon as dew evaporated unto the wilt of the scorching sun. It was high in the sky at the first quarter moon when I disturbed a nest of wild bees and received my first sting, on the eyelid, for lacking awareness. I ran with a frenzied, instinctual panic to plunge my face in the pond, rubbing as it swelled up, almost instantaneously. Airmed pulled me out, slapped on a poultice of chewed leaves, gave me a toke, then explained in her mellifluous tone how plantain would attenuate my histamine reaction to the venom.

"How do you know everything?" I groaned, and her laugh served as salve.

"I took physiology in medical school, but the use of wild herbs is basic knowledge, even to our children; how else can we let them roam freely?"

"I'd hate to see a kid get stung by one of those bastards; it fuckin hurts!"

"Oh, I've seen far worse; you ought to get a grip and be careful next time."

"Next time?! Why don't we get rid of that damn nest right now?"

"Those bees are far more important to this ecosystem than you, while biocides of industrial farming endanger pollinators worldwide. What would you think if some specie of so-called self-conscious giants decided to wipe away New York because its noise or odor was a nuisance?"

Her point had been effectively made, and I felt remorse for my entitlement.

"It's not you, it's your culture," she added, as if in reply to my thoughts. "Besides, if the bees become extinct, human society will follow in four years, at least according to Einstein. Their medicine is a gift, which focuses attention on areas of your body and life requiring healing."

If this meant to imply that my vision, or powers of observation, left room for improvement, then she was correct; were I attuned to my environment, I would not have gotten stung. My immune system, or the absence thereof, developed in artificial conditions, and had consequently been ill-calibrated for response to such natural phenomena as apitoxin. Although the poultice surely helped, by Aeiolus' return at twilight, my left eye was swollen shut so tightly that the pressure alone pained me.

He took one look at my distorted face and smiled broadly.

"You're making me feel better already," he said.

For all the self-deprecating remarks on his appearance, Aeiolus wore disfigurement proudly among a public that silently respected him therefor. After all, how could we do anything but revere, or else fear, the man who had endured such scarification, then made it a source of personal power? I noticed this more under the influence of my own facial deformity, which had dissipated enough to restore depth perception by the time he finally gave me an island tour. Whilst traveling its periphery sunwise via bicycle, my host outlined landmarks and erstory along our route, patiently indulging the multitude of questions I asked in response. Five constantly-staffed watchtowers were among New Shoreham's most distinctive man-made structures, and we went first to the old lighthouse near his homestead. With walls of red brick and a steep slate roof that survived the Superstorm, it still perched nearly 200 feet above the surf at the eastern end of bluffs forming the south coast. Due to natural erosion, this edifice once sat on the edge of a precipice, but in the late 20th century, each of its 2000 tons had been moved inland to safety, where they provided villagers of my day a lookout station, whence I could see Long Island on the western horizon. As we pedaled along the wooded buffer of Aeiolia, its eponymous founder pointed out various pastures, fields, and orchards, describing what was grown by whom, though their exotic names did not yet mean anything to me. Assorted huts, houses, and storage buildings speckled the elevated areas, each evidently built according to its purpose as well as available materials, surrounded by neatly-fenced paddocks wherein livestock grazed peacefully. The agrarian landscape possessed a pleasant rolling characteristic, which lent itself to the formation of numerous freshwater ponds; he recited with great specificity what fish lived in them, when the best berry-picking could be had, and where the wood ducks preferred to nest. Upon being asked if this was too much for me to absorb, I assured him I would remember it all, in a lapse of modesty that caused him to grunt and me immediate regret. Across the road dividing Mykenai from north to south, we entered Akhaia; then farmland gave way to the village wilderness. After passing through its forested ravine, Aeiolus brought me to the southwestern sentinel, a defunct wind turbine accessible by rows of spokes welded alternately on either side. Gazing northward from there, I could see a dozen islanders harvesting peat in a drained swamp, though they were the size of ants by my perspective. We ate lunch whilst watching waves wash the sunny western shore of Elis; further inland, we hiked on densely wooded hillsides of Arkadia that site planners had deemed too steep for sustainable grazing, where selective logging encouraged hybridized pine tree with the best form and greatest potential for growth. "We've harvested enough lumber from indigenous structures and ongoing clearing to meet most of our foreseeable needs, so these stands of timber are for future generations," Aeiolus explained. Between their trunks, I saw tarmac from the former airport, upon which was built a low tunnel of sorts; the ropewalk, he called it, noted for almost a quarter-mile of length, set within a quilt of hay, grain, and hemp fields encompassed by Attika. This once-upon-a-time landing strip lay adjacent to Athenai, the majestic community hall, along with its central infrastructure, whence we went west across silvapastures in northern Arkadia. Pathways through forest gardens led to flourishing Elysian fields, past the omphalos at Delphi, then ended on broad, flat beaches quite unlike those adjoining the base of bluffs. Pointing north, he indicated the sparsely-populated plains comprising sandy Pylos and the midwestern watchtower, also called the Herakleion pillar. This slim pole, over two hundred fifty feet in height, had been erected for an offshore wind farm proposal to support weather monitoring instruments, which were only accessible by rope, with ascenders or winch. My knees felt weak as a tiny figure at the pinnacle greeted us via salute, since its guy wires failed to stop the mast from vibrating in the wind. We walked beside the bustling docks and shops of Ithaka toward a hilltop cemetery engraved between stone walls, with lofty nut trees all around. Sheep rested in the shade or grazed on the underlying sward, though I thought they were goats at first because of their regally curled horns. "These are from my stock," Aeiolus announced; as such, they descended from the Icelandic breed that had scarcely changed in the millennium since their introduction by Vikings, while bearing little resemblance to the archetypal varieties of mainland Europe or the British Isles. These animals were magnificent and alert, with long wool in beautifully colored patterns, but I found the sight of them climbing on monuments vaguely sacrilegious. "I agree," he said, "hence part of the intent. This pomp and circumstance surrounding funerary rites is at best an artifice for the benefit of the living, if not outright profiteering by commodification of tragedy; and the dead, given the choice, should not want to be taken so gravely nor be so abused. Life goes on, and with all these headstones, mowing is impractical here. Grazing is our way of preventing them from being lost to eternity, and if they happen to double as a sheep playground in the interim, so be it." On the northern side of Argos, in an area colloquially known as Old Town, the mideastern sentry overlooked estuaries defining its border with Ithaka from atop a pylon nearly as tall as the weather mast; this tower, in contrast, was heavily built of crisscrossed steel framing, then braced to the ground by thick galvanized cables. It supported microwave dishes and radio antennae used for telecommunications transmission to or from the rest of the world in the halcyon days of yore, but afforded the island's current residents excellent views of the Rhodesian mainland from a platform at its apex. The base sat on a plateau, adjacent to five container-sized underground tanks that had stored diesel fuel for New Shoreham's electricity generation station. Little remained of Block Island Power besides rusty steel buildings, swallowed by honeysuckle, grape, and poison ivy vines. Causeways thence leapfrogged the waterways of Korinth; we followed its isthmus northward to Lakedaimon, a geographically distinct region set apart from the rest of the island by an ample inland harbor on the west. This salt pond connected to the open sea through a tight channel, bounded by a peninsular extremity of the Korn Neck, as the latter was also called, that reached toward Pylos yet did not quite touch. Although the early 21st century found its highest value as real estate, Lakedaimon possessed some of the village's best soils and topography for agriculture; residents during my time seemed especially empowered by vigorous cultivation thereof, along with produce it yielded, while comprising a disproportionate number of the tribe's loveliest women. Rising slowly along the spine, a single straight road of generous width gave access to woodlots and farmsteads via the narrow branches intersecting it.

I struggled to keep up with my guide until we reached the top of the incline, where leaves of canopy trees at their peak of fall color closed in overhead; but felt exhilarated by my flight down the opposite side, whose cedar-lined shoulders were blurred at high speed. Amidst the cooler microclimate of its north-facing descent, leaves had thinned and turned brown; at the bottom, they littered the ground, revealing a large, circular pond separated from the eastern ocean by a narrow land bridge joining Lakedaimon to Kriti. Our stopping place had cobblestones instead of a beach; its shore rose to the southeast, eventually meeting bluffs less dramatic than those of Aeiolia and Akhaia in height, yet more so in their splendid coloration, due to the clay veins for which they were named, elsewise seldom seen on the island. Aeiolus gazed toward them wistfully, his demeanor suddenly downcast as if by some dreadful memory, but I felt it was not my prerogative to pry. After a pensive silence, he suggested we leave our bikes and walk to the northern end, where the coast became sandy again. Periodically peering through binoculars hung around his neck, he warned me that in the event, albeit unlikely, of a boat sighting we would need to hide immediately, either by running to the dunes or diving in the water, whichever might seem more expedient. Walking on the waterfront during day violated taboo because it risked attracting the attention of passing vessels to what was allegedly an uninhabitable location; thus, shoreline activities such as seaweed harvest and shelling only occurred at night, preferably in the dark of the moon.

"Do you have many passing vessels?" I asked him.

"Besides our own, no, thank goddess; they avoid Tartarus like the plague, and enter the Sound via Northfork Canal, if at all; but past precedent does not necessarily affect future outcomes, so we are always vigilant. Let's consider this a special deviation, and keep it to yourself, please."

The fifth village sentinel was another lighthouse, tucked into the dunes of Delos at its northern terminus, dating from the mid-19th century and the fourth erected upon that site. Its builders, evidently intent on it also being the last, constructed the shell entirely of granite blocks a full foot in thickness, and each the weight of several men. Aeiolus described how they were quarried in Connecticut; transported to New Shoreham via sailboat; and dragged thence by oxen. Imagining this epic effort, especially what had been required to set capstones on the steeply-sloped gable rake walls, absent the assistance of hydraulic power equipment, boggled my mind.

This nearly indestructible envelope, combined with a recently-restored roof of slate shakes, protected the structure from the Superstorm as well as its sibling on the southeast, even though it sat perilously exposed to the ocean, just a stone's throw away in three directions. No cover of forest would establish itself on such windswept sands, making the walk there so conspicuous that watches could only be changed at night; since this restriction lengthened shifts, it required teams to occupy the north light. Bounded by sea on both sides, east beach met west at lonely Delos, where they tapered down to a curved spit and disappeared underwater together.

A herd of deer were browsing nearby; they retreated from our arrival but did not hurry, unlike those I had previously seen on the mainland. We watched them leave, then turned to the waves, which rose from either side upon approach to the submerged spine, in unison at times, breaking

against each other in perfect symmetry. My host removed his clothes,
much to my surprise, prompting me to wonder aloud what he was doing.
"Swimming, obviously," he replied, taking long, naked strides into the surf.
"You might do the same; soon the water will be too cold for your comfort."
I trailed behind in underpants with averted eyes until he turned to ask,
"When you get out, what on earth will you wear?"
I had not shed my mores either, and he laughed at my slackjawed demurral.
"Sorry; I forgot that in America men are meant to fear their own bodies."
Voluntary nudity in the presence of another male, excepting virtuality,
constituted a new challenge; yet for the sake of practicality I followed suit,
running after him and diving into the cool water when it reached my thigh.
Calisthenics were his remedy for the cold wind we met upon emergence;
I strained to complete ten poor push-ups under the pressure to achieve,
· which effectively warmed me, while Aeiolus managed over a hundred, not
to impress or embarrass me, though he did both nonetheless, but simply
since that was his normal routine. Despite the wrinkles of an antediluvian
physique, its effort appeared far less, and its form much better than mine.
My admiration thereof, as well as sheer disbelief, impelled me to glance his
direction, where I saw a symmetrical pair of sea monsters tattooed on taut
trapeziuses, pointed snouts touching as in a blue and white Rorschach blot.
They swam synchronously in my peripheral vision with the steady tempo of
his repetitions, and I asked about the image when we had pants on again.
"That is my totem, the great white shark."
"Have your ever seen them?"
"A few, but humanity's last natural predator is long gone."
"Then...I beg your pardon...why would you take it as a totem?"
His hesitation was not to find words; rather, to give them proper gravity.
"Sharks lived without fear of death, though they had to swim constantly
to forestall sinking; mastered infinity through their perceptual powers; and
embodied ancient wisdom - abilities whereto I might aspire in their stead."
As the tide receded, bickering gulls gathered to feed on what nourishment
they could find amidst the seaweed; then Aeiolus gestured enthusiastically
toward a white raptor soaring effortlessly on the thermals above them.
"We must have called her in with the shark medicine," he suggested.
Her broad primary feathers and slightly bent wings reminded me of the
bird that confronted me on the beach, so I remarked upon the similarity.
"Pure white, you say?"
I nodded. "Other than the head, which was small and red."
"You were close enough to tell its wingspan?"
"By far the largest bird I've ever seen," I replied, demonstrating with my
arms outstretched to their limits. "I thought perhaps it was a dream."
"Not a dream, but the profoundest of omens," he said. "To my knowledge,
a single albino vulture frequents Burbarus, and rarely does she venture
this far from shore. I've seen her, though never out here before."
"You think it's the same one? How can you tell from so far away?"
"Lest my face deceive you, know that I see more than you might suspect;
in this case, the key is in her tail. There were once birds of prey with
which the shape could be confused, yet they now are all extinct."
Whilst I gazed reverently at the bird, Aeiolus craned his neck behind me.

"Would you turn around for just a moment?" he asked.
"Face opposite the sun...hold your arms out to the sides again."
I did as the vulture had and he said, "Strange I didn't see it before."
"What is it?"
"The scars on your back resemble a pair of wings; if had a mirror
to show you, it would lay out well enough to develop as a tattoo."
Recalling the bloody head tearing into maggoty gull entrails, I shuddered.
"Of a buzzard? Are you serious?"
"You don't choose your totem; the totem chooses you."
I still found the association unappealing. "Just like that?"
"Are you disappointed or kidding? I know of no animal more powerful
who still roams the sky or sea; you should feel honored instead."
"By a bird that would eat a rotten carcass?"
"Indeed...*Cathartes aura*."
"I beg you pardon?"
"Her scientific name; it means purifying breath."
The mighty vulture flapped thrice, turning northward for the mainland;
when she disappeared into the gray distance, I brushed sand from my skin
and finished dressing. Chilled by bitter winds, I walked ahead of my guide
for a change on the way back to our bicycles. He had seemingly timed the
trek so our arrival would coincide with sunset, and from a stance upon
the isthmus just above its rocky eastern shore, I could see beyond the
pond, over sand dunes, then beach on yonder side, to the western sound
where the horizon lay tangent to our star. The red orb sank slowly, spilling
prismatic waves of color across the sky, whose pristine reflection off the
pond's unruffled surface made a dramatic contrast to the green waves
behind us, already below evening's shadow. Cold or not, I thought I must
have inadvertently been imprisoned in the most beautiful place on Earth.
"I've been all over this planet, and I agree," Aeiolus said, as if in response.
I wonder whether it was a lucky guess, legitimate telepathy, or if he had
brought enough other people to visit that place in such conditions to know
how I would react, past precedents and future outcomes be damned?
We went on foot across Kriti, pushing our bikes toward the twilight along
the pond's reedy northern shore, thence headed home via Lakedaimonian
fields. In the gathering dusk, he attentively noted the health, maturity,
and germination of the crops through which we passed, chiding me when
necessary to keep my footsteps between their rows. We returned to the
main road by a meandering route and rode the rest of the way beneath
a gibbous moon. I thanked him for taking time to show me the island;
in response he thanked me for providing a reason for him to explore.
"I can get so caught up with responsibilities that sometimes distraction
is required, as a reminder for me to worship my beloved habitat."
Airmed was gone upon our return to the house, but she had left a pair
of dinner plates for us. The next day would be my introduction to work,
he announced, along with the recommendation that I go directly to bed.
I felt spent, and did so gladly; there, I fell into the sleep of the dead.

"Treat the Earth well:
it was not given to you by your parents;
it has been loaned to you by your children.
We do not inherit the world from our ancestors;
we borrow it from our descendants."

~ Indigenous American proverb ~

"The care of the Earth is our most ancient and most worthy,
and after all, our most pleasing responsibility.
To cherish what remains of it and to foster
its renewal is our only hope."

~ Wendell Berry ~

SKORPIOS

Aeiolus pounded on my door adamantly, awakening me before dawn;
as I staggered into the dimly-lit kitchen, he pointed toward the counter,
upon which sat a plate of scrambled eggs with sausage, fried potatoes,
greens, salsa and a scoop of soft cheese. Washed down by a steaming
mug of tea, the hearty breakfast energized me; then he indicated that,
after washing the dishes, I would find my destination by heading west.
"Cross the orchard and head over the hillcrest; go through the far gate in
the fencerow, and thence take the wide trail. There will be recently-cut
hemp fields and barns to the north, followed by a bog on its south side.
You'll soon come to a stone monument, overlooking the large fish pond;
follow its bank counterclockwise to pools where you'll be working. If lost,
just tell someone you're looking for Will. Can you remember all of that?"
I nodded. "Make sure to arrive ere the sun is fully above the horizon,"
Aeiolus added on his way out the door. The morning was clear and cool,
leaving a dense blanket of dew whose droplets revealed the otherwise
inconspicuous spiderwebs lining my walk through the swamp. At its far
edge, I met a group of four teenage boys; when asked about Will, they
said that they were going to work with him and invited me to join them.
We exchanged uneasy introductions, while in response to their apparent
bewilderment, I gave an abbreviated outline of how I came to the island.
They had presumably heard rumors of me begotten from Bridget's reports,
because their conversation prior to my appearance was subsequently
derailed by an extensive interrogation concerning life in New York.
"Is it true that some people have to sleep in the street?"
"Do your doors really open automatically?"
"What does synthetic meat taste like?"
"Are any of your organs cloned?"
"Have you ever been mugged?"

"Do you have to wear a respirator outside?"
"Can you see over the smog from atop the Park Towers?"
"Is it true that everyone has machinery implanted in ers body?"
"They really let elders die of heat stroke if there isn't enough power?"
Remembering my first meeting of native-born villagers other than Bridget,
I am amused by their ostensibly simple questions, as by the astonishment
wherewith straightforward answers were received. They seemed especially
interested in the depiction of my cranioplasty - "You must tell Aephaistos,"
the boy named Hemlock said – but I found particular difficulties explaining
how the scenery looked from street level. All of them had seen pictures
of American cities in books dating from around the turn of the century,
so they grasped the basic urban pattern: cuboid domiciles and offices were
stacked repetitively inside titanic, sterile edifices of glass and concrete,
artificially illuminated and conditioned at all times; amidst grids of paved
roads filled with automobile swarms; bounded by walkways conveying
a parade of strangers from bus to train, then back again, for the entire
duration of their lives. What changed since the days of those publications,
aside from the replacement of sidewalks with air-conditioned breezeways,
was that most vertical surfaces in the city were leased out to display an
unending procession of animated advertisements. I eventually realized
these boys had never seen a digital screen or iNterface projection, and
thus could not understand words like brand, model, logo, or commercial;
they possessed as little frame of reference for my world as I did for theirs.
The sun had nearly risen from the ocean by the time we reached Will,
who stood facing it. He was an imposing man of mostly African ancestry
with the muscular build of a professional fighter and a clean-shaven scalp
covered by intricate tattoos. When I introduced myself as Aeiolus' guest,
he appraised me dubiously, then just said, "Let's see what you can do."
Vinyasa yoga began the day, taking me on a crash course in coordination
despite the balance I had from skating. Will explained that this discipline
intended to quiet the mind, by focusing on our intercourse with the animate
atmosphere via pranayama breath and the hard-packed earth supporting
our asanas, thus summoning the vital power of the gods. My inexperienced
emulation of his postures must have looked awkward, as I stumbled or lost
my stance regularly, whilst requiring frequent corrections; though polite,
I knew from their facial expressions my coworkers were also entertained.
Letting egoic thoughts pass as Will instructed, I concentrated on presence
and breath, yet still found myself trembling uncontrollably in several poses,
whereas others I could not hold at all. Watching him left me ashamed
of my inflexibility; however, by the end of the practice, as we focused on
respiratory meditation and gave thanks through ancients chants, I felt
limber nevertheless. It was a good thing, too, because our job consisted
of dragging waterlogged sheaves of hemp stalks from the adjacent pond.
They had been submerged there a week prior for retting, a fermentation
process that separated hurds in the core of a stalk from the long fiber in
its bark, and produced a pungent stench as well. In pairs, we stacked the
putrefied bundles on a trailer with high sides to restrain its load, whose
requisite method made us lift them to one shoulder, reach over the wagon,
then shove the hemp off with our opposite arm, the first acting like a ramp.

I worked beside Will, and even as he took the far heavier butt end, I sensed my weakness constantly holding him back. At one point I became dizzy but pressed on to fulfill perceived expectations; stumbling, I dropped my load in the mud. To my embarrassed apologizing, he replied without judgment, "Mistakes are less efficient than taking time to do it right, so I'll let you set the pace. All I ask is that you give me your best effort; no more, no less."

Once we filled the trailer, I finally received a much-needed break, riding along as the tractor pulled our load to the field whence the hemp had been originally harvested. It was cut high, leaving about six inches of stubble for a ventilated rack whereupon we spread the soggy stalks, parallel to each other and in a single layer for optimal drying; we used only the warmer south-facing slopes for this purpose, in accordance with Will's directions. Around noon, when I thought I might collapse from exhaustion, his wife Grace came to the field carrying a lunch basket for us. While she had an undeniably feminine figure, with curves in all the right places, as they say, she shared the toned solidity of her husband, thus exuding a similar self-assuredness. I felt ravenous by then from the unfamiliar expenditure of energy, and suspect that my hyperbolic expressions of gratitude for the humble meal helped foster in her an early fondness toward me.

"You're not pushing the stranger too hard, are you, dear?"

"No ma'am...I'm just putting some meat on his bones; he aint nearly ready to eat yet," Will quipped, winking at me.

She asked me how I was doing, and I said I rejoiced to be there; in truth, fatigue brought concerns for my ability to endure until sunset, but pride prevented me from letting them show. After she left, we rested on a shady edge of the field, hydrating and digesting in preparation for the next round. Will, who reclined with arms clasped behind his head, began to laugh spontaneously, prompting one of the boys to ask what was so funny. "Two centuries ago, my ancestors were slaves in Kentucky doing this work under the supervision of white men, and I'm just appreciating the irony." Later on, I inquired with him how it could be that technology for processing hemp had not advanced since the American Civil War; and he told me it did, briefly, only to regress immediately. During World War I, a German named George Schlichten developed a hemp decorticator so efficacious it made retting unnecessary, even for production of the finest-quality fabrics. His machine stripped leaves from the plant, then separated long fibers from the pulp of hemp cut and dried in fields, effectively eliminating all of our labor, along with its associated odor. This breakthrough would have permitted cannabis to predominate in American textile factories; and it could have revolutionized paper manufacture by creating, as a byproduct, four times the raw material harvested from tree plantations of equivalent land area. Instead, industrialists who owned timber or the patents on chemicals used to process pulpwood formed a cartel with petrochemical tycoons whose business was threatened by the prospect of hemp-derived hydrocarbons. Under leadership of a prominent newspaper publisher and a corrupt U.S. Treasury Secretary, they suppressed decortication technology via propaganda and Congressional influence, culminating with the passage of the Marihuana Tax Act in 63 B.T., which ensured that hemp cultivation was economically unsustainable, henceforth eliminating their competition.

Schlichten sank into obscurity with his invention, whilst the crusade against cannabis continued in hallowed halls of the United States' government and journalism, under guises of protecting its citizens from violence, apathy, communism, or homosexuality, among other ills, until the present day. Consequently, fabric manufacturing had been based ever since on plastics and cotton, the latter constituting a petroleum product, given that it was grown via machinery powered by fossil fuels, as well as oil-based biocides. Upon advent of glyphosate-ready GMO varieties, chemical agribusinesses strengthened their bureaucratic stranglehold, necessary to uphold hemp prohibition. Considering cotton's inferiority to cannabis in every respect from productivity to durability, soil conditioning to weed competition, its facile monopoly could only be perpetuated by monstrous lobbying power, coupled with egregiously shortsighted laws. For a moment, perhaps fifty years ago, the prevalence of herbicide-resistant weeds in cotton fields caused a crisis of mechanical harvesting; then, under the auspices of a certain presidential candidate, it seemed federal decriminalization of hemp cultivation might stand a fighting chance; yet those dreams were dashed by his assassination. Subsequent events left desertification of the world's last breadbasket in their wake; whereas if Americans had instead cast off the shackles of corporate farming, the nation could have transitioned to hemp via minimal investment in decortication, thereby supplanting its reliance upon tree plantations, toxic textiles, and synthetic building insulation with an organically-grown crop that sequesters atmospheric carbon in the soil.
"But such is not the world we inhabit," Will declared poignantly,
"so we employ the labor intensive methods of my ancestors,
until or unless we develop better equipment ourselves."

I did survive that first afternoon, and the rest of the week, with difficulty. Although I awoke to disconcerting stiffness in my muscles, by the end of our yoga practice, I felt substantially less crippled, whereas my physical self-control improved markedly from one day to the next. Will apparently knew how to push me past soreness during work, always stopping just short of breaking my spirit. I genuinely desired to excel in our monotonous labor; despite my struggle against them, there were still limits on what my body would do. When the last of the hemp had been spread in the sun, he let us quit early, then went to drain the nutrient-rich water of the retting pond onto his fields of winter cereal grains. I hung around whilst he arranged irrigation hoses and rotated valves in order to hear some of his story.
"We aren't pioneers, but Grace and I came early on; she was about your age, while I'd recently gone through my Saturn return. We both grew up on the southern shales of Marcellus, in a shanty town near the fracking rigs and Pennsylvania prison colonies. Our neighbors were of the Amish church, an insular Christian sect that retained its ancestral culture. Theirs was an agrarian community, whose religious order prohibited modern conveniences such as cars, electricity, or government aid, though they would drink soda from Styrofoam cups on occasion without any noticeable moral conflict. Nonetheless, their horse-drawn buggies and strange dress fascinated me; so to satisfy my curiosity, I began helping an elderly couple who couldn't conceive children, and remained stalwart adherents to the old ways.

"I learned traditional farming techniques from them; moreover, I learned to value my work for its own sake, rather than for a wage. It has been said before, but warrants repeating, that they have the most lucrative agriculture in the world because they count their labor as profit, instead of an expense. I soon became spoiled by the taste and sensation of real food in my body, which comes from the ground, instead of from a factory or laboratory – I guess you probably know what I mean by now. On a fall day not unlike this, whilst plowing with a team, I mused on the opportunity to watch them work, and to work beside them, as a sort of modern miracle. The horses were in superb condition, and well-matched; the soil had a perfect moisture content for the job, crumbling as it turned over without dust; the distance betwixt headlands was long enough to lose myself in meditation. Halfway down a furrow, my first epiphany suddenly possessed me; I realized that during a crop's growth, the spiritual energy, if you will, of the farmer and ers methods infuses it, so one ear of our corn is not the same as any other, regardless of what chemists or agronomists might have us think. From then on, how could I consume food produced for the bottom line, by whichever means most profitably prostitute our environment, when I can eat meals cultivated with intention and magic, for direct connection to god's creation, as opposed to financial gain?

"Perhaps a week later, some of the pioneers appeared to do research amongst the Amish, investigating their non-electric tools and equipment. These were not your garden-variety survivalists; upon seeing them, I knew I was in unusual company. They surely thought the same of me; after all, it wasn't quite normal for a young black man to be working alongside the Pennsylvania Dutch. I asked what they were up to, and they told me a little bit about their project – not much, just enough to catch my interest. When I asked if they needed help, they said, as a matter of fact, they did. I ran home to find Grace; told her 'we need to get on board with this', and we came. I've had the privilege, ever since, of creating true nourishment for my community. Because I love my labor, anything I raise embodies such sentiments, whereby we derive a quality of life that cannot be purchased."

His definition of thereof was beginning to have tangible meaning for me; everywhere I looked, and in all the people I met, I saw authentic livelihoods invalidating the socioeconomic pyramid inculcated by mainstream America. My notions of the nature of wealth had been overturned; here were people who worked hard out of a desire to do so, and believed in what they did as intentional service, instead of going to jobs they disliked, merely to prolong a facile consumer existence. With a level vocational playing field, they had no motivation to climb the ladder; in fact, there was no ladder to climb; yet each member of the tribe strove for prosperity of a personal kind. Despite early radioactivity, villagers enjoyed exceptional vitality, as well as life expectancies a decade longer than the national average, no thanks to modern hospital facilities or corporate health insurance. Their health was insured by nourishing food, clean living, real activity, and medicinal herbs. They lived free from obesity, diabetes, or heart disease; absent need of pharmaceutical antidepressants, soporifics, digestive aids, stimulants for concentration, or anti-anxiety psychotropics; all of which were ordinary treatments for standard operating procedure in the land of my genesis.

Will had tractor work to do in his fields of hemp grain during the following week. He planted this variety less densely, to favor seed formation over vegetative growth, and about a moon earlier than the fiber crop, whose quality deteriorated if allowed to flower before harvest. In the interim, I was assigned to the squash harvest, as the only male in a crew of four.

Our task included collecting, cleaning, sorting, and transporting two dozen or so varieties to the hot, dry loft of his barn, where they would be cured for long-term storage and consumption throughout the winter. Whereas I find no shame in it retrospectively, this position emasculated me at the time, which may have been Will's intention. My sexist mores obliged me to pull the heaviest carts or stack crates whenever possible, because I was, in all other respects, the least efficient laborer among us. While I kept to myself for the most part, I could not resist observing the conversation betwixt the young women, who were native-born, thereby learning discreetly what I might of gender dynamics within my peer group. Unlike me, they had gone through initiation; so although eldest, I still had the lowest social status. When my gaze lingered too long in their direction, one would remark on it to the rest, and I wondered if they talked about me as each of the trio glanced singly, amidst shared giggling and whispering. I pretended not to notice or care, but inadvertently overheard a discussion of my body, whose lean condition was apparently not absent merit since it had attracted their attention during our long hours in the sun. I listened to this silently from around a blind corner with a produce box held before me.

"Boo," Will said as he snuck up and gave me a small shove from behind.

In surprise, I dropped the crate, sending buttercup squash rolling into their view from the shady doorway. Panicked with embarrassment that my eavesdropping had been exposed, I hastily crawled to retrieve its evidence.

"I can come down there, if you need some help," one of them, named Kalliope, for whom I had developed a bit of a crush, sang from above.

"No thanks, I'm fine...just fine," I muttered, chagrined by her mockery.

"Yeah, you are," remarked Thaleia in a low tone, provoking all to laughter.

"Good morning, ladies," Will announced, stepping out of his own hiding place and thus breaking the ice. "You're not getting distracted, are you?" Their snickering ended abruptly. "Not at all," they called in melodic chorus. "As I thought," he replied, then asked me, "Can you lend a hand over here?" Some squashes had begun to rot in the field, and these we left for his pigs. The remainder would be graded after aging based on projected shelf life; any fruits with soft spots or blemishes were consumed as soon as possible.

By counting the cartloads we pulled up the ramps into the curing area, I estimated that our harvest amounted to about fifty pounds per villager. Will was the island's largest, but not sole producer; because I never ate winter squash previously, I hoped to enjoy it, as there would seemingly be much to consume in forthcoming months. A few plants of each variety had been individually hand pollinated, then their flowers enclosed in bags, ensuring a supply of seed that bred true to its parent. Cucurbits of the same specie were liable to cross sexually with neighboring plants; such hybrids usually reverted toward the characteristics of their wild ancestors, producing fruits of low sugar content and insipid if not disagreeable flavor.

Once the vines started shriveling, the field was undersown to buckwheat, a short-lived annual green manure that enhanced tilth whilst providing forage for the bees at a time of year without clover or native tree blossoms for nectar sources. Following completion of the harvest, we let in his hogs; they devoured the flowering cover crop, scoured the ground for rejects or weeds to eat, then effectively turned the rich soil in pursuit of grubs, worms, and roots. It amazed me that something as soft as their noses, composed of mere skin and cartilage, could perform the same job as Will's tractor-drawn steel rotovator. I had not seen the animals up close before, but imagined them as fat and indolent, based on the examples shown in television cartoons; his swine, however, were nothing of the sort.

Although muscular overall, I was especially impressed by their necks, which began as large in girth as the skull, then widened until merging with meaty shoulders. These powerful trunks drove their plow-shaped snouts, and I enjoyed listening to them grunt as they dug. All of the dirt appeared the same to me, yet I could tell when one animal found a particularly tasty patch by the others scampering to join it. After the pigs had done their job, the field looked nearly clean, except for an occasional dried-out tendril. We broadcast winter peas and rye into the well-prepared earth next, just in time for several days of gentle rain perfect for germination.

Given hot, dry weather in the subsequent week, Will decided to cut his primary hayfield for the last time that season. This process comprised the most fuel intensive portion of his operations, relying on ethanol derived from the island's feed corn. The distillery, adjacent to the community hall in Athenai, only operated at night because exhaust from its wood and hemp gasification system, which created heat as well as power for the process, would have been visible offshore during the day. Grain went through two fermentations in large vats, warmed by hydronic heat from the furnace; the resultant brew was then separated via stripping plates in rectifying columns. Since I had read that alcohol fuel took more BTUs to produce than it contained, I asked Will how this could possibly be sustainable.

"Ethanol is often described as a net loss of energy, and rightfully so; though only the way it's made in the petroleum economy. Our ethos can not condone waste; ergo, we do things differently here," he explained. "In order to mix with gasoline, your mass-market alcohol must be pure; and as the concentration increases during distillation, so does the energy required to remove the remaining impurities; but if you're not mixing it with gasoline, ethanol that still contains some of the hard-to-remove water will run perfectly well in an appropriately-calibrated spark ignition engine. By distilling to just a 90% concentration, whilst feeding the leftover mash directly to our livestock rather than drying it with natural gas to prevent spoilage during long-distance transport to feedlots, we can make our alcohol using about a third as much invested energy as the industry; furthermore, in our case the energy comes from biomass sources that can't be put in a gas tank, as opposed to petroleum fuels, which could."

Ironically, the associated technology was ancient, and the American government, under aegis of the USDA, published an excellent manual on a similar system, inspired by high oil prices during an Arab embargo almost a century ago. Because history tends to repeat itself, the nation thereafter followed the course dictated by special interests, instead of common sense; the problem thereof being, as Will said, "it isn't very common nowadays." Along with the Schlichten decorticator, a reasonable method of utilizing renewable resources fell by the wayside, in surrender to the insanity of anhydrous ethanol. Extracted from the cellulosic residues of genetically-modified corn, using enzymes spawned via GMO fungi, the 'alternative' increased CO_2 by depleting the soil of organic matter - in order to sell, at best, a fuel additive containing far more energy from petroleum than from photosynthesis that made, as such, a travesty of the word 'biofuel'. He acknowledged corn was not the best feedstock for fuel production in terms of yield per acre; sorghum cane or sugar beets were superior by severalfold; but they became prone to spoilage upon harvest, meaning all fuel production would have to occur within a relatively brief window of time, which already happened to be the busiest of the agricultural season.

"When I arrived, the pioneers had envisioned animal husbandry based entirely on perennial pasture. While I supported their ideal, considering it achievable with sheep, goats, or beef, I thought it a foregone conclusion that we'd need grain if we wanted to feed dairy animals, poultry, or pigs. Because we'd presumably be growing some anyway, I said we might as well treat it as a source of liquid fuel; ethanol removes only about a quarter of corn's caloric content, in the non-structural carbohydrates, leaving all of its more desirable nutrients intact. The benefit of this system is that we can dry, store, and handle our feed with extant, accessible technology, whose flaws lie less in the tools themselves than in how, or why, they are applied. Making fuel throughout the year lets us get by on a smaller still, creates a manageable stream of spent grain, and ensures via cogeneration we will have hot water for the community center whenever it's needed."

Whilst the hay dried, he assigned me to plant garlic during the day and haul seaweed for home gardens at night. Working on the breezy east beach beneath the ethereal glow of moonlight offered a pleasant change of pace from sweaty toil in sun-parched fields. Three days after cutting the grass, Will raked it into windrows; then he sent me a message through Aeiolus, indicating that I should take the night off, in order to arrive by noon the next day with plenty of rest, long pants, and a good pair of gloves. The meadow in question did not make much of an impression at first sight; yet upon survey of the work entailed by our harvest, its size astounded me. Will's red tractor and baler looked like a deformed ant at the opposite side, gobbling up the final swath and leaving compressed green pellets behind. I met Hemlock and Diomedes there, who knew me from the retting pools, along with Thaleia and Polyhymnia, whom I joined for the squash harvest; Kalliope would have been a distraction, so her absence was for the best, especially considering my ignorance of her new relationship with Diomedes, which put us in competition. Stretching the field's length were row after row of regularly-spaced rectangular bundles - over twelve hundred, as it turned out, though I grew anxious in my initial attempt to estimate a total.

"We're not going to get them all today, are we?" I asked hesitantly.
"He's not going to leave them out tonight," came the unanimous response.
When baling was finished, Hemlock, the smallest among us, ran down to help unhook the implement, connecting a trailer in its place. They drove to

where we stood at the high end of the field and Will flashed a toothy grin. "It's a big one," he hollered over the roar of the tractor, gesturing behind him excitedly, then passed a greasy bandana to me for use as a dust mask. At my reluctance to put it on, he said, "Trust me; you'll be thankful later." Hemlock drove, crawling forward with Will cheering from the trailer deck. "Come on - the job won't do itself whilst we're wasting daylight. Bring me some hay; my wife's waiting and I intend to be in bed with her by sunrise." Albeit theoretically dry, the bales felt unreasonably heavy for their size. I started out carrying them in front of me, with back arched and elbows held high, thereby inviting premature fatigue, until I noticed the women hoisting hay to their shoulders for longer trips as they conversed easily. Diomedes took one on either side at hip height, walking with strict focus and bent knees, but Will could grab the strings of two bales in one hand, rearranging them as if they were made of goosedown. His rate did not slacken as the stack got tall; at its sixth layer, he threw them overhead with implausible accuracy, seeming to be unreasonably pleased by his success. Building another rank, he quickly disposed of the accumulated pile and harassed us good-naturedly, saying that he should be struggling to catch up with us, not vice versa. Once finished, we drove the load to his barn, reversing the process. Hemlock tore down the stack, setting bales along the edges of the trailer within convenient reach of us four on the ground; whilst we moved them toward the back, Will organized; yet in spite of our industriousness more than an hour elapsed ere we began the process anew. "Everyone ready to start working now?" he asked. The women laughed; neither Diomedes nor Hemlock replied; I feigned a smile to hide my dismay. "Sorry yall, but it's gonna be a real late dinner unless we pick up the pace." So it went, over and over and over again. My body progressed from tired to exhausted to numb; its exposed flesh itched, swelled, and bled from the constant abrasion. Will kept up the group élan with assorted exclamations that he meant to be humorous; "Look, the job's practically doing itself," or, "Don't worry; it's all downhill from here." On the fifth load, when the sky grew dark and distant lightning flashed, he scowled. "Yall should pray to hold off that rain, 'cause there will be hell to pay if it gets on my hay." Night arrived as we unloaded the sixth trailer; then Grace came bearing refreshments. "You'd better take that away; they haven't earned it yet," he said, winking at us; though he relented after she appealed on our behalf. "Since we'll be working in the dark anyhow...they're lucky I'm hungry too." The tractor had electric lights, whereby we picked up the final load, amidst ominous reverberations of thunder; a handful of droplets fell as we finished stacking it under cover of the barn. "Just enough pressure to galvanize our crew in the home stretch," Will declared. He thanked us for helping and sent us home, rushing back out to retrieve the baler; with its many moving parts, stowing the apparatus inside before the storm was imperative, given the susceptibility of steel to corrosion in the salty breezes on the island. "See you next spring?" Diomedes asked when our hands clasped in farewell. "Maybe," I told him reluctantly as they parted, "though I don't know if I'll be much use; unlike some of yall, I can't carry two bales at a time all day." "Nonsense," he said. "You will, with practice. This isn't my first rodeo." "Do you come often?" I inquired.

"Any chance I get." He wiped sweat off his filthy brow. "I wouldn't miss it."
"You must be some kind of sadist; that's a lot of damn work."
"Just wait," he laughed. "The first cut of spring is wetter and much larger."
"Yikes," I groaned. "Hard for me to imagine doing more than this at once."
"There's always more; it's hardly a challenge if it doesn't test your limits."
"Yeah, but don't you ever exceed them?"
"Hell yes," Diomedes replied, smiling despite discomfort. "That's my goal!"
I began then to understand what Will meant to convey about the economics
of Amish farming. By a change of perspective, albeit easier said than done,
the nature of work would shift from toil shirked toward exertion sought.
In the interim, with what appeared a nimble feat of geometry and physics,
he had maneuvered the baler backwards into the barn on his first attempt.
The heavens waited until he killed the engine, then opened immediately;
we listened as a wall of rain rushed from across the field like a freight train.
Will threw his head back, cackling in celebration, and clapped my shoulder,
yelling over the reverberation of huge droplets that pounded his metal roof.
"It's the greatest sound in the world. If you pay attention, you'll know
when you're living right by the gods smiling with favor upon your labor!"

When the earth dried sufficiently for us to drive again without compaction,
we returned to the hemp stalks. Will had devised rig for processing them
that I thought rather ingenious, and it was certainly more efficient than
methods from the Civil War era. A hydraulic decorticator straddled the
back of a small dump truck, run by a power takeoff from its diesel motor.
Walkboards along either side provided standing room for operators who
fed the machine; stalks reached them via a folding conveyor, loaded by two
people on the ground. The continuous combed slivers of long hemp fiber
were dispensed onto a platform hanging over the cab, whilst the hurds
dropped into the bed below, ready for transport to their next destination.
With everything properly cleaned, calibrated, and lubricated, the system
moved like clockwork; its only shortcoming, as far as I could tell, lay in the
time and effort required to lift the decorticator off of, then onto, the truck
when it had to be dumped. Severing the hemp at the outfeed rollers each
time, we delivered slivers to the textile mill before they could get marred.
This gave me frequent occasions to accost Bridget, for whom my passion
was renewed, though rationally I knew it to be hopeless; my respect for
Diomedes, if nothing else, obliged me to abandon my momentary crush
on Kalliope. From there, we would bring the hurds to a barn that needed
bedding, a homestead lacking mulch, or, in absence of another use, to the
village stockpile, thus making them available for compost and hempcrete.
Whereas he did not smoke at work, Will routinely offered a joint of his fine
sativa-dominant buds upon its conclusion for those who were so inclined.
Airmed cured her plants in the house, sampling them freely, albeit in small
quantities and typically with guests, throughout the day; yet I never saw
Aeiolus indulging in marijuana during my service to its industrial relative.
Reflecting on his previous life as an openly pot-smoking figurehead, and the
fact that the island was effectively beyond jurisdiction of law enforcement,
I took it for granted he would use cannabis recreationally; so at dinner
alone with him one night, I wondered aloud about their relationship.

"You're really going straight for the pith, aren't you?" he asked.
"Well, your position on the issue is a mystery to me," I told him.
"Because humanity's interaction with psychoactive cannabis is perhaps the most complicated, yet understated among entheogens. If you must know of mine, although currently on hiatus, I will take a tincture for headache or nausea; and I'll smoke in ceremony on occasion, or use it as a psychedelic. Did you get to read my thesis on the commodification of counterculture?" I said I had not, but that Alexander Fremont's biography alluded thereto, thus pointing out the double-standard in his use of 'my', which he ignored.
"I asserted then and still opine, albeit differently, that its heroes found fame or drew attention as much in spite of, as due to, their addictions; while in the entire War Of Drugs, marijuana has been more successfully weaponized in the service of empire than by the evolutionary opposition. I believe it has led to apathetic acceptance, disorganized thinking, illicit capitalism, and demotivation more than it has ever propagated change."
"Easy to say, since it's a hypothesis that can't be tested," I argued.
"True enough, but consider for a moment that over half of the food calories consumed in America come from corn, which is, economically, its largest legal crop; and yet the value of the American marijuana harvest consistently exceeds that of corn, while the prospect of revolution becomes increasingly remote. I would therefore posit my hypothesis as self-evident. There comes a time in any serious interaction with cannabis when one must entertain the likelihood that the plant is breeding us, as well as vice versa; for testimony, I submit how much diversity has unfolded via our symbiosis. Only after accepting this role can you cultivate a truly conscious connection with the plant, which may have more to do with abstinence than inebriation. I'll gladly acknowledge how she transformed me, by opening doors to ways of thinking, feeling, and being, of whose existence I was unaware before; she adds new depth to our experience, or eases hardship; her therapeutic potential is enormous; her profound healing prowess cures even cancer. Marijuana is also a muse; as such, a seductive mistress; thus, until you can lay the pipe aside - with unconditional affection and appreciation, instead of reluctance - you risk making yourself her slave, regardless of any fantasies to the contrary. Like tools, the merits of our spiritual technologies are not necessarily intrinsic to the substances, but the means whereby and ends wherefore we use them. The plant is a potential guide or ally whilst you are the traveler; and as you give yourself to the relationship, you should remain open to it changing. If ritualized, you could be served by imbibing daily at times; in others, a decade of sobriety might be justified. I generally find partaking more often than, say, once a week leads toward tolerance; such that instead of going through emotional breakthroughs or existential crises, people get inebriated – which has benefited humanity, although it is not the plant's highest and best purpose for me any longer. If you seriously think marijuana enhances performance, elevates work ethic, or increases endurance, I want to know what you're smoking and where I can get some. You see, I've had that very notion when stoned, but never when I've been sober observing somebody else who just smoked. Beware the trap of habitual marijuana consumption; once addicted, humans are prone to delusions about its effects, thereby reinforcing their habits,

so countless regular users can earnestly deny they have actual dependence. I've been there myself, of course, and seen it happen in unwitting others, often to their detriment, as to our specie's. Given the reality we inhabit, moments of delusion are essential; but it's easy to forget that a little goes a long way, and there is a price to pay. Cannabis is a powerful psychoactive, dangerously powerful much of the time, since she does not overtly seem so. Lest you forget, she is a succubus, yet I suspect you already know this."

Nodding in assent, I asked him, "What about people who smoke, say, for quality of life, or as an escape from work at the end of the day?"

"I like to think that a truly empowered person would shift the conditions of ers life, eliminating the need to escape at its source. I love my work, and if I started feeling like I needed to get away from it, I would rather stop."

"That's not a luxury everybody has!" I protested.

"And so you must concede how recreational marijuana can readily be manipulated to perpetuate the status quo. From my perspective, a vast gulf lies between escape and celebration, while for you they are the same."

Although I had not thought of it as such, by reviewing my own experience with city weed in compulsory education, I saw the veracity of his position. "Herein lies one of the government's best kept secrets and most insidious conspiracies. By criminalizing cannabis, they made a narcotic drug from sacred medicine; the would-be counterculture just got too high to notice."

He went to the library then, returning with a reference book on the crop. "Let's briefly examine its effect on the efforts to legalize industrial hemp. One of the strongest arguments was that its cannabinoid content is so low consumption for intoxication would be ineffective. Many hemp advocates, however, also used marijuana recreationally, and could not resist conflating these two distinct applications in an overarching 'pro-cannabis' movement. Personally, I sought legalization of both; but if they were kept separate, the argument for industrial hemp would have been stronger and had more chance of success. This always comprised the most important issue to my mind, since prohibition of hemp was totally effective, hence depriving us of a valuable component in the transition to a sustainable human future; whereas prohibition of psychoactive cannabis has been utterly impotent, a fact underscored by its continued status as the most valuable crop in America, whence the federal government still receives no tax revenue. We suffer the inconvenience of inflated prices, unfortunate deterioration of quality by chemical cultivation, paranoia due to legal repercussions, mandatory minimum sentences, and the world's highest incarceration rate; yet most who want to buy it can do so, and use it without getting caught. Those who have such privilege did the country a great disservice, via their failure to withhold the recreational agenda from public discourse on hemp. I understand as well as anyone that this debate takes place in the forum of the obscene, but such is the nature of public discourse. Above all, the inability of stoners to observe how the psychoactive cannabis movement undermined the legalization of industrial hemp is the tragic quintessence of cognitive consequences that can accompany habitual marijuana use."

He paused then, inhaling deeply. "You should take what I say with a grain or two of salt, though. Half a lifetime ago, I smoked because it was illegal; and as a self-proclaimed expert on getting high, I sang a different tune."

NARRATOR: "This isn't a fucking piece of evidence. This is a person; he's a friend of mine, and you're not going to bury him in the fucking garden."
ANGELFACE: "He was killed serving Project Mayhem, sir."
NARRATOR: "This is Bob..."
SPACE MONKEY: "But sir, in Project Mayhem, we have no names."
NARRATOR: "No, you listen to me. This is a man, and he has a name, and it is Robert Paulson."

~ FIGHT CLUB ~

"A human being is a part of a whole, called by us Universe,
a part limited in time and space. He experiences himself,
his thoughts and feelings as something separated from the rest,
a kind of optical delusion of his consciousness.
This delusion is a kind of prison for us,
restricting us to our personal desires and
to affection for a few persons nearest to us.
Our task must be to free ourselves from this prison
by widening our circle of compassion to embrace all
living creatures and the whole of nature in its beauty."

~ Albert Einstein ~

KHEIRON

The implicit trust wherewith villagers interacted impressed me early. Nobody used locks; food, labor, and tools were freely given whenever requested or required; every person seemed to have enough to thrive, hence they did not strive for more. Airmed and Aeiolus lived in one of the island's larger residences, which verged on ostentatious in comparison to the rest, but its value was for enjoyment by all. They had built a library for their tribe; made the guest house available to any in need of medical treatment or space from an angry spouse; while sharing the abundance of their large kitchen with visitors at weekend brunches and dinner parties. Community members had only a few prescriptive obligations to fulfill; for example, the 180 or so residents eligible to serve as sentries were responsible for six hours of duty per week, though these shifts could be bartered amongst them without restriction. Elsewise, there was neither money nor an alternative medium of exchange in the village; the pioneers, however, had undisclosed investments to procure goods from the mainland. Aeiolus indicated that in the beginning they used polished fragments of clam shells as internal currency, akin to the wampum of extinct tribes from the northeastern woodlands; but this system led to regrettable disagreement over relative valuation of commodities and each other's labor. He thought the beads might have been cursed, because it was European settlers who appropriated their heritage in the first place, ultimately without success; whereas its indigenous creators had made wampum for ceremony, marking agreements, or recording erstory. Plagued by dissension, the modern tribe formed committees and held interminable meetings to institute standards that were never universally satisfactory. In addition to facilitating wealth accumulation, their use of wampum became a negative-sum-game for the whole, since time and effort spent on economic regulation would have been better invested in humanifestation of the very resources whose exchange rate had provoked such consternation. The graver danger Aeiolus foresaw was that by quantifying its members' contribution, currency defined their efforts within a finite scope, despite the fundamental vision of a culture to which people would give as much as they could regardless of accounting. "I expect it sounds idealistic to the point of impossibility, and in a different group it very well might be; yet here we've replaced monetization with the ethic and expectation, instilled from childhood, that everyone in our village shall give according to ers abilities, and receive according to ers needs." Individual benefit was thus based entirely in the prosperity of the tribe, as a step toward the ulterior goal of invalidating theft as a concept.

"How do you handle crimes besides stealing?" I asked.

He furrowed his brows, then bowed his head, pressing into anguished temples with the thumb and outstretched fingers of his left hand. "You're bound to hear the tale sometime; I suppose now is as good as any." Three years prior to my arrival, the tribe had adopted a wandering refugee in circumstances similar to mine, except that he was in his later twenties; a skilled mechanic who seemed to acculturate well, filling a valuable niche whilst vocally appreciating his new community. Aeiolus remembered him as upbeat and quick with a joke; the only cause for concern stemmed from his propensity for alcohol. Other villagers drank ceremonially or in occasional celebrations, if at all; this man, on the contrary, took the drug regularly for the expressed purpose of intoxication. He was gregarious and entertaining under its influence, so they met his loud voice or indecency with tolerance and made efforts to discourage the habit. The mechanic laughed them off, saying, "I'll do as I damn well please"; until what pleased him extended to the rape of a girl half his age who previously considered the man her friend. When called before Council to explain, he claimed in his defense she had encouraged him. Her mother attested that, from the extent of her bruises and subsequent bleeding, the act was obviously not consensual, but violent. Although the girl admitted she did not physically resist him, the councilors understood this to be out of fear or surprise, neither of which could he have reasonably construed as her permission. Rather than repenting, the mechanic further inculpated himself with his rebuttal, declaring that where he came from, a woman's verbal 'no' often meant 'yes'. "She was still a child," Aeiolus told me, "making his vicious violation so much more egregious; yet in any case, the cardinal rule, which I urge you not to forget, my friend, is that all of our interactions here are voluntary. It is never acceptable to force someone, age and gender notwithstanding." Council deliberated arduously on his disposition. Several members even supported execution; however, to introduce judicial power of life or death over another person would send them down a slippery slope, whose moral consequences were too far-reaching for them to comfortably contemplate. Instead, they agreed with apprehension to discreetly castrate the mechanic, while the girl and her family took an oath of silence to protect him socially. "It was the most difficult decision we've ever made. I performed the operation myself, then kept him in restraints until he healed, remaining mute and stoic for the duration. I interpreted this behavior as penitence, in hopes that his vanity had prevented him from apologizing aloud."

Upon release, the mechanic returned to home and work, his formerly jovial demeanor replaced thenceforth by subdued brooding. Whereas the crime had been kept secret from tribe, and the councilors who knew of it treated him with courtesy, he could feel their disapproval, or perhaps the burden of his conscience in the aftermath of castration. A few weeks later he stole a kayak, then fled the island, thereby forcing them to disclose what had transpired; they kept his victim's name secret, but fabricated a mutual agreement to ostracism as reason for the mechanic's disappearance.

"You lied?" I exclaimed indelicately.

"Yes," he sighed. "We did not want to unnecessarily alarm the villagers, and fervently hoped that would be the end of it; how naive. If there were transmitters in our seacraft, we could have been immediately alerted and tracked him easily; however, none of us planned for such a turn of events. We believe in giving people the benefit of the doubt, to foster a culture wherein they have the chance to choose what is right of their own accord. While they will often do so, the inherent nature of that choice allows for the horrible wickedness and awful hostility of which some are capable."

A tempestuous night at the first quarter moon forced the sentry in Argos to vacate her post; amid descent, she glimpsed by lightning the wake of a motorized boat approaching from the north. Notifying the other sentinels via radio, she stayed atop the tower despite the conditions until the vessel came near enough for her to see through night glasses that it decelerated about a mile offshore, aimed toward Old Harbor; another flash revealed it was a pontoon catamaran with at least two dozen people aboard.

"The mechanic knew we were poorly armed; thus he probably expected a modest force to have no problem overrunning us with a surprise attack in darkness, based on his knowledge of the island." The gang gambled on their ability to land in secrecy, and the six sentinels wagered that the pirates would not be monitoring all of the VHF channels. Because they could only communicate with each other initially, those at the lighthouses and southwest windmill went to awaken Council members, whilst the young woman in Argos monitored the situation. Stationed atop the weather mast on the west coast was Kastor, a childless man of nineteen years who decided to take the defense of the village into his own hands. He awoke his father, Amadeus the engineer, and persuaded him to wire charges of waterproof dynamite, which they kept on hand for demolition or moving the submerged boulders dislodged sometimes by storms. After collecting the SCUBA gear used for cleaning the undersides of sailing vessels, Kastor went to the harbor, where he intended to hide in submersion, secure the bomb upon the pontoon boat before landing, then detonate it remotely with an electric blasting machine. According to Aeiolus the engineer refused to participate at first, on grounds that there were too many variables in calculating the appropriate amount of explosive and no means to perform the requisite sequence of tests on their connections. Kastor begged his father to use all he could, asking rhetorically if his wiring had ever been faulty before, with a reminder that time was of the essence, since their tribe would be ill-prepared to face predacious foes in combat. Amadeus ultimately agreed, proposing to place and blast the dynamite in his son's stead, but Kastor stood resolutely by his own assessment: he was young, fast, agile, able to see well in darkness, and as a farmer, demographically expendable; his father, conversely, was an elder of the village, indispensable to its technological development, whose vision had markedly declined. The engineer reluctantly accompanied his son to the harbor, and Kastor slipped into the water without being seen; then, mere moments before the invaders aboard it disembarked, their boat exploded. Either the blast or subsequent drowning killed most of them; the rest, deafened and wounded, were executed whilst floundering in the shallows, which roiled red by dawn. Sentries and councilors collected the corpses, along with as many of the dismembered body parts as they could find. Whereas the village was saved, its deliverer, brave Kastor, had died. Remains of the gang were suspended on prominent display by a cable strung from atop the northeastern bluffs at Clay Head, thus giving the second wave of would-be conquistadors, who appeared near noon on the third day, a macabre warning rather than the easy looting they anticipated. After idling momentarily and a few warning shots they left, never to return. "I trust you now realize why we don't allow immigrants to leave the island. Your surprise arrival was especially disconcerting for some, arousing fears that have lain uneasily in wait, due to its ominous parallels with his story." This finally made sense of the awkwardness I felt in many social situations.

"You should also know this is why my daughter grieves. Although not yet sixteen at the time, she loved Kastor dearly, and planned to marry him after her initiation. They often took the same shifts to maximize their free time together; hence, it was Bridget who first saw the boat. Because she stood watch over the harbor through events there that led to his demise, they had no chance for a proper goodbye. She doesn't do it consciously, but I know she blames me for his death to this day, and justifiably so."

My throat tightened with compassion evoked by the tragedy; I forgave her caustic attitude towards me; then my voice cracked as I asked, "Why you?"

"If I had advocated the mechanic's execution, Council probably would have agreed. My failure to do so is one that I will regret to the end of my life, whose consequence cannot be undone; I can only avoid making the same mistake again. While intending the castration to cure his diseased soul, we created a monster, and it is because of me this evil still hangs over us."

"What do you mean?"

He lowered his good eye to a fist clenched so tight its knuckles were white. "The girl whom he raped vanished a week later. Since she left no note, we don't know for certain whether she chose to leave or was abducted. However, we did not find his body after the harbor ambush, which would have been identified easily by its distinctive tattoos, and I am therefore obliged to imagine that he is plotting his retaliation as we speak."

Despite Aeiolus' frequent references to its Council, a comprehensive understanding of the tribe's self governance eluded me for some time. As an outsider, all I saw of the island's administration was his passage through the house on his way to or from various meetings. Whilst reading minutes archived in the library, I learned that the original members were closely knit by years of preliminary conferences, collective investment, and their common vision. Initially, they made decisions via strict consensus, wherein individuals could object to, thus effectively vetoing, any proposal. With a small group, and planning its sole focus, this bureaucracy worked well enough, validating their underlying ideal of a completely participatory government. Once they moved to New Shoreham, however, the pioneers discovered that their chosen system required too much of the available human energy, which would prove to be the limiting factor in development of the village. Among new recruits, insignificant perspectival differences were exaggerated by the onus of stopping the process to address every objection. Debates devolved to semantics; resentments built on all sides; by their attachment to consensus decision making, they could no longer sense the mission in common, so the perfect arose as enemy of the good. Aeiolus, along with several other founders, observed that the government was inherently conservative, given the unanimous agreement required for anything to change, thereby placing it at odds with their community's goal – expeditious evolution of a solution-oriented model for cultural transition. What they intended as total inclusivity had been held hostage, subject to the tyranny of a minority; and before it could be further entrenched, the community abandoned unanimity for a more efficient representative administration, whose existence meant to guarantee personal autonomy. By quadrennial election, villagers thenceforth appointed ten councilors to represent all constituent hamlets, trades, and demographics; but the youth delegates, one of each gender, chose their own successors upon initiation. For avoidance of the competitive either/or mentality to which majority rule is prone they made decision via the former process, except that a single veto could be overruled if the remaining eleven agreed the respective objection was not based on concern for common welfare, and as such, unprincipled; yet in practice, this condition of consensus minus one seldom occurred. Councilors convened at every full moon, as well as whenever necessary to address matters of exigency. They posted notes from their meetings in Athenai, and then took personal responsibility for further dissemination. Whereas any adult was welcome, they were asked not to speak, except in extreme circumstances or unless elsewise specified, because this process relied on their trust that all interests would be encompassed by the circle, whose jurisdiction had been limited to only issues affecting the whole tribe. All other authority was decentralized, insofar as the hamlets determined, amongst themselves or by whatever process they saw fit, the resolution of neighborhood conflicts. Committees and task teams acted autonomously inside their respective arenas of expertise, fostering a sort of meritocracy, which empowered those best qualified to decide the nature of their service. Council could make recommendations, requests, or reports, but the final mandate resided with whoever did the work on behalf of the community.

In addition to the seat of Council, their community center afforded venues for many of the villagers activities, especially as winter advanced. It was the first structure built by pioneers upon arrival, and remained one of the largest, most technologically sophisticated edifices on the island. Like their domiciles, the hall had been designed for passive conditioning, with the best salvaged glazing installed in south walls, whence it shone on the heat-storing thermal mass floor during the winter but received shade against unwanted solar gain in summer from awnings or eave overhangs.

Fenestration in the other walls was configured to maximize daylighting, cross ventilation, and convective cooling. This basic pattern begat interior climates that stayed basically comfortable throughout the year, an implicit prescript of building guidelines since mechanical cooling was unavailable, while fires for heating could only be made at night, and were discouraged even then. Absent electrical systems, homes often drew domestic water from wells via handpump or windmill; energy for cooking came from solar ovens and small stoves fueled by peat, wood, or alcohol, whereas raw food was preferred much of the time. By pooling their material as well as labor resources in a central complex, the villagers thence provided themselves access to some of the modern amenities that they might otherwise lack. The floorplan had been dictated to a large extent by the concrete slab of a former airport terminal upon which it stood, and the new construction enclosed an airy, squarish central chamber with lower wings to either side. Supporting its vast vaulted roof were phenomenal hammerbeam trusses hewed from peeled round poles, harvested during the initial 'worst first' selective logging of Mykenai's young forests, thereby conjuring the grand ambience of a medieval cathedral and endearing rusticity of an Appalachian log cabin at once. I studied the timberframe's complex joinery details in admiration of how a structure with overarching geometric precision could be made of such rough material under the application of skillful diligence. Adzed, contorted rafters formed a steep gable, covered by a solid deck of salvaged lumber that had been whitewashed to render a finished ceiling for the room below, and insulated above with a layer of strawbales from the pioneers' first grain harvest, which were protected from the elements by a waterproof membrane; a sacrificial thatch of phragmites reeds prevented early photodegradation of the latter. The multipurpose space beneath this aesthetic roof typically functioned as a dining hall, but with the furniture stowed under the stage on the west side, it could also be used for large meetings, dances, or theatrical performances; on such occasions, balconies and hammocks strung between the trusses offered extra seating capacity.

A welcoming masonry heater at the east had built-in ovens, as well as luxurious radiant benches, whilst village artwork of all media adorned the hempcrete walls. There were sculptures integral to the interior plaster, mosaics of embedded shells and precious stones, tapestries with finely-embroidered mandalas, framed charcoal drawings, paintings on canvas, and gorgeous curtains. These decorations celebrated the plentiful skills of the tribe, as they honored its mores through use of indigenous materials. The eastern wing off the main hall lay adjacent to the ethanol distillery, whose gasification system created the hot water, along with electrical power; this annex contained the utilities, kitchen, and bathing fixtures.

Due to their central location, the public toilets collected enough solid waste to support a methane digester, thus producing cooking gas for the facility. Its spa included a hot tub, wood-fired sauna, cold plunge pool, walk-in showers, and laundry room, open to everyone; the kitchen, conversely, was only for designated staff, who served meals at predetermined hours, but sustenance could still be had throughout the day by asking politely. It usually teemed with the extensive enterprise entailed by preserving and embellishing produce from larger farms. Depending on the season, the culinary crew made pickles, sauerkraut, jams, nut butters, hemp oil, pesto, salsa, or rendered lard from dawn into the night; while they used interludes for non-food purposes, like dyeing wool or dipping candles. The west wing of the community center further accommodated cottage industry. Smaller studios were available to those who preferred solitude in pursuit of their crafts, complementing a large common space for others amenable to music and conversation, especially in the fiber arts. Past the sewing tables lay the bindery, then a well-equipped woodshop, though only open to villagers trained by Kristos, the master carpenter, to utilize such machinery unsupervised. Crazy by reputation, and among the eldest men upon the island, he was identifiable from a distance by an unruly shock of white hair that looked as if it might jump off his head any moment to attack. At our first meeting, he lectured me on how tools, perhaps even more than the psychedelics of Terence McKenna's stoned ape theory promulgated in Food of the Gods, had influenced early hominid evolution, since they relied on both of our unique endowments – consciousness and prehensile hands. "I well know your society, which would have you amputate your defining anatomical asset in favor of reliance upon a system of automation and robotics. By learning the trades, you shall be cured of this insanity," the disheveled old maniac told me with a firmly focused glare when Will introduced us. "Lest you forget, manual, manufacture, manipulate, and manuscript all derive from *manus*, the hu-man hand of humanifestation." Common infrastructure hence supplied the foundation of the community's self-sufficiency, as it epitomized our prosperity. Whereas I typically took meals with Aeiolus, Airmed, and their guests, or ate beside my coworkers, I did make a point of visiting Athenai for dinner at least once per week. The place supplied a lively change of pace, permitting me to meet other villagers while making myself, the ominous outsider, approachable in a public setting. I picked the occasions of special events whenever possible; my favorites were banquets held in honor of individual members as they shared the stories of their lives prior to recruitment for the tribe, or else dramatic plays performed by the children, who provided the script, set, costumes, and actors for their productions. If nothing else, music often accompanied dinner, which obliterated the horizons of what I thought I knew about such things. The synthetic frequencies of my past proved to be mere noise in comparison to the acoustic artistry of the islanders, from the newgrass of *Manisses*, invoking the nimble fingerpicking and folk songs of their pioneers; to the delightful lyres of Erato and Terpsikhore; or performances on the grand piano by Aeiolus, whose dozen digits gave him unparalleled dexterity, coupling with the resonant quality of the hall to render compositions of baroque and classical composers magnificently.

In December, the villagers began decorating in preparation for Pannyxia, the winter solstice festival. An early snow caught the village by surprise, inundating us knee-deep in blinding whiteness such as I had never seen; life and work slowed accordingly whilst we all dug out miles of pathways, but one task that could not wait was consecration of a ceremonial spruce therefor, from atop Parnassos. I joined an expedition of other young men to this end, though it devolved unto blasphemy as we dragged our sacrifice over a mile of impedimental slush to Athenai, slipping, sliding, cursing, and laughing at ourselves throughout the whole ill-conceived trek. We had to compress its lower limbs with ratchet straps just to get them past the double doors; using ropes and pulleys, we erected the tree in the center of the space, so large that its topmost limbs nearly touched the gable ridge. Once braced by framing, the children were able to climb upon it, hanging bunches of berries, popcorn strings, shells, and jewelry of glass or metal; then they carved out nesting perches amidst their handiwork, whereby the dining room could be secretly surveyed during community meals. I had the subsequent honor of participating in the butchering of Airmed and Aeiolus' turkeys, which they raised specifically for the feast marking the year's longest night, and spent autumn foraging in their orchard. The appointed date was so cold that frost affixed plucked carcasses to stainless eviscerating tables straight out of the scalding vat, requiring us to plunge our hands therein periodically to restore sensation. Despite my lifelong consumption of meat, I never killed or butchered an animal before; Aeiolus believed the experience should be mandatory for any carnivorous adult, if only to know whence it came. He emphasized the importance of giving death to his stock as conscientiously and painlessly as possible, in order to imbue the flesh thus harvested with metaphysical health. "The consumption of turkey is typically associated with Thanksgiving Day," he said amidst our slaughter, "another kind of harvest feast, ostensibly commemorating the American settlement by Europeans; albeit to my mind a ritualized satire of how colonists civilized this region. The immigrants that legendarily began the tradition greeted their new home by stealing corn from natives of the Province Lands as soon as they stepped ashore. After anchoring near Plymouth, the majority perished in their first winter; then, in spite of its reputation for theft, the Christian colony was saved by the Wampanoag, who brought venison for the historical Thanksgiving. In return, the pilgrims gave New England aboriginals disease and despair; preemptively murdered their leaders; coerced sale of their territory; and when these failed, forced them from their homes via military power or by simply burning villages to the ground. Some thanksgiving, if you ask me. "Nowadays, families across the United States come together each year to celebrate their marauding nation's heritage by gathering around a platter of turkey, the Americas' wild contribution to our panoply of domesticated livestock; however, even if they are privileged enough to eat a live-raised bird, it is invariably spawned by artificial insemination. The commodity variety of ubiquitous confined feeding operations has been so inbred for breast size that the tom is anatomically incapable of mating, because his legs cannot support his body weight; he spends life suspended from a sling, milked for semen as electronic probes stimulate his prostate.

"The country has hence enshrined the genesis of its manifest destiny in a vainglorious holiday, observed via gratitude expressed over the corpse of a native animal incapable of having sex with itself, due to our intervention; yet most Americans do not know, while many now eat cloned meat instead. This is the false thanks, and the perversion, begat by spiritual bankruptcy."

More than three hundred villagers came to Athenai for Pannyxia, one of the few affairs wherein mores condoned recreational alcohol consumption. Aegipan, a goatherd who was also the eldest man in the community, kept bees at the periphery of his pastures, for pollination and his fermentation, making from their honey sassafras-root brew, which happened to be rich in a chemical precursor of X. Although the trolls of my trade were synthetic, the millennial generation had access to phenethylamines of natural origin, dispensed from a shadow economy of plastic baggies that left its addicts ignorant of, or indifferent to, how their insatiable appetites demanded deforestation in South America and Southeast Asia, where formerly-renewable sources of safrole grew; just as those preceding them had been so easily prompted in the War Of Drugs to overlook exotic social and environmental damages borne for their heroin and cocaine habits, by obscuring or assuaging the guilt thereof with its causative substances. Our patriarch, on the other hand, offered libations from an organic vintage completely of his own creation, which aptly promoted caroling, revelry, and flirtation. The turkey, begotten by sexual intercourse in this case, I deemed the best I ever tasted – moist, finely-textured meat from athletic animals who had roamed, flown, and lived the existence evolution intended. The sumptuous gravy was no doubt enriched by their diverse diet of bugs and plants, in contrast to a drug-laden, chemically-adulterated ration of lifeless grain formulated for factory farms; but the satisfaction I gained by helping bring them to the table made a sauce of flavor beyond compare.

Airmed and Aeiolus also celebrated their wedding anniversary at yuletide; for the occasion they gave a concert with Linos, the village orchestra. The pair had resorted to busking at times whilst sailing abroad, thereby acquiring a wide repertoire, which comprised rock operas and mock-epic renditions of popular songs from American culture prior to the Exchange. Airmed sang beautifully; one of my favorites was 'My Heart Will Go On', accompanied by a very drunk Aegipan on the flute, Aeiolus on piano, and Amadeus on an electric viola. For their final act, they reprized the power ballad 'I Would Do Anything For Love (But I Won't Do That)', joined by ribald echoes of an increasingly bacchanalian audience for certain lines, most notably, "I just pray to the gods of sex and drugs and rock and roll!" I would later learn that the gender roles had been comically reversed to showcase Airmed's voice, allowing Aeiolus to focus on his instrument; nonetheless, it was he who brought the house down during the duet coda as he crooned, "Will you cater to every fantasy I've got? Will you hose me down with holy water, if I get too hot?" with her stroking his burnt face. I stood in the back, grinning, though without seeing the music video I had only begun to appreciate the humor; and found myself beside Bridget.

"Happy birthday," I whispered, leaning toward her momentarily.

"Indeed," she groaned. "How did you know?"

It was not the 'thank you' of my hopes; yet having a secret seemed clever.

"A little bird told me." I feigned nonchalance, staring straight ahead.
"Whatever," she replied dismissively upon the realization I would not tell.
"It's so embarrassing that they do this, and that this is whence I came."
"I think its lovely," I remarked as the couple twirled onstage. "What is it?"
She stared at her parents, perhaps feeling disenchanted with partnership.
"An awful song, which they repurposed for their prothalamion."
"Prothalamion?" I asked.
"Do you hear an echo in here?" she joked. "Those were their wedding vows."
"I beg your pardon?"
"The four 'that's'," Bridget elaborated. "As in, I won't do 'that'."
Reading the lyric sheet later, I learned the promises Airmed so fervently
declaimed to her husband of forty years, before the entire tribe, backed by
string sextet, clarinet, and drum kit, were that she would never:
"...forget the way you feel right now;"
"...forgive myself if we don't go all the way tonight;"
"...do it better than I do it with you, so long;" or
"...stop dreaming of you every night of my life."
As the music ended, Aeiolus swooped Airmed from the floor with
a flourish, kissing her passionately. The audience cheered joyously
at what they had done; the players of Linos embraced one another;
and elders laughed uproariously over a Meat Loaf joke that they alone
could understand. Children went to bed during the intermission, because
the next performance was of a more burlesque nature, in overt adoration
of human physique and sexuality. For anyone not yet too inebriated, the
theatrical dialogue resounded with ironic humor, mysticism, and parable,
as well as its flagrant instigation of debauchery; yet betwixt the cannabis-
infused deserts, opium-laced spliffs, and Aegipan's sassafras mead, the
Pannyxia soon degenerated from literary criticism to ritualized eroticism,
then ecstatic dance to orgiastic chaos, as its subject matter intimated.
"Enjoy your youthful practice for initiation," Bridget said, grazing
my shoulder as she left for her own bed, much to my regret.
"How do you mean?" I called after her quickly-receding silhouette.
"Chthonic boundary dissolution is not the only way to meet the goddess."
In truth, she was the only goddess I wished to encounter, but given her
departure, my prolonged celibacy, and collectively compromised inhibitions,
I became elsewise drawn into carnal indulgences. I am sorry to say that,
other than glimpses of anatomy, fleeting fragments of ecstasy, and the
residual sights or sensations of bodily secretions shared, all I can recall
prior to recovering from my hangover the next day on the floor is this:
whilst gazing upon the vibrant figures and smiling faces among whom
I would weather the dark, cold months of winter, feelings of security
and appreciation filled me, mingling with those of narcotic confusion.
My life felt so awesome, so deeply good, that I could hardly
believe I had really lived for a mere quarter of a year.

"It's what you do that makes your soul."

~ Barbara Kingsolver, *Animal Dreams* ~

"Each man delights in the work which suits him best."

~ Homer, *The Odyssey* ~

"If you'd been shown how to do things with the minimum of strain and the maximum of awareness, you'd enjoy even honest toil."

~ Aldous Huxley, *Island* ~

AIGIKAMPOS

Aegipan, who was a pioneer, farmer, and the widower of Amaltheia, died in his sleep just after his memorable performance of 'My Heart Will Go On' at the Pannyxia. I had only conversed with him once, when sent to his house by Will in pursuit of a plumbing fitting, and he thereby detained me with an hour's discourse of the microclimate effects on fungal endophytes in pasture grasses. Because I did not know him as the other villagers had, I gladly volunteered to take on extra sentry duty during the funerary rites. His reputation stemmed partially from a knack for repairing and rebuilding antique equipment, including the miniature combine he acquired on the village's behalf, which still ran well despite two decades of vigorous use. His compound spread across the Arkadian uplands northwest of the Fresh Fish Pond, where he kept an ample herd of dairy goats with his daughter, Elithyia. As mistress of the cheese caves and the doula sought most often, she had been stretched by the obligation to care for her father as he aged. Will, who lived nearby, helped with the heavy work as Aegipan's health declined; consequently, he assumed the obligation of caring for the land and animals left behind, even before she asked him to do so. Although sorrowful, the patriarch's death was not untimely, since winter facilitated a relatively convenient transition of responsibility. With field crops harvested, essential work would be limited to the daily chores of providing feed and water until spring came, if one could ignore the daunting lists of maintenance tasks that were endemic on every farm, never to be completed. Will took the former in stride readily, as he already performed them for his own stock, while beset by concerns about the latter. Aegipan managed to keep his herd and homestead healthy through his elder years, but the scope of his enterprises in Arkadia had been established by a younger edition of himself, then slipped toward decrepitude in lockstep with his body, due partially to the tribe's reliance on his mechanical skills. Many fences, buildings, and implements literally hung by a thread, in the form of hemp twine; the labor required to produce knotless quarter-mile lengths preferred for baling imbued this material with such value that it enjoyed a long cycle of reuse through the community. After hay was fed or straw mulch spread, the string might be made into macramé; employed for nets and trellises; braided as rope; or lashed around bundles of the hemp stalks, like those whence it came, prior to submersion in the retting pools. However, only at Aegipan's had I seen baler twine serving as goat fence, or as a structural connector to replace nails in barn framing. Elsewise, the farm was held together via the telekinetic force of his intent; hence, upon his death, the place seemingly began spontaneous self-destruction. Will brought me with him to help move some feeders and field shelters, mired in the ice of low-lying areas that were sheltered from north wind but would be mucked up by hooves when the ground thawed. It was a fine, cold day, with sapphire skies whose unobstructed sun reflected off the remaining crust of solstice snow, which had thawed and refrozen. As we explored, he kicked at loose fenceposts, pointed out areas where weeds were getting a foothold in the pasture, then bemoaned old water hydrants, leaking from corrosion. We fed hay and distillery grains whilst there, prompting me to admit that Aegipan's barn was not particularly conducive to the purpose; it had been built for use as an interim dairy only until completion of a newer, more sanitary slab-on-grade version in the cove below. The original layout, still unchanged generation later, provided no direct pathways, thus compelling me to swivel my body as I wove bales through an obstacle course of columns and implements ever absent sufficient room. Principal posts that were set directly in the earth, presumably out of haste, subsequently rotted at their bases. Low ceilings and the structure's great depth left its interior quite dark. Brisk winds on the hilltop location had gotten under the barn's metal roofing, pulling it from the framing to which it was originally fastened; sheets flapped and the clattered in the breeze, as snowmelt passed freely through the open screwholes, whose leaking thereby started decomposition of the purlins - lashed, once again, with baler twine because nails would no longer fasten them. The rafters were scant in size, salvaged and probably on their way to decay at the time of framing; strained by its span, the roof's deflection had increased alarmingly since then. Will commented that it might collapse beneath the next heavy snow load; a risk he neither could nor would afford.

"If I am to take it on, I'm going to need a better barn," he declared. In an oblique way, the trip therefore invited help; to my knowledge, I was available for the job, and told him so. In fact, his request came as a relief; following the challenges of autumn, winter's indolence made me anxious. Cold or not, I felt eager to get outside and immerse myself in physical work. Together we donned the fantastic mode of thinking that is the hallmark of new construction, beginning with a landwalk to ascertain the optimal location for a new barn. We rejected the windswept site of the existing building in favor of a well-drained bench, sheltered on the north, whose gentle grade gave convenient access to several fields by its position at a four-way intersection of fences. Whereas this required us to cut, re-brace, and add several gates, the end result would prove our efforts worthwhile - a circumferential barnyard favorable to livestock rotation, via connections

to four separate paddocks, which also allowed room for maneuvering of
farm equipment or vehicles. Enjoying a reprieve from the chill in his cozy
home, we made plans over mate lattes and hemp cookies left by Grace.
Upon her return, she glanced past her husband's shoulder at a list of
features and functions, inquiring as to what we were doing; since he
seemed tongue-tied, I overzealously described the design of our new
barn for Aegipan's farm, receiving a reproachful glare from Will.
"Oh, really?" His wife's hands moved to her hips as she addressed
him assertively. "When were you going to ask for my permission?"
"Well, the idea sort of...just came up," he replied with a sheepish grin.
"Don't pull that on me; I know you better than yourself, sir, and there is
no way that this idea 'just came up'. Aren't you busy enough already?"
She softened her tone then to tell me she was three months pregnant;
in response, I offered my timid congratulations, whilst Will spoke quickly.
"But darling, that's all the more reason...if we are going have a family,
this is my last good chance to do so, and for our children or whoever else to
take care of that place as it deserves, they will certainly need a new barn
before a decade passes. If its built now, we get to start with the benefit..."
"Don't you 'darling' me," Grace said sharply; then, in my direction;
"I'd guess he's probably rehearsed this speech countless times,
along with whatever line he used to hook you into his escapade."
I politely indicated my eagerness to help, but refused to take sides in
a marital conflict, moving for the door; she ordered me to sit, citing the
fact that Will always did what he wanted anyhow. Although turned toward
me discreetly, she saw his wink and slapped him square across the face.
"Oww!" he whined, rubbing her crimson handprint with hyperbolic injury.
"Behold your champion," she exclaimed, swiveling next to deliver a forceful
punch on his arm; he clenched the impression left by her knuckles, wincing.
"Look at you – pathetic! I'm going to kick your ass and take the belt, wuss."
"That's what they all say," he declared. "Don't worry; I'll get it back later."

After drawing relevant equipment to scale, then reckoning areas
required for livestock, storage, drying, and miscellaneous functions,
Will thought a two-story barn measuring 30 feet by 60 was appropriate.
The ground floor would be pole construction, whose movable wall panels
fit betwixt consistently spaced posts to permit flexibility in configuration
of the space; he planned to enclose the long wall of the second level with
siding, thus protecting hay and other stored crops from windblown rain,
while large double doors at either end worked as windscoops, to augment
ventilation for purposes like drying lumber. This configuration presented
difficulties during our investigation of the community's inventory, upon
discovery that the necessary framing materials were not available therein.
Because I had previously encountered some fascinating manuals on timber
engineering and mechanical properties of wood in Aeiolus' library, the barn
finally offered meaningful opportunities to apply my formerly superfluous
intellectual aptitudes, by performing structure analysis or bending strength
calculations based on information gleaned from these books. For example,
I knew his intended uses for the second floor implied live loads in excess
of sixty pounds per square foot; just as the practical limitations of sawn

lumber implied a central beam, splitting the building lengthwise in two spans of fifteen feet. My math indicated that we needed 2" x 12" joists to safely carry the load, larger than any on hand. Moreover, the coveted girders would be 8" x 14" and almost 700 pounds each with a paltry dozen feet between the posts supporting them; yet if they were any closer the barn would have failed to fulfill its fundamental purpose, since the equipment for which it was designed could not fit inside. "Remember that your equations assume dry material," Will said, drawing from his experience with timberframe raisings in the Amish community, "so you should allow an inch on the wide face and a half to the other for shrinkage. Besides, even if we could get sufficient clear logs to mill them – we can't – I think it unwise to put up timbers that large before they dry, and I don't have years to wait; perhaps a month, according to Grace." Turning to options in steel, we located a stash of galvanized guardrails behind the salvage shed, fortuitously compatible in length to the span of the barn's five bays. Their profile meant to resist the force of a car hitting perpendicular to the direction of our proposed floor load; but by overlapping two pieces, then welding a pair of such assemblies back to back, Aephaistos created girders that would not be prone to torsion, whose strength characteristics rivaled those of I-beams; and at half the weight of comparable pine girts, they could be lifted by just the two of us. "Their rigidity comes from the empty space within, you see," aphorized the elderly metallurgist when he delivered them.
The remaining framing could reasonably be sought in wood, preferable as a more readily renewable resource than metal, and Will consulted other members of the Forestry Team about cutting live timber for this purpose, from Arkadian forest that Aeiolus had told me was for future generations. "They don't need to be the best trees," he petitioned. "Just straight enough for sixteen foot lengths and perhaps as many inches in diameter." As it happened, an exposed grove of hybrid pine atop Olympos had been hit by a recent ice storm. Although these trees were actively tapped for pitch and turpentine, their long-term management plan was lumber production; which all parties agreed would be served by removal of those whose leaders were broken. Upon initial survey of the stand, Will despaired, as floor joists alone would require all the long butt logs, leaving none suitable for rafters. "What about trusses?" I asked, after he tallied standing board feet thrice. The physics behind such structures fascinated me from when I first saw the dining hall; using the inherent rigidity of triangles, spans were only limited by a designer's imagination and strength of connections betwixt their sides. "We'd still want continuous top chords," he said with some audible concern. "Not if it's hammerbeam," I argued, and Will laughed, relieving the tension. "True in theory, but we're framing a barn, not a cathedral. I hope someday you have time for that kind of craftsmanship; we need to get this up quick." "What about splice joints and a midspan top plate?" I suggested next. "Ugh," he groaned, kneeling to scratch his head, "sounds like a clusterfuck, or every barn I've ever been in. I'm sick of queen posts in haylofts and such nonsense; I'm over that paradigm and just want an open floor for once." Wracking my brain for a solution to redeem my naiveté, a traditional barn shape ingrained by books arose behind my eyelids, then refused to fade.

"Well, what do you think of a gambrel roof?" I inquired hopefully.
"I've never built one," he replied. "I'm not opposed, so long as it works."
Seizing a stick, I excitedly scratched my truss idea in the snow underfoot;
the four slopes were defined by half of an octagon, with a slightly smaller
octagon revolved and inscribed within, so that its vertices met the rafters
at their midpoints, whilst its own sides tied the roof planes to each other.
"We'd have to give up two feet of floor space at the eaves," I explained,
pointing out vertical struts at the edges, "but there are no walls to build."
"No walls, no siding...headroom everywhere...no interior posts...that IS
elegant," he declared after a quiet stare. "How long are these rafters?"
"About eleven-six," I said, estimating the trigonometry in my head.
"Seems legit," he agreed, "though I'm no math whiz. If you're right,
we can almost build the thing out of toothpicks. I'm just concerned
that your plan transfers the entire roof load to the exterior girders."
"No worries; it's practically the same condition as the central floor beam,"
I assured him, outlining and computing the loads in an adjacent sketch.
"How much hay would it hold, if stacked solid up to these collar braces?"
"Maybe twenty-three hundred bales," I answered, based on my arithmetic.
"Better than I'd hoped, then," Will ruminated as a grin crept over his face.
"We've really gone back to the very genesis of architecture," he mused,
gesturing to schematics conceived upon the earth, rather than his desk.
Looking at me quizzically, he asked, "Where did you learn to do this?"
Until then, I had not considered what I was learning; I simply absorbed
seemingly random information on whichever subject caught my interest.
"From observation, and books, I guess. It's funny...I never thought whilst
reading that I'd have a reason to use them for something substantial."
"Aside from farming, building is about as substantial as it gets," he said.
"From the way you think, I'd bet there will be use for you here a while yet."

According to folklore, timber is best cut during the lunation's last quarter,
when more of its sap lies in the roots. Our design coalesced just before the
new moon, and so I joined Will the next day to witness how, with only the
assistance of an antique chainsaw, tapered wedges, and a sledgehammer,
he could drop every trunk precisely where he wanted, regardless of the
direction it leaned. By carefully weaving trees between their neighbors,
he successfully left the rest of the forest undamaged, absent evidence
of his logging except for their stumps, scattered woodchips, and the
momentary thunder that echoed over the valley as they crashed down.
"Like judo," he said, referring to a combat sport in which he trained, whose
name came from the Japanese words *ju*, for 'gentleness', and *tao*, or 'way'.
"How so?" I failed to see the connection between martial arts and logging.
"It's philosophical precept as much as it is self-defense," he elaborated.
"The goal on the mat is to turn your opponent's own body weight against
them through technique, causing them to move with minimal effort instead
of brute force. Here, the tree is not our adversary, yet we still harness the
potential energy therein, letting gravity do the work. You want to fell one?"
I responded enthusiastically, and he gave me a brief demonstration of
chainsaw operation, including the danger of it kicking back into my face.
Lending me his chaps and hard hat, Will said that I was not to cut trees

without them. Beginning by limbing under his supervision, I developed a feel for the machine. Its cutting teeth were well sharpened; driven by the ethanol-fueled engine I held, they threw plumes of dust with lethal efficacy and little of my effort, indeed. When satisfied by my competency, Will chose a pine listing away from the skidroad where he wanted it to land, showed how to lay out my cuts via sight lines on the saw's motor cowling, then stepped back and left me to do as he instructed. I was amazed that the small cross section of intact fiber in the hinge could prevent such a large object from falling the way gravity would have dictated; yet as I pounded on the wedges, each inch they penetrated the kerf moved its crown by feet, until bypassing at last the center of mass.

"Timber!" I called, emulating him.

All went well initially; the tree fell toward narrow alley in which I had aimed the face notch; but at about twenty degrees from vertical, the trunk veered off sidewise, thus hanging up on one its neighbors, much to my dismay. Will came over and inspected the stump.

"I did everything you said," I insisted defensively. "What happened?"

"The hinge broke," he told me simply. "Let this be a lesson to us both; I didn't give you enough information to compensate for side lean."

"How do we deal with it now?" I asked, looking to the entangled crowns.

"I'm loathe to cut a tree that has another hung in it since the physics can be unpredictable, so I'm going to make this one roll off. Give me that saw, get out of the way, and don't do what I'm about to show you on your own." Darting the tip in and out of the mangled hinge, Will managed to sever the trunk completely without pinching his bar therein. Employing a cant hook for torque, he strained to rotate the hung pine, until eventually the heavier portion of its canopy pointed skyward. The limbs fell around the far side amidst tumultuous cracking as the tree struggled to turn out of the bind.

"There she goes," he muttered, expectorating in the snow, and it finally plummeted freely. Will stood before the stump, watching with a hand on his hip and the other resting on his peavey handle, when a thick dead limb, snapped off during the twist, hit dead center atop his head, breaking in twain on impact. While I saw the series of events culminating with his collapse, they unfolded so quickly that I was powerless to prevent them, and ran to Will's motionless figure in a panic. His eyes were clenched shut; then he rubbed his jaw, grimacing but still alive, by the grace of the gods.

"Just give me a minute," he mumbled as I knelt on the bloodstained ground. "Second lesson: don't cut timber by yourself. If that limb wasn't so rotten, I would have needed you to carry me out of here." He blinked, frowning. "I'm a bad teacher; even after talking about looking for hazards and wearing safety equipment, I violated all of my own rules."

"Are you all right?" I inquired, concerned by a massive protuberance that grew from the wound on his tattooed scalp with each heartbeat.

"Yeah, I'll survive - as long as you don't tell my wife I nearly killed myself."

"I won't, though your lump there is going to be hard for her to ignore." Will probed the knot carefully, then examined his reddened fingertips.

"It looks pretty bad, huh?" he asked, and I nodded affirmatively.

"Fuck," he said. "I guess they aren't called widowmakers for nothing."

Whereas I could intuit the close relationship Airmed had with her daughter, the conversations that occurred betwixt them in my presence were never quite natural. Bridget always seemed put off by me, or holding back from candor in some way, until the day I stumbled upon their mutual confidence inadvertently. A unseasonable warm spell had thawed the frozen ground, such that Will and I churned our log depot into a quagmire. I ran home at lunch to replace my saturated socks; there I heard the women talking heatedly through the open kitchen window facing the guest house. I did not mean to listen in on their discussion, but as it happened, they had not observed my presence, and its topic was, of all worldly possibilities, me.

"He is in love with you," Airmed remarked, catching my attention.

"He most certainly is not," Bridget scoffed. "That dance takes two."

"Forgive me, I stand corrected; he's been struck by Cupid's arrow, rather."

"Sure, he's infatuated...and his is a fatuous infatuation," Bridget replied scathingly, then she started giggling; perhaps she was simply amused by her own paronomasia, but the seemingly callous glee tore my heart apart.

"It worries me that you are so hardened against him already."

"I'm not against him, but come on...he's still a child!"

"Age is far from everything," Airmed said.

"Says she who married a man almost twice her own," Bridget quipped.

"Case in point," her mother shot back, "since we are well-pleased with the fortune whereby we found each other; yet in this small pool, you may not be, and I'd hate to see such discrimination unduly limiting your prospects."

"Yeah? It may very well be that relationships are overrated."

"I beg to differ...in your case, I'd say they are underrated."

"What makes you think I need your advice on men?" Bridget snapped, her volume rising. "You think there aren't any who share my bed?"

"While we both know that's not love, I hope for your sake there are."

"Oh, there are plenty, trust me," she announced in a low tone.

"Uh-huh," Airmed replied. I thought her voice betrayed doubts, which I fervently wished to have basis in reality, as the notion of Bridget with someone else, regardless of who he might be, sickened me. "Besides," she went on, "He's always lurking, listening when he shouldn't... overthinking his actions, and constantly apologizing. He tries too hard, and eats too fast." She paused, then concluded unequivocally, "He's strange."

"As is your father," Airmed observed, "and in our time together, what I've discovered, which you might consider, is that stranger can be interesting."

"Strangers bring problems," Bridget declared, shrill with resentment.

"They also bring solutions," her mother added calmly.

"Why all the persuasion? Did he put you up to this?"

She waited a moment to respond. "Thou doth protest too much, methinks."

"Forsooth," Bridget mocked, and hissed dismissively, "psst...interesting..."

"Honestly, at times you make me pity whoever may play the fool you marry, assuming he survives the courtship. How did you become so judgmental?"

"I learned from the best."

"Dear goddess," her mother lamented, "I've created a monster."

The silence that followed broke when Bridget stifled a snicker; then Airmed shed her solemnity as well, and their shared clarion laughter rang over the orchard. I loped away stealthily on all fours, assuaging pain in my chest where brutal condescension had impaled me, yet still hoping for a chance. Mine was a fatuous infatuation, as Bridget said; raised by a culture whose objects of worship, be they celebrities, wealth, or religious idols, were so far removed from myself, what could I do but aspire to the unattainable? 'Thank you Airmed,' I prayed. 'If nothing else, please let me be interesting.'

To maximize the length of our workdays, I made a practice of meeting Will before dawn for calisthenics - combining the Greek *kallos*, or 'beauty', with *sthenos*, 'strength' - which necessarily preceded our yoga, given the cold. His unspoken motive, and my consequent benefit, constituted training for labor whose physical demands were new to me; the first of these came via skidding, as engaging therein absent proper warm-up and coordination would have been downright dangerous. Although he preferred horses for the purpose, their dietary requirements and potential erosion had caused concern amongst early site planners, so we utilized a tractor to drag our logs to an improvised lumberyard where he set up a portable bandsaw. I assisted from the ground, rolling them around, handling choker chains, and marveling at my growing ability to move tons of mass with the proper amount of force efficiently applied via leverage or momentum. Such work felt great for my body as well as my soul, inducing me to sleep more soundly than ever, strenuous enough to keep me sweating in frigid weather, which I deemed splendid. We cut the butt end of timber for floor joists, prioritizing our yield of rafters from the narrower bole above, based on the premise that those with wane at an end or drying checks could make the shorter collar ties, "since I think I misplaced my board stretcher," Will joked. Curved lengths, along with small, knotty tops, became purlins and studs. Whilst Will ran the mill, I staged logs, then handled them again as lumber. My muscles rejoiced at this exertion, and I celebrated my metamorphosis from the weakling I was upon arrival. I found myself eagerly lifting more boards at once than necessary to test my athleticism, empowered by the thrill of participating in the entire construction process, from conception to completion. Producing the barn materials ourselves out of standing trees and so little embedded energy, selectively harvested on adjacent land, then dried by the wind and sun, comprised an endeavor as pregnant with spiritual significance for me as it was with noise and sawdust. Aeiolus taught that civilization, via its global economy, promoted the ruination of the planet by the simple disconnection of human beings from the sources of their existence; and the village was an exercise to "bring the effects of our lives within the horizons of our lived experience." Through my labor with Will, I began to understand the wisdom of such an ostensibly simple goal. Surely if people saw the fields in which their food was grown, or the forests whence their shelter arose, they would curtail their consumption; but in absence of a visible, tangible, comprehensible correlation between a consumeristic lifestyle and the vital environment supporting it, they were easily led by the artifices of media, religion, and government to accept the wishful fallacy that technology could somehow sustain their extravagance, disposing of its waste as they slumbered. "We have demonstrated our prowess for destroying the world with the black magic of our unconsciousness," he said, "an ungrounded spell, whereby we sacrifice the world upon the altar of a cash register or stock exchange to appease a false god. The destruction we unknowingly beget is a testament to how powerful we truly are; regrettably, most people have no concept of the awful feat our kind has accomplished. Can you imagine what might emerge if we tapped the potential of our consciousness instead?"

I got a good taste of this during the construction project, whose process lasted less than a month from the time lumber had been cut and stickered to dry in the solar kiln; yet it was one of self-discovery that went back to phylogenesis, revealing my intrinsic facility for physical humanifestation. Despite a lack of relevant education, I knew, as though by osmosis, how to do what had to be done once put in such a position. This did not occur without effort; rather, I strove daily to embody the ethos of impeccability impressed on me by Aeiolus. My meditation lay in the continual pursuit of perfection, with the understanding that my objective was unachievable, the point of the path being its endless potential for self-improvement.

If I saw any deviation from straight, square, or plumb, I rushed to adjust. Whilst framing together, Will often asked me, "Can it ride?" as I fussed until satisfied that the connection could not be made noticeably better. After stepping back to examine my work, he would say, "Look at these materials. You keep forgetting we're building a barn; it aint no piano." When I self-consciously justified my dedication to 'better than adequate' as part of a spiritual practice, he backpedaled a bit. "I grok the reason," he admitted, "because I do the same in yoga, capoeira, and martial arts. As far as building is concerned, I can tolerate your perfectionism, as long as you can tolerate my reminders that someday we must finish the job."

I knew his remark to be partially in jest, because we were getting it done faster than either of us expected we could. By the completion of roofing, I had surmounted the lingering vertigo from my Manhattan jump, dancing across the open framing and carrying the long metal panels with aplomb. Standing at the ridge to gaze over the island, I savored the exhilarating rewards of fulfillment, while supported by the universe palpably through my newfound fitness, purpose, and dexterity. Most of all, I reveled in the knowledge that, using my own mind and hands, I had created something of real quality and durability, whose service to my community may outlast me.

I was never one for superstitious notions of eternity, which hold appeal for so many, but the view I enjoyed atop the barn catalyzed a fundamental shift in my perspective. Regardless of heaven or hell; karma, reincarnation or cryogenics, I realized I would have a life beyond this in my effects on the world I will leave behind. For the first time, I possessed an articulated reason to exist, more meaningful than mere fulfillment of biological caprices, addictions, or the appetite for sensations and stimuli: to contribute as much as I could to the welfare of my tribe, and hence, the sustainable perpetuation of my specie.

"My benefactor said that when a man embarks on the paths of sorcery he becomes aware, in a gradual manner, that ordinary life has been forever left behind; that knowledge is indeed a frightening affair; that the means of the ordinary world are no longer a buffer for him; and that he must adopt a new way of life if he is going to survive...The frightening nature of knowledge leaves one no alternative but to become a warrior."

~ Carlos Castaneda, A Separate Reality ~

"It is not the oath that makes us believe the man, but the man that makes us believe the oath."

~ Aeskhulos, 2525-2456 B.T. ~

DEUKALION

Members of the tribe endeavored to provide for their needs from the island whenever possible. This default was simultaneously an existential quest, preparation for the long-anticipated collapse of modern civilization, and a practical expedient for the sake of security. They integrated their support systems harmoniously, on the principle that products of one should always become the inputs of another, with an eye toward the eventual elimination of waste as a concept. In terms of food, fuel, and fiber, the village was completely self-sufficient; while most resources not strictly renewable were repurposed from New Shoreham's forsaken ruins, such as cable, pipe fittings or fasteners, further bolstering its independence from the mainland. An early job of mine, for example, had been to remove thousands of stainless steel screws from the composite decking of erstwhile boardwalks. According to Aeiolus, selecting a coastal site took advantage of its former inhabitants' propensity for corrosion-resistant materials, many of which could still be used after forty years abandonment. "When the shit hits the fan," he said, "we'll just have to make the best we can of manufactured goods left behind, in order to soften the technological contraction. For all of our resourcefulness, we cannot yet fabricate screws, let alone something as complex as a tire. These are challenges we pioneers leave to future generations, perhaps yours; and I know not how they will be addressed; yet I do know that necessity is the matron of innovation." In absence of this necessity, the islanders did import a few commodities, including hydrated lime for plaster and replacement parts for sophisticated machinery. Although some of New Shoreham's upscale preexisting homes had salvageable metal roof panels, most were built with asphalt or cedar shingles, which deteriorated long ago. Thus, when plans for Will's barn solidified, he submitted a request to the Materials Acquisition Committee for industrially-produced panels with factory-applied paint, primer, and galvanization. To utilize an expedient like this reminded me that the tribe comprised a transitional strategy, not an end state – even if such a thing could exist amidst the dynamics of reality. Total isolation from the world beyond the horizon was neither an explicit aim, nor was it sustainable. In our case, alternatives would have been thatch, or to spend years riving, then applying, shakes from a slow-growing, immature, and limited supply of white oak, to compose a roof for the barn with a much shorter lifespan. Since industry-wide recycling rates for steel exceeded 80%, MAC deemed Will's petition for some relatively thin sheets therefrom, after milling all his lumber, a reasonable compromise betwixt practicality and ecological ideals. When the pioneers settled on Block Island, Aeiolus commissioned a custom 50' aluminum catamaran affectionately named *Kismet*, built by a boatyard near Boston for these sorts of imports. Among the numerous benefits of multihulled design, the greatest may be in potential speed. A bluewater monohull typically gains resistance to overturning from its weighted keel, a downward-facing fin that tends to sink to the bottom; the elsewise hollow vessel displaces water, creating hydrodynamic drag due to its consequently large wetted surface area. Catamarans, on the other hand, derive lateral stability from the distance separating two hulls, which displace very little, reducing friction, deadweight and draught; thus they are able to sail faster, as on shallower seas. Aeiolus' boat drew just shy of three feet empty, with sufficient buoyancy to carry two tons of cargo routinely, in addition to its stockpiled supplies, fresh water, and crew. When the protruding rudders were retracted, the *Kismet* could also be safely run aground, perpendicular to a beach, resting its twin *vakas* on the bottom; whereas a monohull would be unbalanced, tending to heel over whilst perched upon its single keel. Albeit at least as old as civilization, sailing is, to my mind, still one of our most elegant and direct technological applications of renewable energy. By simply maneuvering pieces of fabric, a boat can be made to move in any direction, and travel everywhere in the world with deep enough water to stay afloat, simply because air moves. Although one cannot sail directly toward the eye of the wind, headway may be counterintuitively had going thereto obliquely; tacking back and forth in a zigzagging series of turns, sailors may harness the power of a breeze to effectively work against it. Unless running free downwind, pressure upon sails leans their mast away from the wind, lifting the bilge, such that a monohull's maximum sail area is limited by the ability of its weighted keel to counterbalance this condition without capsizing. Due to the inherent stability afforded by its width, a catamaran will scarcely tip where a keelboat might heel twenty-five degrees, and can safely fly more sail than a monohull of comparable size. Aeiolus hence specified a bi-plane rig for his; while requiring a pair of crew, installation of a mast for each *vaka* allowed the *Kismet* to travel faster. The space between them provided a broad platform suited to transporting bulky goods since it remained relatively level and high above the waterline; while a close-hauled monohull regularly takes waves over its narrow deck. Besides cost, the disadvantages of a sailing cat lie in maneuverability; and loss of momentum amidst a tack makes it prone to getting caught in irons. Ergo, for heading upwind on rough seas, a keelboat is preferred by some. The *Wyrd* was such a vessel, whose forty-two foot hull hailed from New Zealand and a racing pedigree, uniquely constructed of solid wood via the cold-formed triple diagonal method. Although lighter than a similarly sized boat of fiberglass, the *Wyrd* boasted ten tons empty, nearly half of which resided in the lead keel extending almost seven feet below the waterline. With just a mainsail and large genoa, the Bermuda sloop rig could be sailed singlehanded. Airmed purchased it to live aboard during medical school; soon thereafter, on her first solo voyage, she rescued Alexander Fremont. As of my deliverance from death, her boat had been afloat forty-five years. There were miscellaneous skiffs, canoes, kayaks, rowboats, and rafts on the island also, used for fishing, recreation, or as dinghies; yet only the *Kismet* and *Wyrd* ventured upon the ocean, always leaving and returning to the harbor in darkness. Both carried hemp sails and rigging of native manufacture, harking back to American sailing ships of yore, or perhaps *The Fates*. Whereas the *Kismet* was equipped for mercantile transport, Airmed and Aeiolus reserved the *Wyrd* to cruise or conduct reconnaissance on behalf of Council, keeping a finger on the world's sociopolitical pulse via furtive excursions into range of wifi. It had served as their primary vehicle for recruitment in the past, among other uses; as when they found me on the way home with Amadeus from a hospital visit to diagnose his leukemia. Another of my winter assignments, begun in earnest after Will's barn had been dried-in, was to painstakingly replace the *Wyrd*'s teak deck under the supervision of Kristos. Upon the death of centenarian Aegipan, he became the eldest living member of the community, famous for retaining dexterous craftsmanship in spite of age and showing no indications of slowing down. I felt frustrated, verging on miserable, with our work by the second week. As if stripping and scraping of petrified adhesive were not bad enough, the scribing of complex curves in rough planks of local locust, as on *The Fates*, proved even more tedious; whilst as consequence of the same flavonoids that gave the wood its reputed durability, dust generated therefrom made my eyes itch and sinuses drip constantly, whether I was on or off the job. Its grain, quite opposite the pine with which I grew familiar through Will, was so strong and convoluted that the effort of shaping requisite pieces of the project seemed like carving a jigsaw puzzle from stone – except in my case, after investing hours of labor to create the perfect fit, one might be rejected for a split that appeared during fastening.

"Jesus!" I exclaimed, struggling to extricate a defective board.

"Another carpenter, allegedly," Kristos responded, though I had not spoken to him directly. "What size counterbore are you using?" Unlike me, he found delight in the challenge, muttering animatedly to his tools, materials, and ghosts about the miracle of every cut or screw because I refused to entertain his dialogue. Due to my rotten attitude, I experienced the process as monotonous rather than mystical.

"Well, that's just fascinating," I quipped, out of caustic exhaustion.

"Indeed." Overlooking my disdain, he took this for an invitation to converse. "Rumor has it you're reading the Bible. Have you learned of Jesus, then?" I knew not why at the time, since his question was not overtly threatening; ubt it begat a profound sense of dread, as if he called a subconscious bluff. My culture had conquered the world under the sign of the cross, yet I could scarcely recall the myth thereof. I retreated to some words ingrained by TV religious services from my infancy, when my mother still feigned faith.

"The son of God, whose birth was by a virgin and heralded by wise men... during his ministry, he cured the sick, fed the hungry, and preached the gospel...he was crucified, died, and was buried, but on the third day he rose again, in fulfillment of the scriptures, and his kingdom will have no end." "So the Council of Nicaea still rules the day," Kristos said, chuckling. "I beg your pardon?" "Oh, you don't know?" he asked astonishedly, turning my sarcasm back on me. "It's only the most significant ecumenical gathering in our age, which determined the course of history for the majority of two millennia." I listened attentively as he explained how a politician, general, and saint, named Constantine the Great, used the meme of Europe's 'new god' to lay foundations for what would become the Byzantine and Holy Roman empires, whilst making himself their sole ruler; however, his most enduring legacy, by design or by chance, was an empire of consciousness that lasted from the fourth century *Anno Domini* to the present day, called Christianity. Although largely responsible for this religion as we know it, records show Constantine was a superstitious secularist, as successful in economic as in military strategy. When neutrality served his career, he idly watched his imperial predecessors' bloody persecution of Christians; but a decade later, he captured Rome with their sigil freshly marked on the shields of his army. "Neither faith nor religious freedom were among his aspirations; his sole motivation was evidently imperial unification by military domination; ergo, the only message that could convince Constantine to accept the sign of the cross, purported to have struck him in a vision, said *In Hoc Signo Vinces* – 'in this sign, you shall conquer' – which is about as far as one can stray from whatever message the mythical messiah might actually preach." Kristos then flipped an U.S. quarter-dollar coin to me, minted in 2001 A.D. "It seems old habits die hard," he remarked, gesturing toward the mainland. His token came to rest heads-up on my palm. "In God We Trust," I read. "A fair translation," he agreed, "and whereas the United States might be the first to print such blasphemy on paper currency, subjugation of the commonwealth through the marriage of monetary policy and religion is yet another innovation of Constantine's. As in America today, he declared the artifacts of pagan temples to be imperial property; instructed his minions to confiscate and melt them down; then reissued their precious metals as coins with his face struck on them, lest any doubt his absolute authority. Although today's masters of finance may be ignorant of it, they also owe a tremendous debt to him for drafting blueprints of their tactics to extort from lower classes through devaluation of their currency. In Rome's empire the gold standard was reserved for transactions of the elite, while common people were involuntarily subjected to incessant dilution of their bronze with base metals. Wall Street is just this mechanism's logical extension; by circumventing physical currency, today's digital, symbolic money simply utilizes a fraudulent basis more efficiently, whose markets inevitably convey wealth to the center via unchecked commodification of the sacred." The parallels to my native culture had me captivated by then. "That's kind of brilliant - terrible, of course, but for an emperor, brilliant." Kristos nodded. "Constantine was brilliant; moreover, he possessed moral flexibility of which Machiavelli only dreamed. Who else could ruthlessly conquer neighbors as easily as he could issue edicts of religious freedom, the difference being in what he deemed politically expedient at the time? This was a man who found mere military subjugation of Germanic tribes too merciful, so he humiliated them with the messages he minted on coins he made of their hallowed relics; someone apt to parade the decapitated heads of his vanquished opponents through Rome or serve them at the dinner table; a ruler who killed his wife and eldest son, solely to show other heirs his willingness to do so in order to protect his throne."

"But didn't you say he founded Christianity a moment ago?" I asked.

"More so than any savior," Kristos declared, exacerbating my confusion. In fact, the ecumenical council Constantine convened, whose proceedings were echoed by my declamation of the Nicene Creed, marked the end of an ideological battle between Christian doctrines that began in Alexandria. One school of thought, led by Arius, believed Jesus had been created by God, and was hence distinct from the Father; a belief encapsulated in a passage from John, whence the Lamb of God tells the disciples: "I go away, and I am coming back to you. If you loved me, you would be glad that I am going to the Father, for the Father is greater than I."

"Arius' logic was elegant, and simple enough for a child to understand," Kristos elaborated. "If God begat Jesus, then the one begotten has a beginning, and there was a time the Christ did not exist. Accordingly, Jesus may have arisen from nothing, but is by definition not eternal."

The majority of bishops who came to Nicaea contended that Jesus shared with the Father, equal and unique divinity, a facile view upheld by numbers as by its conduciveness to imperialist ambitions. In making a prophet who had walked among the common people uniquely consubstantial with God, the sought to position the church as middleman between a disempowered population and a savior accessible only through hierarchical institutions. Whereas it may have seemed like theological or philosophical discourse on its surface, Constantine conceived his council as a strictly deceptive process to achieve convention; by bringing out of swarming, disparate memes that ranged from the Neo-Arian *heteroousios* (different than God) to *homoios* (like god) or *homoousios* (of the same substance as God) a single and thus easily-controllable cult of personality. The '*homoiousian* compromise', as it were, concluded a debate two months long, albeit not via acceptance; rather, by stating that Jesus was 'of similar substance to God', *homoiousios* alienated many who thought Jesus unlike the Father; and it anathematized those Arians who objected to the very use of *ousios* in the conversation, on grounds that to speak of God's 'substance' at all constituted profanity. This doctrine, ostensibly for pacification, disappeared after serving its true purpose, which was to prepare the ground for predomination of *homoousios* and repression of Arianism as blasphemy. An edict of Constantine decreed:

"If any text composed by Arius should be found, it shall be handed over to the flames, so that not only will the evil of his teaching be obliterated, but nothing will be left even to remind anyone of him. And I hereby make a public order, that if someone is discovered to have hidden a text by Arius, and not to have immediately brought it forward and destroyed it by fire, his penalty shall be death."

"What fascinates me, more than the severity of the threat Arius posed to Constantine's orthodoxy, is that same emperor's uncanny facility for reconciling his own beliefs with the state religion, which might appear to be mutually exclusive. On the eve of his death, he took his baptism in the river Jordan, a place chosen because it was written that Jesus did so also. While his political agenda, promulgated by the Council at Nicaea, had been to expunge the views of Arius from all record, after deeming them heresy, in his paradoxical final hour he selected as baptizer Eusebius of Nicomedia, the man primarily responsible for organizing, leading, and recording the Arian faith, despite its persecution. The Emperor previously exiled this same bishop for his desperate opposition at the infamous Nicaean synod, whose confession he felt compelled to 'subscribe with hand only, not heart'."

From *sub–scribere* - 'under the spell' - I realized upon further rumination, when I first observed the overlapping linguistic and occult usages of 'spell'.

"Ergo, Constantine left to Rome a Christianity of idolatry and fallacy, harnessing vernacular fashion for his empire, without evident spiritual qualms about reserving for himself rites in the very tradition he had not just prohibited, nor merely exterminated, but utterly erased from history – enjoying a privilege that, as Augustus, he asserted was his alone to exercise. The English idiom 'not worth one iota' refers to anything so insignificant it does not merit discussion; but in the case of *homoousios* and *homoiousios*, a difference of one iota catalyzed the greatest semantic argument in the history of Western civilization - whether the progeny of God was at heart essentially like the rest of creation or not. That culture has long since submitted to priests who posture as conduits to the Word; and though their interpretations were irrelevant to his own beliefs, those powers are preserved by the works of Constantine from his day to ours, perhaps best immortalized in the Gospel according to Matthew: 'For truly I say to you, until Heaven and Earth pass away, not an iota, not a dot, will pass from the Law until all is accomplished' – unless, of course, you're the one writing it."

I idly turned over the coin he had tossed, part of a commemorative series, featuring my home state of New York in this case. "Gateway to Freedom' had been stamped on its reverse face, alongside a familiarly iconic statue, whose name was emblazoned on the front. "Liberty," I enunciated slowly.

"Funny you should say that," Kristos remarked. "In Latin, the word *liber*, whence it derived, means 'free'; but it's also the noun for paper, or a book; the difference lies, yet again, in the emphasis placed on its iota. You'll find these languages are far from dead, and their etymology is akin to Qabalah."

"I don't actually know what that is," I admitted, chagrined.

"It is the study of esoteric information embedded in ancient scriptures via allegorical, rhetorical, and numerological dimensions, particularly of the Old Testament, or Torah, as it is called in the Hebrew tradition; whereby the absence of vowels or punctuation permits a reader to unveil double entendre and subliminal messages. Similar principles apply to our other mythology because language is alive; and by reading between the lines, or multiple times, you may find more inside than first meets the eye."

His lesson ended abruptly, so we could prepare for an impending shower; yet whilst musing afterward on the semantics of *liber*, I noticed that the ambiguity of the iota therein might be construed as 'text will set you free'.

I spent the subsequent night reading the New Testament, as preparation for his pedagogy the next day. After we had set up and established an efficient routine, I led with one of my carefully premeditated inquiries. "You said yesterday that church and state conspire to corrupt the savior's message for imperialist ambitions; which means Jesus must have preached something else instead. I'd like to know what, then, is the real gospel?"

Kristos smiled slyly beneath his untamed beard. "That is the question, and I'm glad you're listening. Every word you've read was in the books of Matthew, Mark, Luke, and John - canonical scriptures, from the Greek verb *kanon*, to rule - but they are only the tip of the iceberg. We also have the Apocrypha, which means 'hidden away' – gnostic texts either purged from the New Testament during one of its numerous transcriptions, or legendary heresies hiding from the light of day in desert caves. I've been compiling, translating, editing, and analyzing them for much of my life; the results, along with exegesis, I intend to publish soon as a kind of psychedelic bible."

"What's psychedelic about old scrolls and tired dogma?" I wondered aloud.

"How can you ask such a question?!" Kristos moaned, flabbergasted. "Let's break it down, shall we? Psychedelic, from *psyche* and *delos*, also Greek, for mind-manifesting. *Psyche*, from *psychein*, to breathe; breath being the animating spirit, atmosphere, air, or Yahweh, the semitic god. To be psychedelic is hence to reveal god, and my manuscript certainly does, insofar as it re-minds us that divinity lies within all of us, accessible via our very own consciousness, rather than some non-endogenous institution."

Still unfamiliar with etymology, I was thus incapable of sharing his enthusiasm – from *enthousiasmos*, 'inspired by God', I later learned. "It is the imagination that argues for the divine spark within human beings. It is literally a descent of the world's soul into all of us," he declaimed.

"Is that out of the Apocrypha?"

"No, though it is holy scripture, from the gospel of Terence McKenna."

"Aha!" I exclaimed. "I thought it sounded familiar."

"You know him?" Kristos inquired, raising a bright, bushy eyebrow.

"I wouldn't say so, but I did read Food of the Gods, and am a fan."

"Did you tell Aeiolus?"

"Yeah...it actually came up on my first day out of bed, when I asked about the lectures Airmed said were recorded on his computer."

"What was his response?"

"That I'm not supposed to partake in the knowledge of the Apple."

"I wonder what he's up to," he mumbled, stroking his beard and apparently disinclined to say more as he sharpened his chisels on the Arkansas stone.

"So...where were we?...yes...tell me, do you know of Judas Iscariot?"

I answered him with confidence, given my painstaking reviewed the Bible.

"Sure; he was the apostle who betrayed Jesus for a ransom of silver."

"According to the Canonical gospels," he amended; I nodded in hesitant recognition of this distinction. "Would you like to read the Book of Judas?"

I scoffed at the thought of the martyr being exalted by an informant.

"It's no joke," he declared. "Such a scripture exists."

My attitude suddenly became serious. "What does it say?"

"The eternity promised by his messiah is not one of physical resurrection;

while crucifixion was not a sacrifice to absolve sin, but a premeditated and theatrical means for Jesus to enter the imperishable realm of a gracious God that demands no suffering. Judas just followed his instructions in a long chain of skillfully planned events; the eleven other Apostles who ultimately stoned him to death repudiated the ministry of their savior for a world of religious hierarchy, carnal rituals, and attachments of the ego." The implications were staggering, if I accepted the existence of the document to which he referred; Kristos had compelling evidence.

"You believe in this gospel?" I queried him.

"More so than the rest; though I meet all of them with skepticism, at least Judas has papyrus dating from two millennia ago, whereas others were translated and altered Lord only knows how many times in the interim. What reason besides its authenticity could there possibly be to keep secret the true story of one who so nobly followed in the footsteps of his teacher?"

His version of the Christ myth appealed to my emotional preferences as well as intuitive archetypes, by representing Jesus as multidimensional, and thus a more fully human being. Compared to the morally incorruptible savior of modern bibles, this was an engaging protagonist who made sense; enough to even merit worship, perhaps. I mused then on the mysteries Constantine had erased from common knowledge but saved for himself; the undiluted basis of Arius' cult, effaced by imperial censorship; inspiration that could lead aspiring Christians to the divine inside them, absent need of any church. Might it not have been a testament such as that which Judas would leave, revealed (*re-velare*, to uncover; from *velum*, a veil) at last?

"I must retract what I said earlier, and apologize for my ignorance; I now see old scrolls can indeed be psychedelic," I told him with humility.

"No apology necessary; nonetheless, you should know our sole extant source of Judas' testament is not a scroll, but rather an Egyptian codex."

"What's that?" I asked; like Qabalah, this word was new to me.

"Basically a book, comprising multiple sheets of paper or parchment bound on one edge, so named from Latin *caudex*, for tree trunk, or block of wood; though both codices and scrolls would fall within the definition of *liber*."

"Which also means inner bark," I added, recollecting its dictionary entry; Kristos nodded approvingly at the connotation. "Whether or not the text you've mentioned is authentic, it just shifted my paradigm completely."

"Beloved, believe not every spirit, but try the spirits whether they are of God, because many false prophets are gone out into the world," he said, winking. "First Epistle of John, widely acknowledged as baptizer of Jesus. And if you think this is a paradigmatic shift, wait until I share with you my thesis that, if such a personage existed, the messiah was really a woman."

As our labor gradually proceeded I succumbed to the perception it would never end. There were days when we recovered less than ten square feet, an area scarcely visible on a boat of such size. Kristos seemed ageless, as if he had already gone to and returned from the godhead's luminous cloud, because his keen mind and steady pace betrayed no sign of doing anything but continuing as always. Although eternally committed to the decking's expedient completion, he cared naught for its rate of progress. Winter was wet, cold, and dim; our shifts, weather permitting, spanned the entire space from dawn to dusk, whose length had grown wearying by then. To maintain my attention for this duration, I adopted his habits of eating small morsels and drinking frequently, as I avoided sitting down or losing momentum. Still, the switch from forceful exertion to indomitable patience did not come naturally. While my work with Will felt like climbing toward a visible mountain summit, this was akin to crossing a continent on foot, requiring a different strategy to manage my energy, along with a sense of hopelessness; as in sailing, the goal forever receding beyond the horizon. Afterward, my appreciation of the task emerged in ways it could not before. Conceptions of vertical and horizontal characterized the Arkadian barn; our concerns were for square intersections, trigonometry, resistance to bending, or bearing loads to the Earth. While I used, to a large extent, similar materials and technologies on the *Wyrd*, the carpentry thereof was a whole trade unto itself, involving not only curves instead of lines but arcs compounded, then dimensionally complexified, whereby elemental forms flow in and out of each other seamlessly; of tension, flexibility, buoyancy; without flat planes, insofar as these are conceived via our mental artifice. By embracing eternal labor, I learned how to be present and recognize the magic of life; no matter what my endeavor, it constantly offered me the choice to evolve my understanding of the world, which was, as such, a gift.

Amidst the revelation of this providence, Kristos sought my opinions on his hermeneutic Gospel of Judas, which I had read the previous evening.

"You asked last week about the real message of the messiah; now I wonder if you can answer for yourself," he said as I passed the drill.

"God resides inside all of us," I replied.

His head shook in dissatisfaction with my response or ambivalence.

"While that may be true, did Jesus need to die for you to know?"

I frowned, set down my board, and considered the catechism seriously.

"Look not to divinity, but to Christ's humanity."

"Jesus is a paragon," I began, "who shows the way to a heroik death."

"Getting closer; from Greek; *her-oikos*, protector of the home, incidentally. What do you think it is that made the heroes of their culture notable?"

I contemplated the myths for a moment. "They were unafraid of death...?"

"Although that, too, may of archetypal heroes be true, would you include the likewise fearless suicides, soldiers, or psychopaths among them?"

He paused for poignant emphasis. "Have you heard the tale of Kastor yet?"

I nodded with a sense of foreboding and thoughts of Bridget's iciness.

"Would you call him a hero?"

"Absolutely!" I cried, shocked that Kristos even asked.

"Let me assure you he was terrified of dying since he had so much for which to live; and he did so sickened by premonition." He pointed to the weather mast whence Kastor had been stationed on the fateful night. "We call it the Herakleion pillar, 'glory of the protector', from *kleiein*, to proclaim; hence Kleio, the erstorian's muse. I presume you're familiar with Herakles, too?"

"Somewhat...I gather that he was a demigod who slew his own children, and as atonement had to complete twelve feats believed to be impossible."

Kristos agreed. "As I'd like to recast the life of Christ, so would I change the story of Alkmene's son, because what defines our greatest heroes is not their superhuman abilities, nor a lack of fear; rather, it is their choice of a life exemplifying their principles. They thereby achieve true liberty, or total freedom, which is tantamount to total responsibility; responding with ability, and the ability to respond. Fear is created by the mind, and thus a choice; fearlessness in the face of death is just an expression of a deeper life experience, based on these qualities. The most free are those who can be loyal to ethos and protect their homeland, not only despite fear of, but even unto their end if necessary. It is neither death, nor how they died, that makes them heroik; it is how they lived until their final breath."

After contemplating this more thoroughly, I remarked, "It seems the hardest sacrifice would be the one made when no one is watching."

"Indeed - if your reputation no longer matters, it is also the truest gift. Our mythology, however, is alive, and needs renewal from time to time; idolizing those we do see, via cults of celebrity, reminds us that, like Jung's collective unconscious, humanity's soul is akin to the ocean floor. We might think of ourselves as islands, yet beneath the surface we are one connected landmass, and the vast seas of separation that we perceive are imaginary. 'No man is an island, entire of itself...every man is a piece of the continent, a part of the mainland; if a clod be washed away by the sea, the whole is less...any man's death diminishes me, because I am involved in mankind; and therefore never send to know for whom the bell tolls; it tolls for thee.' "

"Sounds familiar," I remarked.

"I'm not surprised, since the turn of phrase has been recycled by writers and musicians for years; it comes from John Donne, a metaphysical poet, mystic priest, and politician from the turn of the seventeenth century.

My point is that Kastor saw himself as such an inextricable part of this island that he willingly gave his life; I pray he may live on in our salvation."

By reading <u>Food of the Gods</u> and Genesis, I had formed new views on the Tree of Knowledge, Original Sin, and what salvation therefrom might mean.

"So the story of a hero who challenged religious institutions, their vengeful God, and notions of our inherent evil was corrupted to reinforce them?"

"Yes," Kristos said, "but as with Eden, echoes of the original message still permeate imperial propaganda. In the Gospel of John, Jesus proclaims, 'I am the way, the truth, and the life', but the path to God is not through a messiah worshiped in places of monumental architecture, whose masters of ceremony are rich white men festooned with the robes and jewels of consumer fetishism. Even Paul, schizophrenic though he may have been, wrote in his letter to the Romans, 'All who are led by the spirit of God are children of God'; their path is marked by detachment from ideology and commitment to principles. Examples can be found in personages from Leonidas to Sokrates, Jesus to Judas, Steinem to Goodall, Gandhi to Fremont. My favorite hero is Nikolai Ivanovich Vavilov, a Russian agronomist who, through his curiosity about the genesis of our subsistence, determined the geographic origins of his culture's staple crops. He saw the genetic diversity of his commonwealth as a fountainhead of its security, so he devoted his life to collecting, cultivating, and conserving it. His titanic contributions notwithstanding, I must admit that he perpetuated the fallacious concept of increasing crop yields to end hunger; we now know starvation and indigence are consequences of the overproduction whereon stratified societies rely. For this error, I forgive him, since he came too early to see civilization needed replacement rather than repair; moreover, because his vision begat the world's largest collection of plant genetics in Leningrad. At that time, which happened to be the outset of World War II, Vavilov was arrested for dissenting against the pseudoscience of acquired inheritance, promulgated by Lysenko and upheld by the regime of Stalin. His first sentence was death; then commuted to twenty years incarceration; nonetheless, he died after two years in prison, of malnutrition, ironically."

"How tragic; it sounds like a Dostoyevsky novel."

"Worse, in fact, because unlike Fyodor's most notorious protagonists, Vavilov was an upstanding man, a seeker of truth, a would-be servant to evolution and the common welfare. The benefits of his heroism came a year later, when Hitler invaded Leningrad, whose seed bank had been left unprotected. Inspired by their deceased mentor, Vavilov's assistants protected his life's work from the incursions of Nazis; by the time the siege ended in spring, nine had voluntarily died of starvation, whilst guarding a collection that either might have fed them or been the future of their nation. I endeavor to carry forward such efforts in an era of rapid environmental transition, with respect not only to the atmospheric composition or erratic weather, but also extremes of UV radiation and a preponderance of plant diseases. I've witnessed the stranglehold of U.S. agribusiness, legislative criminalization of seed saving, genetic commodification, and the sabotage of non-proprietary crops by designer pests or bioengineered epidemics. I've examined millions of plants in field trials to find the handful of mutants that can endure our harsh conditions; I've grown out thousands of crosses to foster the diversity required for a resilient economy (*oikos-nomos*). Heroik deeds surround us, in myths and history, legends and literature; we've had plenty of practice, since the evolutionary imperative to protect our home, family, and tribe is older than our specie. As Alexander Fremont said, we can be victims of our history, or we can choose transcendence. Freedom is here; the time has come; let us take it, now, once, and for all. The responsibility therein obliges us to be like Christ, ready and willing to give life for our beliefs, because failure to do so would be their abdication. I'm not advocating martyrdom per se, since it is far from the best way; but by twisting the mythic messiah into an entity not of this realm, ruling elites have perpetrated the illusion that divinity and heroik sacrifice are beyond reach, accessible to us only as spectators or through the insidious lens of their institutions. Via moral flexibility, along with control of written information, Constantine's ilk appropriated one of our greatest warriors of consciousness, whose sermons would tear down the walls of imperial morality, materialism, and monetary policy, as a weapon of oppression."

Kristos bore more than a bit of resentment toward this aspect of the past, and I wondered if some perverse enjoyment of frustration might have tied him to the mortal world, feeding his vigor regardless of age. Two thousand years later he remained avidly embroiled in a crusade to remove the facade of religious hegemony for the sake of healthier tradition. I thence learned, when used in service of a creation greater than the individual, life becomes a power that is ours to give, not a possession of which we may be deprived. Whereas my work with Will begat the concrescence of a reason to live, through my dialectic with Kristos, I discovered a reason to die.

"Love is a smoke made with the fume of sighs,
being purged, fire sparkling in lovers' eyes,
being vexed, a sea nourished with lovers' tears.
What is it else? A madness most discreet,
a choking gall, and a preserving sweet."

~ William Shakespeare, Romeo & Juliet ~

"They both listened silently to the water,
which to them was not just water,
but the voice of life, the voice of Being,
the voice of perpetual Becoming."

~ Hermann Hesse, Siddhartha ~

IKTHEUS

To my amazement, the *Wyrd* project did end, although the theology,
philosophy, and monotony thereof so absorbed me that I felt legitimately
surprised upon looking up from my work and finding none remained to do.
Sun broke through the cumulus blanket, which had plagued our photovoltaic
system from the beginning, as we collected Kristos' tools; wincing, I noticed
my accumulated locust splinters, forcibly driven beneath the skin by numb
planing or chiseling, then later squeezed out of their itchy, white pustules.
A spell of unseasonably warm weather settled over the island thereafter,
conducive to applying finish on the decking, with only the incipient birdsong
or distant laughter of children to accompany labor that was silent, for once.
Aeiolus visited the boat's slip whilst Kristos and I subsequently refitted it.
The village presbyter stood beside me as our handiwork was inspected by
his younger colleague. Running his gaze and fingertips across the joints,
Aeiolus stopped on the bow, where shapes had been especially challenging;
then raised his intact eyebrow, turning to Kristos, who nodded at me.
"This is impressive, better than the work of some finishing carpenters I've
known and more than I could have do with your minimal training," he said.
"Thank you, sir." I blushed proudly, allowing a pause before introducing a
topic of my long reflection, which I had resisted discussing for lack of an
opportunity in a neutral forum, outside his house. "I've been thinking..."
"...sounds dangerous," Aeiolus joked; I waited for Kristos to stop laughing.
"Since this is done now, I'd like to build my own place; being dependent
on you feels parasitic. Between leftovers from Will's barn and what I can
salvage from the boat, if you'll let me, I have a solid start on the materials.
Once the roof is on, I could carve out time in the evenings next season..."
"What happened to you?" Aeiolus exclaimed with an appalled glare.
"I sent you here to be cured of materialism, not infected thereby."
I expected him to support my aspirations toward self-actualization;

moreover, I figured he and Airmed were eager for me to leave the nest so they could savor their marriage in privacy at last. I shook my head from confusion and attempted to defend myself, but the right words escaped me, undoubtedly because I elided the truth. As spring approached, my desire for female companionship grew into a psyche-consuming fireball; yet I knew that my prospects in this regard were certainly not helped by living under their roof as a child. I meant, and failed, to express how my excitement for the next chapter did not at all diminish my appreciation for their care; rather than watching me continue to fumble, Kristos interceded with scripture, restating Aeiolus' intended meaning in different terms.

"What kind of people shall we be? We are out of control. We are basically, severely addicted to things, and cannot stop ourselves; and we know, or we should know, that there is not enough petroleum, heavy metals, and so forth in the planet to give all the thing addicts all of the things that we know they must have in order to be happy."

"Amen; thanks be to Terence," Aeiolus agreed, but I was verging on anger. "I think your judgment is unreasonable and unfair! There must be some projection going on, since I'm not consuming petroleum or heavy metal; I'm proposing to use salvaged and local materials to build my own shelter, as a humanifestation of ethics you've taught me. How else did the two you create your homes? Do you believe I'm not ready for this rite of passage? How am I different from anyone else? How is my project unlike any other?"

Kristos meandered down the pier, mumbling to himself with feigned senility. I involuntarily glanced at Bridget's hut, which sat above the harbor's east shore, clearly visible albeit half a mile distant; to my relief, Aeiolus missed this as he shaded his gaze, peering southward. A sea breeze rose from the day's warmth, bringing birdsong from the marsh; when he faced me again, his expression had softened, at least to the degree his scars would permit.

"Be mindful of your possessions. The things you own end up owning you." He went on to inform me that he and Airmed were taking a trip as soon as we finished fitting out the boat, asking me to proceed with all expediency, in order for their departure to meet an auspicious window of weather.

"I want to discuss this notion of yours further, yet exigency dictates it must wait until I return. Will you stay in Aeiolia for the next few weeks, to keep an eye on things and do the animal chores in our absence, please?"

"Of course," I said, glad to have some modicum of reconciliation after my reactive outburst, "though it seems like a risky time for sailing."

"We've seen worse," he replied. "Besides, it can't be helped in this case."

"Why is that?" I asked ingenuously.

"We have a meeting to attend." He issued a tired, or annoyed, sigh. Whereas I could have left the subject alone, curiosity seized me, and I wondered aloud why they needed to leave the island.

"Because we're outside of the network," he answered abruptly, "and for them to come here would be an unthinkable security breach."

"What I mean is that a few weeks strikes me as a long time," I said, vaguely aware of overstepping my position, "unless you're seeing 'them' in person."

"We hope it won't be so long, but the wind is unpredictable," he began, shrugging. "Since you can't leave, I suppose it won't hurt if you know we are going to Washington and visiting some old friends from the Agency."

This astonished me. "Are you trying to get yourself killed?!"
"Quite the opposite," he laughed grimly. "We have what you might call an arrangement for mutual benefit. Our village has not hidden from the world these many years by chance alone. If you found this area on the iNterface, all you would see is ocean, and it is not radioactivity wherefore the flight plans of private aircraft avoid us. The secret to our seclusion, the reason we enjoy sovereignty on this island, is that Airmed and I possess secret information about the American government, which its masters wish to remain as such. They know, if anything suspicious ever befalls either of us, or our community, this will all be made public."
I could imagine the electorate-turned-proletariat, despite delusion, would not gladly receive proof a presidential candidate's assassination had been orchestrated by the Agency; whilst its reputation would probably not be helped by the fact their operation was a failure.
"Information concerning Alexander Fremont?"
"Among others...and that's all I'm going to say, so you can stop asking."
"You're serious? You've really blackmailed the United States?"
"In a manner of speaking," he replied curtly.
"Wouldn't it be a catalyst if these conspiracies were unmasked? Instead of making deals with the devil, shouldn't you tell citizens the truth?"
Aeiolus glared askance, then solemnly shook his head.
"Americans don't want to know the truth, nor do they deserve it any longer. Once upon a time we thought transparency might instigate change; while their country had more chances than I can count amidst the sociopolitical climate following the Exchange, we judged that our measly efforts to hold the system accountable were too little, too late. Instead we took to heart the trite, but oft-unheeded advice of Mohandas Gandhi, and became the change we wish to see in the world; for my part, I gave up one life so this place could be born. Perhaps I would elsewhere have been more effective; then again, perhaps not. Because I've committed to this path, for better or worse, it doesn't matter; the only choice left now is to strive for the better. I don't believe that anyone can revolutionize the way America lives; yet we can evolutionize one island, and let this be enough for us. Lest you forget, the rest will have to take care of itself."
During his soliloquy, Aeiolus' demeanor had turned dour and downcast; I felt uncomfortable in such moments, unable to help him out of the morass. As a cloud crossed the sun, his hands briefly between his closed eyes.
"You're still young, and I'm just a bitter old man. Beware of my bias or it will bring you down, too," he concluded. "Have some fun whilst we're gone; enjoy the weather if you can. We should be back before the next moon."

I appreciated their house so much when I had it to myself that I began in earnest to reconsider my building project. Since the chores were far from onerous, I did some repair or disposed of an unfinished project each day beyond my instructions, to curry favor with Aeiolus; but still spent most of the time exploring unfamiliar parts of the island, visiting with neighbors, reading books, and even indulging in sunbathing on the warmest afternoons. Bridget came by on such an occasion, barely acknowledging my presence, which did not speak well of musculature I had thought was hard-wrought.

She went directly to rummaging in her former bedroom, then the closets;
I trailed behind, asking what she sought, and whether I could help.
"I'm looking for my fishing tackle; but no, you cannot."
Slamming doors, she growled with frustration, "Well, I have to tie them."
I listening to a few minutes of commotion and tiptoed back upstairs,
whereupon I craned my head around the door jamb to behold its source.
"What do you want?" she demanded in a voice sharp as the razor she held.
"Umm...nothing...I'm just curious to know why you were in here, rather
than outdoors, enjoying the beautiful weather," I ventured cautiously.
"I might ask you same thing," Bridget retorted with a trace of disdain.
"Oh...I was outside when you arrived," I reminded her, undiscouraged.
"Well, don't let me deprive you," she said aloof. "It is a beautiful day,
which is why I want to be out fishing, instead of getting ready to go."
She sat at a desk, boxes of furs and feathers strewn about on the floor
in chaotic abandon, with a freestanding vise before her, whose pointed
jaws held a tiny fishhook, whence hung a spool of finely-spun red thread.
"Do you want to learn, or not?" she asked in an impatient, accusatory tone,
motioning for me to sit. At a pace that was almost incomprehensible,
she took me through the process of fashioning a fly: attaching the tail,
dubbing its body with waxed animal fur, wrapping a tiny hackle feather
from a rooster around the shank to make a plume of barbs that would
simulate legs and wings, forming the head with a Gordian knot of sorts.
She dabbed on a little pine resin to prevent it from coming untied, hooked
the lure on her hat brim, and began anew. I strained to bring the fly into
focus, whilst her skillful fingers moved to create it with unerring precision.
"You want a turn?" she asked, after tying a dozen or so of varying styles.
I looked at my cut, calloused, hands, riddled with splinters and hangnails.
"I'm not sure that I'd be any good," I replied, slightly intimidated.
"That's a relief, because I'm not sure that I would want to see you try."
Packing her tackle, she casually asked, "Have you ever gone fishing before?"
I shook my head, heart skipping beats as I realized
this might have been the prelude to an invitation.
"Unless you have something better to do here, you could
paddle for me. I'll even teach you a thing or two, if I can."
I did not have something better to do than watch as she trotted ahead.
The rod she held was a work of her art in itself, made from tapered lengths
of split bamboo, neatly bound by countless wraps of thread, terminating
in a carefully carved handgrip at its butt end. I carried her creel and net
until we came to the fresh pond monument, panting, where we awkwardly
launched our canoe, amidst a flock of ducks that quacked with indignation
at the disruption. She took the bow, thus permitting me to gaze upon her
athletic back, arms and shoulders, revealed in all their glory by a sleeveless
gown of excruciating translucence whilst they paddled with exquisite form.
"Take us over there," she ordered, pointing across the pond at a clump of
budding shrubs. Although I did my best to oblige her, I had never been in
a canoe, and Bridget was quick to criticize my technique, or lack thereof.
"What are you doing?! When you paddle on that side, it turns us away,"
or, "Stop splashing so much...you're scaring off all the fish already!"
By the time we reached the far side I had developed a feel for the motions,

whose effort suited my body well. Observing my companion, I gained some small sense of how to control speed and direction with backward strokes. "Shhh," she whispered as we approached, laying her paddle under the thwarts. "Take us in slowly...stop...turn a little...hold that position." She assembled the lengths of her angling rod, fed line through its eyelets, then tied a fly from her hat on the thin leader, which was connected by a thicker, floating cord of waxed hemp to a spool on the reel. Giving this wand several quick, practiced flicks, she soon achieved the steady rhythm of a metronome whilst line flew over her head in a tight loop, flipped over, then reversed direction, longer with each pass, until finally sent loose. Dropping straight and level, it gently tucked the fly into shadows below willows that hung from atop a steep bank. After a moment of stillness, I saw what looked like a large bubble; jerking upward, Bridget lifted the entire cast at once. Her rod bent; the taut leader swung sideways, slicing the surface; and a fish jumped, in excess of twice its own length above the pond, flashing brilliantly as it thrashed in the sunlight. She pulled some line and it ran yet again; whenever her quarry leapt or swam toward us, she gained another bit. It was close beside our canoe in less than a minute of this dance, roiling the water with paces against a short, elastic leash.

"Do you want the net?" I thought to ask eventually.

"No thanks," she replied, deftly leading her catch to a submerged hand. Seizing its curved lower lip firmly betwixt her thumb and forefinger, Bridget removed the fly, then lifted the fish for examination; streamlined in body, with a deep green back, light belly, and wide maw for gulping large meals. "Smallmouth, thirteen inches; a good start," she announced to nobody in particular; her exhibition of *techne* had impressed and affected me more. Releasing the bass, Bridget mentioned it was a predator that would restrain the prolific reproduction of sunfish, thereby preventing them from stunting; an essential role since she considered the prey species both trophically and culinarily better for eating. Smallmouths bred earliest, she told me; but in basses as well as sunfish the males took responsibility for nest construction, along with guarding eggs, then the fry. Assuming her catch spooked their spawning beds, she bade me move further down the bank, where her next few casts caught sunnies; flat, sinewy creatures that displayed their broad sides as they dove to make surprising jumps from deep below; close-lipped, with tall dorsal fins reinforced by needle-like spines; present in a wide array of iridescent markings. Some were sensationally speckled in blaze orange and turquoise; others had slate-colored backs, with blue and red splashed on their flanks; while the least glamorous bore countless shades of green scales bisected by dark bars. Any bigger than my hand went into the creel. A few flying insects emerged, the first harbingers of spring I had yet seen; upon touching the water, fish took them as they did Bridget's handmade imitations. These were mayflies, from the order *Ephemeroptera*, so named because after a year of submersion, the nymph's metamorphosis gave rise to a one-day fly; the purpose of its brief life was to mate, lay eggs, then die. Their hatch dimpled the elsewise glassy surface of a nearly windless pond, whose shoreline showcased the turning over of seasons; withered stalks from autumn's spent cattails standing in stark contrast to a backdrop of verdant alder catkins or yellow witch hazel blossoms. Although distant

passersby waved amicably, we had the entire basin to ourselves except for
songbirds and ducks. The surroundings seemed serene; I daresay romantic.
When she judged that we had enough fish for a meal in the dinner basket,
Bridget asked whether I wanted to practice casting, passing her rod.
"You really should learn whilst standing ashore, but here we are;
the stroke is from two o'clock to ten. Don't swing until you feel
weight loading the tip; and use tension to flick it the opposite way."
Despite my frenetic efforts waving her pole, the fly barely moved initially.
"It's easier after you have the line paid out," she said, pulling some
through the guides for me as I laid her pole along the gunwale; then I
made sweeping arcs overhead, slapping the water with each stroke.
"Ten to two," she corrected, smiling. "A gentle motion of the wrist.
You're swinging your whole arm, as if wielding a sword in a battle."
Next I got a fixed length to remain airborne, albeit cracking like a whip.
"Let the rod do the work; you'll feel it throwing the line as it turns over."
Whereas I could not form the tight, level loops Bridget had, my rhythm
was finally effective. "Cast it out," she suggested. "On your backstroke
haul in at the end, and let forward momentum take its slack therewith."
I meant to follow her instructions; yet the whole length fell in a snarled pile
directly in front of me. I stiffened from frustration as she began laughing.
"I'm sorry; it's not as easy as it looks, and you're actually doing quite well
for a novice. Watch me again, now that you have a grasp on the concept."
Disentangling my nest, she straightened the line with lithe motions.
"If I was casting, I'd let it go here, flat on the surface," Bridget
demonstrated, snatching the fly back just prior to making contact.
Determined to succeed under her aegis, I took the rod once more.
"On this stroke, haul in and loose," she encouraged amid my next attempt,
which laid out smoothly, except that the leader hooked sideways at the end.
"Good! You'll be a professional in no time," she teased approvingly.
I was staring at the glistening skin of her naked legs, naturally, rather than
my lure when a fish delicately rose to the latter. Although dimly aware of
an eddy thence created, I did not immediately recognize its significance.
"Set the hook!" she called urgently.
"How do you mean?"
"Pull back! You have to sink the point before it spits out your fly!"
Springing into action, I felt the vibrating weight of a live organism
fighting against my drag. Tracing its run abreast of us, Bridget yelled,
"Be ready for a jump; keep the tension!" A bronze bass fluttered mid-leap,
exerting force that attested to mastery of its environs, despite a small size.
"What now?" I wondered, stupefied by the thrill.
"If it comes toward us, strip in the line; if it dives hard, you can feed a bit
out, but keep it taut. Don't jerk or let it slacken, lest you lose the hook."
The agile smallmouth soon submitted and I reeled without much resistance;
yet halfway in, the water churned momentarily; then there was none at all.
"Ah, it's gone!" I lamented.
My line grew tight again and the rod slowly bent double, drawn down
by some obstinate anchor at its far end. I pulled from different angles,
figuring I had snagged a log or the bottom, until I felt an unmistakable tug
in response. My grip slipped and my fingers burned as cord hastened away;

all I could do was prevent entanglement on my feet as it went to the deep.
    "What's happening?" I asked Bridget, feckless and confused.
    "I think you've caught another," she replied, attentively looking forward.
The reel sang at high pitch as it spun, dropping to a hum when near empty.
    "Get a hand on your line, and control it this time," she commanded.
    I cautiously brought in some of the almost unyielding length; suddenly,
the fish switched direction, heading for the pond's center. Hand over hand
stripped in the loose line; at last, finding my seemingly massive quarry still
attached, I engaged with renewed focus. For anxious minutes I knew only
the connection between us, sensing from my side every thrust of its tail
and each change in course. Bridget coached me in a low, calming voice.
    "It's probably going to jump; when it does, give up just a little.
    Don't yank; this is a fish strong enough to break the leader."
While I remain uncertain which of us was more shocked, I never saw the
shape that burst forth from the reservoir outside books; lean and pointed,
akin to a missile or the extinct barracuda, with shining skin of verdigris.
    "Holy fuck, it's huge!" I yelled as it dove, sending out a cascade of ripples.
    "I know," Bridget cried, betraying her own excitement.
    "That's the biggest pickerel I've ever seen!"
    "What should I do?"
    "You'll have to exhaust it," she declared. "Their teeth are sharp,
    so beware of it cutting the line by running side to side if you can."
With her guidance, I strove to land the relentless fish, line going back
and forth as in a tug of war. I ultimately brought it alongside the canoe,
where, rather than swimming, it stood like a cobra, tail-walking furiously.
Unsure of how to handle the situation myself, I watched Bridget in one
fluid motion, lock her ankles under the seat, place her waist on a gunwale,
then lean out inconceivably far, almost swamping us. Grabbing the leader
without pause, she deftly slipped her net beneath the fish, lifting it in an
admirable feat of core strength, balance, coordination, and flexibility.
    Her positioning therein, coupled with water splashed on her scant gown,
had exposed her elysian physique to a degree that inevitably transfixed me;
fortunately, she fixated on our catch. Laying it in the bilge, she slipped
her fingers under a gill flap, hence opening the serrated jaws safely.
    "Hold it down for me, will you please?"
I hesitantly wrapped one hand around the tail, clamping my other just
above the dorsal fin. Via forceps, patience, and veterinary dexterity,
she delivered the bass I hooked originally from within the esophagus.
    "It's not a pickerel," she exclaimed abruptly; "this is a northern pike!"
Esox lucius, she noted, were not found on the island since the turn of the
century, when Aeiolus was our age; and thus believed to be extirpated.
    "No doubt about it," she said, counting the sensory pores on its head, then
pointing out spotted markings and reddish fins, which meant nothing to me.
    "I thought I knew all the species in here," she mused. "Just goes to show
that nature still has a few tricks up her sleeve, or lurking in dark recesses."
    Bridget guessed the pike at ten years old, indicating a genetically viable
population had survived the Exchange and subsequent climate change.
    It reached from my fingertips to shoulder, exceeding two feet in length;
taking it from me, she estimated, "Four pounds at least, maybe even five,"

with pride, as if the catch was hers; and to a large extent, it had been.
Supporting behind the pectoral fins, she submerged this glorious predator,
weaving her arms so oxygenated water passed over its gills whilst offering
me a view of her breasts, probably unintentional but sublime nonetheless.
Recovering from shock, the pike began writhing; Bridget released the tail,
and in two strokes it was gone, perhaps never to be seen by humans again.
"Do you think it will live?" I wondered when our gazes met.
"Let's hope so," she replied, shifting hers back to the depths.
"There can't be more than a few in here, and I saw no sign of injury."
"Miraculous," I remarked, as much about her as anything else.
"Indeed...and a fine job of angling, by the way," she added.
"Thanks." I blushed happily. "I couldn't have done it without you."
"I know," Bridget said matter-of-factly. "Don't get too eager, though;
this was a noteworthy day of fishing, the likes of which are not often had."
She turned to the bass that flopped feebly on the bottom at intervals,
mouth opening and closing as it suffocated between them. Reaching her
forceps deep inside, she extricated the fly, then put it into the creel.
"Don't you release those?" I asked.
"Not this one; you must eat your first fish. Besides, by hesitating you
managed to snag her in the gut, and so, in a sense, she's already dead."
Remembering how marvelously the acrobatic smallmouth had jumped,
I felt remorse; still better to be a respectful participant in the circle of
life than a passive consumer, I reminded myself. We caught wild animals
on lures that were handmade from furs and feathers of her family's farm;
I figured we would need to dive in the water and snatch its denizens with
bare hands to be any further immersed in the source of our sustenance.
A sudden wave of frigid water interrupted my reverie; Bridget squinted
at me from the opposite end of the canoe, paddle poised like a weapon.
"What was that for?" I yelped.
"A wake up call; you're ogling...none too subtly, I might add."
Surprised and dismayed, I reflexively volleyed back a splash of my own;
she growled playfully and gave me a thorough drenching. As I went for
another swing, she blocked my paddle with hers, which I slipped around,
riposting on the inside; she parried this, then caught me in the solar plexus
with a counterthrust, sending me to my back. Bridget stood, pressing
me down in the water that sloshed in the bilge and glaring fiercely.
"Do you intend to return ashore without swimming?"
I dropped my paddle, raised my palms in surrender, and nodded.
"Good, because I'm getting hungry," she laughed, liberating me.
The sky had grown overcast; its chill was readily, excruciatingly evident
through her moist dress. I paddled vigorously for warmth on the trip home;
after we drained the canoe, she announced, "I'll race you," taking off with
her gear. I numbly followed, carrying her heavily-laden creel; under the
competitive pressure, I kept up but was unable to pass, and did not object
to running a short distance behind her, preoccupied by fantasies of how
it might be to spend the night with such a goddess. Once I reached the
front door of her parents' house, she high-fived me, saying, "Nice try."
"Kind of unfair...to start without warning...isn't it?" I wheezed.
"Sorry if you're not used to that." She smiled broadly. "Although my way

is closer to real life, you call it next time, if you think you can beat me."
Whilst Bridget bathed, I scoured drawers for my most flattering clothes;
emerging in only a towel, she went quietly upstairs. When finished with
my shower, I met her in the kitchen, where she examined me inquisitively.
"How did you get this?" she asked, fingering the lapel of my vest.
"The recyclery," I replied, as if to an accusation. "Is something wrong?"
Her hesitation intimated secrecy. "It's just awfully fancy for gutting fish."
Stunning one with a blow of her knife handle, she showed how to clean their
body cavities. "Some scrape off the scales, but I cook them until crispy,"
Bridget explained. As I eviscerated spiny sunnies, she filleted the bass,
leaving behind little besides its brave head and a gleaming rib cage; then
spread the fish on a tray, sprinkling them with salt, herbs, chopped garlic,
and kumquat juice. Recommending they be left to marinate for a while,
she brought out a chessboard. "You've played before, haven't you?"
    I had not; she described the game as mental exercise, set it up, and
walked me through its multitudinous idiosyncrasies. We were members
of a culture that ostensibly evolved past warfare, except as an ironic or
symbolic pastime, retained perhaps so we would not forget the barbaric
behavior of our forebears. She corrected most of my moves in our initial
match, beating me in six; by the second game, I had a firmer grasp on the
differences betwixt the pieces, and began to foresee danger a step or two
ahead. Amidst my agonizing study of the board, Bridget heated a skillet of
bacon grease and dropped fish therein, spattering violently. Whenever I
finally made a decision, she glanced at the state of my failing kingdom, then
adjusted her own to take advantage thereof without any apparent thought.
Although I paused to evaluate each position, she vanquished me again ere
the food was cooked, calling her triumphant maneuvers from the stove.
Setting a platter of crisp, brown fish atop a bed of cold-frame greens on
the table, she arranged the chess set for a third round. We picked tender
flakes of white flesh from their tiny bones during the game; every time she
captured mine, Bridget taunted me; "Come on, you're not even trying."
In truth, I was more interested in her than in chess; a woman not only of
unparalleled beauty, but competence, confidence, and intelligence also.
That her talents underscored my inadequacies augmented my attraction,
along with the way she tucked her unruly hair behind her ear when it fell
across her delightful features, thus allowing it to do so over and again.
    "I see my mistake now," I observed as she deposed my king
        with a calculated push of her outstretched forefinger.
    She looked at the analog clock. "Want to play another?"
    I forced myself to wait for the appearance of nonchalance. "Sure."
"Set it up; I'll be right back," Bridget directed as she sprang upstairs,
returning with a collection of quills, bottles, and brushes soon thereafter;
then we paused to smoke an aromatic bowl of cannabis before continuing.
I know not whether she let the fourth game go longer than necessary or my
strategy posed a credible threat, but from an outside perspective I might
have been battling myself since she spent the duration drawing on my skin.
Started at my left fingertips, she painted the nails black, thence drew wavy
rays down my phalanges, as if to represent an energetic vibration; they
intertwined in a capillary web that spread up my arm to the shoulder.

"It's temporary - squid ink," she said, restraining me firmly.
"I'm not concerned; just ticklish, and wondering what you're up to."
"If you're struggling, tell yourself that your future life depends on not moving because my task cannot be interrupted. You pay attention to the game; I'll worry about what I'm doing." Her tone indicated this was no trifling ritual, so I obeyed. She moved her pieces with nary a glance toward the board, at least one hand constantly engaged in the application of her design, which began to form intelligible shapes as it crept above my wrist. There were myriad eyes, lidless at first; next, tessellated faces appeared to join them. These became skulls, in whose sockets seeds germinated, spawning vines with books for leaves and spiral stems dividing repeatedly. By then she had gone beyond my elbow, ordering me to maintain various awkward poses. "If you think your part is challenging, imagine mine," she decreed, seizing my queen. I could no longer see once she required my arm extended sidewise, palm forward, whilst decorating my shoulder. Our game continued until her trance ended, and only then did she permit me to examine her illustration, whose outline was approximately the same as our pike, with a fan-shaped tail covering the back of my hand. Spots on its flanks were replaced by her detailed eyeballs and seeds; curling tendrils and bones filled the voids between. Its head, however, she had rendered as the prow of a sailing monohull; a matching pair of elegant sea creatures similar to the sharks from Aeiolus' tattoo crossed in front of the bowsprit, forming an X with sagittal symmetry; their snouts faced toward and framed the half-sunken sun, stylized as a yin-yang bisected by a wavy horizon.
"Aren't their tails oriented the wrong way?" I asked, pointing to the image. Bridget smiled sentimentally. "Those are dolphins, my friend, not fishes."
I had encountered the name previously, first in reference to Fremont's Sterile Seas; later, upon a spine in his library, Island of the Blue Dolphins. I eventually learned that the name came from *delphis*, Greek for womb.
"What are they?"
"Most magnificent among marine mammals," she told me, "gone the way of their relatives, the whales; but dolphins had intelligence to rival ours, with a culture of tool use, language, recreation, and more we don't know. They could slay humanity's last surviving predator, the sharks for which you mistook them; like us, they participated in elaborate courtship rituals, foreplay, even face-to-face intercourse. The biocidal assertion of human supremacy dictated their destruction; first as food or as sport, then by commercial fishing and pollution. Now I hold them solely in memory."
This conjured memories of the desperate night whereon I faced extinction from the ribcage of the whale, prior to being rescued by her parents.
"Wait...you've seen them?"
"I was a small child," she sighed. "It may have been my first coherent memory; my father says they were likely some of last seen alive in the wild. We were sailing offshore, near Newfoundland on light airs and calm swells when a mating pair began sounding off the bow, attracted to the pressure wave, I suppose. I watched them writhing joyously, weaving through each other's paths at times by diving underwater, or else leaping clear out of it. According to my parents, I intended to jump in with them; and if I knew then what I do now, I probably still would have, albeit deathly cold.

The awareness such beauty could exist in this world has stayed with me inextricably since; that it can be lost forever out of mere carelessness is a source of grief I will bear until my end. To behold these animals dancing, even once...what a gift! Yet, upon my initiation, I had the chance to do so again, swimming in their midst. It was like flying, and I decided then to discover during this life how I will reincarnate as a dolphin in the next."

"You'll have to go back in time, though, to find them," I said tactlessly. "I don't mind; I'm no stranger to time travel," Bridget replied, holding my stare momentarily; "Your move," she prodded, with a nod to the board.

Rather than taking the pawn and bishop I offered as bait, she jumped her knight toward the center. Seeing it would thus threaten my king in another move, as could her queen from directly across, I employed castling, a maneuver she had shown at the outset that allowed moving the rook and king at once, albeit only under special conditions. Rather than attacking my suddenly exposed rook, however, her knight went for a mere pawn.

"Check," she announced, evidently unimpressed with my clever tactics. I smote the offensive knight with my rook, which her queen subsequently captured. Since my castled-side knight then stood at risk between them, I withdrew my queen to a safer position, whilst still threatening her own. For Bridget to attack would have cost a rook; so her queen retreated one space as well. I brought mine over to protect the king, leaving options on all sides; then she moved her as-yet unused bishop just behind the other, already in play, though trapped amidst pawns at my end of the board. I followed through with moving my knight, thereby blocking her queen and endangering the second bishop; but instead of delivering the latter from harm's way, she placed an apparently irrelevant pawn in front of my king, where it posed no visible hazard. After my knight had taken the bishop, her queen went to the final rank, crossing the space I had just vacated.

"Check and checkmate," she declared. "A legitimate game nonetheless." While I did not see this initially, her judgment was correct. Any attempt of mine to capture the offensive queen made my king vulnerable, due to her pawn being promoted upon reaching my first row; hence, I begrudgingly conceded defeat. Noting that darkness had fallen, Bridget prepared to leave; I volunteered to clean and accompanied her as far as the door.

"Thank you," she added, stopping at its threshold, "for such a nice day." I felt unsure what response propriety begged; a handshake seemed stilted, so I opened my arms for a hug. Mercifully, she reciprocated, pressing the warm, inviting length of her exquisite figure against mine and we shared a deep, pleasant breath in unison. Convinced she had let our embrace last longer than strictly necessary, I leaned in to kiss her when we parted.

Bridget stepped back, eyebrows lifted, instantly cold and glowering.

"I'm sorry," I stammered, "I just got carried away..."

"Ugh," she groaned after a scowling appraisal. Hands raised as a blockade, she placed them on my chest and pushed resolutely, turning her face aside. "This is all...so...wrong. We had a good time, but now you've ruined it."

She closed the door firmly behind her, leaving me alone to beat myself up through the wee hours of the night.

"I now think of the brain as a receiver of the phenomenon of consciousness. I don't believe consciousness is generated inside the brain any more than I believe television programs are made inside my TV. The box is too small."

"You are an explorer, and you represent our species,
and the greatest good you can do is to bring back a new idea,
because our world is endangered by the absence of good ideas.
Our world is in crisis because of the absence of consciousness, and
so to whatever degree any one of us can bring back a small piece of
the picture and contribute it to the building of the new paradigm,
then we participate in the redemption of the human spirit;
and that, after all, is what it's really all about."

~ Terence Kemp McKenna ~

" 'Goodbye, Terry,' I said, 'now you are free.'
I liked the thought of Terence's ashes, the last remnants
of his mortal substance, mixing with the water and soil
and trees of the place where we had spent our childhood.
His molecules and atoms will diffuse out into the world from there.
Eventually, they might mingle with parts of himself deposited
in different places. Eventually, he will be everywhere."

~ Dennis Jon McKenna ~
The Brotherood of the Screaming Abyss

 ARIES

Silver clouds brought bitter rain for days thenceforth, wherein I paced the house restlessly, or writhed in bed with the frustration of failed ambition.
If Bridget did not see me as an equal, my challenge would be striving to become one or else die of heartbreak in the process. I went to the library, first to cultivate myself in her realms of power, then to keep my mind off of shameful self pity and loathing. There I began with what I had not yet read from the collected Terence McKenna, followed by adjacent titles in Class 4 of the universal decimal system. Aeiolus' policy decreed all circuit breakers should be turned off during electrical storms; hence I studied by a candle lantern that lit my way whenever selecting another volume from the cases. Whilst unloading the section on ayahoaska and tryptamines, I noticed the care with which the shelves themselves had been constructed. In daily use, such details could easily be missed; but somebody had evidently taken the time to bookmatch narrow boards of red cedar; thus their sapwood, knots, and figuring were joined with glue as if by a mirror down the centerline.
After removing the books, whose antique odors overwhelmed all others, I stuck my head inside one of the compartments, discovering that albeit cut

before my birth, the lumber still retained the fragrance of its parent tree. Horizontal cedar paneling lined the back of the cabinet, blind-nailed to its casework so the shelves could be adjusted independently; yet behind where the works of Terence had lain, I noticed vertical grain boards, which did not belong. Examining the anomalous area more closely, I realized the carpentry successfully achieved an illusion of seamless perfection, thence concealing what was, in fact, a hidden floating panel that hinged down once I unwittingly released its spring closure by pushing thereupon. A breath of stale air escaped the dark compartment beyond; shivering as if some repressed spirit fled over my shoulder, I calmed myself with notions of how the pressure equalization betwixt wall cavity and room attested to Aeiolus' impeccable craftsmanship. Reaching in hesitantly, my fingertips grazed finely-textured metal that seemed strangely warm just as a great bolt of lightning tore the sky asunder. I recovered from the shock to examine a rectangular prism, larger than but proportioned similarly to the dictionary on the lectern, with rounded edges and corners, whose entire metallic surface appeared work-hardened by thousands of overlapping hammer blows. The container had weight, though not nearly as much as solid steel; from my assumption it was hollow, I sought a seam, yet my hands found none and I saw only the lamp flame flickering on the reflective surface. I left the library, dark by design for the longevity of its contents, then went to the kitchen, where I hoped daylight admitted by its southerly fenestration would permit a better view despite the sullen storm. As I passed the woodstove, my left hand, cradling the box under my arm, felt drawn thereto. I stopped reflexively and allowed my hand to move a bit closer, testing the tugging sensation, which increased until it yanked the metal case to the cooktop, nearly crushing my fingers on impact. I had made a fire for breakfast because the spring rains brought a chill; remembering that the range was hot, I struggled to pry the object away, singeing my hand in the process. When my panic subsided, I thought to slide it off the edge using potholders, setting it on the heat-absorbing slab. I knew little about the arcane art of electromagnetism except what Aeiolus pointed out; specifically, how everything in my former life relied upon it, insofar as magnets were essential components of modern civilization's motors, speakers, railways, relays, servers, and circuit boards. Turning the box around, I finally ascertained a barely-visible seam whose irregular course wrapped its four narrow faces, like a hairline fracture vanishing into the depressions of its peened exterior. The polished finish was apparently quite soft, since it left the battle with the stove markedly scratched and scuffed. I figured I had already gotten in over my head, yet curiosity about what lay within banished consideration of repercussions from my mind. Starting with a knife and mallet, I attempted to open a gap, but grew wary of damaging the box further after the tip of my blade broke off, embedded in the crevice. I stretched on the floor staring at this riddle, became frustrated, then smoked some herb, subsequently observing that two skillets might adhere to the opposing sides and provide me with grips. While the principle worked, in practice I did not exert enough force to open the vessel before dislodging the pans. Covering it with pots of water to expedite cooling, I returned the magnetic case when I could comfortably touch the cooktop again, which the tore the object from me with intimidating strength, my caution notwithstanding. Next I removed a large griddle from the pantry, whose rim sat neatly outside the perimeter of the box, leaving about a square foot of metal in direct contact. Even given balanced handholds, the cast iron resisted my pull, so I stood on hot pads atop the range, straddling my challenge, lifting via legs as well as my back. The box indeed split in twain, where nestled between was Aeiolus' Apple – a personal computer of antiquity, predating both the iLap and iTab, with a Liquidmetal casing. The once-glossy topcoat had faded from an age more than twice that of yours truly; within its iconic logo, Alexander Fremont's six-pronged sigil shone green. Soft upholstery cradled his machine, whose seam was protected by adhesive tape like occult grimoires in the library. I lifted it onto the counter and removed the seal, preserving this for later replacement, whilst knowing Aeiolus would notice my trespass if he checked. A pair of power cords lay coiled beneath the laptop, one labeled 120 AC with a standard plug, beside a homemade version with integral voltage converter, heat-shrunk fuseholder, and tag reading 24 DC. Along the laptop's outside edges were various orifices for external memory, data transfer, or interface with sensory appendages; catching its front lip on my fingertip, I lifted the screen, surprised to see a mechanical keyboard. Such features accounted for the computer's weight and thickness; I could not imagine why the manufacturer hesitated to abandon this configuration, given the likelihood that any of its many parts or ports might malfunction. Then I suddenly understood how the iNterface and intelligent prosthetics of my day had coevolved with the control of information. By the planned obsolescence of hardware, as well as a lack of user serviceability, Apple made automatic backups and remote data storage not just convenient, but a veritable necessity in the societal competition to stay atop fashion trends via incessant upgrades to newer models. The corporation eventually judged devices designed based on battery capacity to be most profitable, thence leading to wifi connections only, the thinnest possible touchscreens, cordless charging, and an absence of physical memory, ostensibly for the sake of conserving materials. By my generation, users leased their iTabs rather than owning them; purchased licenses to access iNterface service; and if they neglected to turn in their displays for mandatory replacement during a prescribed period, the latter were remotely deactivated. In an era of increasing scarcity, Apple thus ensured such devices would be recycled; moreover, omnipotent surveillance and censorship arose naturally from the American consumer fetishes Fremont had decried before his assassination. His computer failed to spring to life at my initial push of its power button, leaving me in a momentary anticlimax. Since the lightning was still distant, given five to ten seconds separating flash from audible thunder, I activated a 24 VDC circuit, consciously violating his protocol, and plugged the proper power adapter in an outlet. The two-dimensional LED screen came alight; following a ponderously slow boot, I manually signed in as a guest because the machine did not recognize me without my ID. It displayed an arctic sun enveloped by a dramatic perihelion, rising over water full of icebergs; below these app icons were arrayed in a row parallel to the background's horizon. I kept touching the unresponsive screen out of habit, then begrudgingly submitted to the necessity of the keyboard and mouse. What immediately arrested my attention was the coincidence of my reading that morning with a blank folder therein labeled 'Terence, pre-Resurrection'. Upon opening it, I encountered a collection of scripture from the 20th century A.D., sporting intriguing titles like 'A Crisis of Consciousness' or 'History Ends in Green'. Although I deemed the operating system sufficiently intuitive to navigate via its anachronistic hardware, I exerted significant volition and patience as I browsed glitchy item descriptions, whereas the iNterface would have predicted or preempted my own commands; in hindsight, I wonder which. The first file comprised a grainy, unstable video recording with distorted, scratchy audio that was poorly synched. Nonetheless, Terence appeared, alive and lecturing on human evolution in his distinctive, quasi-alien voice; next I astonishedly realized I had not seen digital media in over half a year. Resolution aside, the bard's facility with linguistics, idiosyncratic sense of humor, spirited curiosity, and above all, the wisdom thus conveyed, were readily manifest, maybe more so by him speaking than through his writing. Settling in with a bowl of fine cannabis, I allowed his gospel to permeate my awareness. He led with a hilarious Rumi joke that went over my head at the time; yet by the end, I sat on the edge of my seat in rapt attention to a genuine prophet, enigmatic, perceptive, earnest, and fearless, whose eloquence was not only indefatigable, but evidently enhanced by duration. I turned on an upstairs circuit at the conclusion of 'Evolving Times', then moved to Bridget's room, still bestrewn from the wake of our fishing expedition, so I could practice my fly-tying during the next episode. I thought Terence truly rivaled Aeiolus in rhetoric and vocabulary as he extemporaneously prognosticated the method and means of his own deification in 'Shamans Among the Machines'; whether he knew it or not, the question remains. He chillingly articulated the illusions dangled via civilization's cybernetics, virtuality, and life-extending medical perversions; "...a pseudo-immortality opens up ahead of us, as a kind of pay-off for our devotion to the program of machine evolution, and machine intelligence." I spent much of the day engaged in this way, checking frequently on the battery charge, which held steady; the Apple proved efficient for such a primitive device. Despite my tattooed hand shaking from concentration, I did tolerably well with my flies; after I had a few I judged sufficiently convincing to catch fish, I restored order by organizing the furs, feathers, and paraphernalia of Bridget's craft. Perhaps due to my emotional struggle with rejection, or the disquieting sense of her morphogenetic impression in the space, my gaze fell upon 'Eros and the Eschaton' whilst perusing her father's archive for an additional Terence lecture to accompany my efforts. Hypnotizing me at the outset, he said, "We get it in the eroticism of media and society, but really what Eros means in the Greek sense is a kind of unity of nature; a kind of all-pervasive order that bridges one ontological level to another. This is not permitted in the official worldview of civilization." Laughing heartily, I applauded along with the recorded audience when he quipped, "What's so progressive about media? It's the spreading of darkness at the speed of light." The room dimmed abruptly as if his ghost was summoned, and I listened in somber reverence to him portraying drug use as a spiritual technology I had never experienced, yet desired deeply.

"What psychedelics do, in terms of their impact on the physical brain and organism of human beings, is they withdraw cultural programming; they dissolve cultural assumptions; they lift you out of that reassuring crystalline matrix of interlocking truths which are lies, and instead they throw you into the presence of the great 'Who Knows?'; the mystery that has been banished from western thought since the rise of Christianity."
This final syllable begat one of those rare moments of power, wherein I simultaneously saw the purple sky rent by a trident of lightning through the northern window; the computer screen went blank; and in the flash, Aeiolus' figure materialized beside me. I leapt back; he shut the Apple, snatched the adapter therefrom, then opened its fuseholder in a single swift motion. "Hold out your hand," he commanded, leaving no room for argument; I did so, and the sweat pooled in my lifeline sizzled as the molten fuse landed.
"Fuck - that's hot!" I exclaimed, dropping it on the floor.
"Of course, and your burnt palm gives a mere glimpse of the powers you have conjured." He looked to the laptop. "How did you get past the case?"
I briefly described my inadvertent discovery of its magnetic properties, then my efforts with the stove, skillets, and griddle, to which he said, "You're lucky; yet an innovative approach nevertheless." He allowed a long pause, punctuated by a grunt. "So you knowingly disobeyed my instruction to keep the power off during electrical storms; you failed to seek permission to use my computer; and now you may have destroyed it as a consequence."
I trembled reticently, contemplated making excuses, but humbly apologized instead; confessing the truth, I began with my relationship to psychedelics. "In New York I did drugs all the time; it was my way of life, you might say, which almost killed me. Terence, though, has shown me a totally different approach, a way of healing, learning from, reconnecting with the creation wherefrom we're alienated. The case was so strange and perplexing I couldn't resist the riddle; once I found the computer inside, it answered a lot of my questions. I'm sorry; I only meant to take a peek, and know I should have asked, but thought you weren't coming back until next week..."
"You should have," he interjected. "Our plans changed, due to weather."
I heard Airmed walking downstairs, no longer silent since the issue had been defused, as Aeiolus sat on the bed, staring at the tempest to the west. "He left the world on this very day, you know, at the new moon in Aries, a period of clairvoyance and transformation, some sixty-six years ago. Today our calendar begins anew with the sixty-seventh to commemorate his own concrescence in the psychonauticon. What do make of that?"
My throat tightened. "I think it seems like quite a coincidence."
"Coincidence? You heard the bard say it himself in that lecture; 'A coincidence is what you have leftover when you apply a bad theory'."
He flipped the switch for a wall sconce on the same 24 VDC circuit as the outlet and it illuminated the space readily. "So the breaker didn't pop..." he muttered to himself; then to me, "I presume the inverter is off at least?"
I nodded, wondering meekly, "Shall I get a new fuse, to test the Apple?"
I could feel the sting of a blister rising from my singed palm, as a surge of nauseating anxiety spread through my stomach. He shook his head dispassionately, watching inky evening creep across the sky. "It does not matter, unless you can change whether the motherboard

was just fried. In any case, I must bid you speak of this to no one."
I swallowed uneasily under the weight of my potential guilt; Aeiolus had
turned toward me, noticing the drawing on my left arm by the electric light.
He arose, strode across the room, seized my wrist, lifted the sleeve, and
traced the image up to my shoulder with the fingertips of his other hand.
"Bridget drew this?" he asked, examining the symbology it comprised with
a focus intimating that her artwork communicated more to him than me.
"She did." My heart sank, recollecting the tragic end of our day together.
"For Christ's sake; now I grok why you want to move out," he concluded,
much to my chagrin. "Face reality, or at least be less melodramatic. She's
an adult, after all; you're still an egg. You'd best put it out of your mind,
and pull yourself together, or you'll never be a man, let alone a warrior."

Upon their return from Washington, Airmed soon became absorbed by
preparations for the growing season, commenting on how well I had done
with her garden in the interim. Meanwhile, Aeiolus alternately wandered
and brooded determinedly; if not for the intensity of his facial expressions,
I might have mistaken him for an aimless old man in the throes of dementia.
Eliding my inquiry about their secret meeting, he said only that the trip was
a slog amidst unpleasant conditions. After contending with peripatetic
light airs en route to the Chesapeake Bay, whence Alexander Fremont
disappeared, they had to reef the sails for beating in excessive headwind,
vicious chop, bone-chilling rain, and blinding fog throughout the slog home.
Their arrival at the island, however, accompanied a burgeoning warmth,
which coupled with the soggy winter to foster a uniform shade of green on
the pastures again. I helped him herd the yearling ewes out of the barn,
since the danger of accidental impregnation passed with the increase in
day length. The first quarter moon, neatly cloven by the Earth's shadow
as it waxed, hung bright white and high in the sapphire sky at midday.
"You're ready to be initiated," Aeiolus announced, gazing overhead when
we had finished with the sheep. "The quickening is seven days hence.
Meet me at the Sourcerers' Pond an hour before the crack between the
worlds. Until then, cut out sweets, cheese, and ferments from your diet;
consider taking a break from cannabis as well. You should be well rested;
I'd recommend eating a hearty breakfast that day, but nothing after noon.
You need to bring only warm bedding, water, and your full attention."

Three young men besides me met at the Lakedaimonian isthmus on
the appointed date, two of whom I already knew by way of our shared
work with Will. Diomedes was a brilliant, handsome young man of Argos,
so respected for his intellect that he served as a youth member in Council.
He intended to wed Kalliope, one of the beautiful daughters of Mnemosyne,
the longtime village scribe; his father-in-law would then be Musaios, who
came to the island as a young man with his parents, Kyntheia and Endymion.
Although they had since gone on to Elysium, their articulate sons were still
instrumental to annual rituals, Haroun as an orator, Musaios as a poet and
playwright. His wife Mnemosyne was sister to Elithyia the doula, along with
Phaedo, a plasterer, all three of them from the late Amaltheia and Aegipan.
Phaedo married Sutra, a daughter Kristos and his deceased wife, Miriam,

who was manager of the bindery; they had Seneca and his younger brother
Hemlock, also in attendance at the initiation. As nephew of Mnemosyne,
he would become cousin to Diomedes by the latter's marriage to Kalliope.
Idomeneus of Kriti, the remaining participant, I recognized by reputation,
or as an acquaintance; a giant in stature, eyes aflame with animal wildness,
albeit no threat to me personally. We exchanged introductions and friendly
conversation regarding our plans for the still-provisional end of winter,
but the ambience had grown apprehensively solemn by Aeiolus' arrival.
"A perfect evening," he declared in greeting. "You should give thanks;
last year, the ceremony fell on a night much colder than this,
which can make the experience ever more challenging."
We walked in the open toward Delos across the calico cobbles lining
Cattle Drive Cove, beneath the vibrant incipience of sunset as he told of the
Delphinion oracle's decree that no births or deaths would occur thereon.
Near the island's northern end, we stopped at a depression in the dunes
where a small fire of reeds, grass, and driftwood had been laid; motioning
for us to sit around it, our hierophant led us through breathing exercises
and sacred Tibetan chants; then, after a prolonged silence, he spoke again.
"A tribe called the Kogi once dwelled in the high mountains of Colombia;
the elder brother of modern civilization, according to their mythology,
and watched with horror as their younger sibling consumed the earth on
which both cultures depended. Kogi shamans believed themselves directly
responsible for helping mother nature maintain a harmonious balance by
their actions in the spirit world, accessed through ritual and meditation.
These gnostic warriors, who peacefully contended with the depredations
of their little brother in mystical realms, were chosen at birth and taken
inside a cave where they spent nine years in preparation for the weighty
obligation of ensuring the continuation of our universe as they knew it.
The *mamas* thus grew up in almost total darkness whilst elders taught them
mysteries of creation; and at the end of this training they left the chamber
to behold for the first time a daylit world that was previously unimaginable.
While we might like to think ourselves a sort of resurrected elder brother in
their stead to the society across the sea, our isolated village is not the Kogi.
We do not possess millennia of unbroken traditional wisdom to build upon;
since our connections to ancestors, homeland, and heritage were severed
we've seen ourselves as spiritual orphans, cast into a vast, unfamiliar abyss,
searching inveterately for salvation, purpose, or identity, though they never
seem to come easily. We borrow ceremonial elements from extinct societies
or concoct inelegant practices on our own, for the sake of future progeny
who may someday revive the cultural inheritance whereof we are deprived.
Those young Colombian shamans abided their entire childhoods in ulterior
senses before introduction to the visible universe; you, on the other hand,
have experienced the world of sunlight that life harvests from your birth.
You will now witness the dimensions of eternity, whose membrane hitherto
has been concealed from view. Until you make it, the journey is indefinable;
afterward, even more so; yet the name thereto we give is entheogenesis,
from the Greek for origin of the divinity within us; and if you are willing,
the vo-yage ahead might epitomize the imperatives of your existence."
Aeiolus withdrew a pouch from his knapsack, containing a quahog shell,

ENTHEOGENESIS · Origin of the Divinity within Us

some twine, and a few pieces of wood, identifiable as cedar by their smell, like his library shelves. Whispering a prayer of intent, he looped the cord over the ends of a bow, inserted a spindle perpendicular to the axis of an arrow, twisted half a turn so it was tightly wrapped at the midpoint, then said, "When you wish to summon the power of fire, you should first ask," prior to enacting a miracle, albeit common technique amidst our past, that certainly would have helped me if I had such during my Burbarian exodus. He laid a small, flat shake of cedar on the sand with charred notches along its edges, beneath one of which he next slipped a thin flake of birch bark. Clenching the fireboard with gnarled, prehensile toes, he placed the tip of his interlaced stick into this opening, holding the clam shell down on its top end whilst he sawed the bow back and forth. The cord encircling the spindle forced it to twirl, sunwise on the push stroke, opposite on the pull. Going slowly at first, the wooden pieces squealed as they rubbed on each other; his pace accelerated, then they began humming. Soon a tendril of smoke curled up from the scrap of bark below; once it grew into a ribbon, he transferred the tiny cone of charred dust thence created to a finely-shredded nest of milkweed pods and cattail heads. The ember glowed as he blew, more intensely with every breath, thus engulfing him in a cloud of smoke; after the seventh, it burst alight. Aeiolus raised the burning tinder, flames licking his fingers, to proclaim, "Give thanks and praise," before tucking it inside the heart of the tepee he had previously constructed. We watched silently as the blaze took hold; when established in earnest, he poured a glass jar of liquid into a charred kettle, setting this on the fire. "Our endeavor here is to transcend within mere generations the civilization whence we came, which lays just a few miles away, and whose mythology depicts itself as the apotheosis of creation. Despite this masturbatory fixation upon cultural aggrandizement, in comparison to the rest of life, it bears a striking resemblance to the organization of ants and termites. These are also socially stratified, with a small royal class upheld by castes; they can achieve staggering population densities, stripping habitat bare, then conquering new territory. They employ armies, make war, and invade foreign colonies; enslave their neighbors, build skyscrapers, and rely on air conditioning. Although intelligence is an indefinite, subjectively evaluated quality, biologists around the world would once have agreed that insects exhibiting conformity to swarm behavior, while remarkably prosperous in their range, biomass and diversity, are far from the nature's greatest achievement of societal complexity. Rather than in our own kingdom, I believe we must look beyond animals for such communities; amongst fungi, the intricate invisible reticulum interconnecting all living things. We are inclined to only notice them when they form fruiting bodies for dissemination of their spores; yet the fungi permeate our soils, constantly replenishing them via transubstantiation of organic matter and minerals. Most plants on this planet depend on mycorhizal or endophytic symbiosis, an intercourse by which disparate organisms interpenetrate each other to synergistically exchange nutrients for energy, through a matrimony so complete they may be indistinguishable at their concrescence. Fungi join mutually beneficial partnerships with algae to beget lichens, entwined to such an extent that they resemble neither of their component organisms, and serve as environmental pioneers, leading the succession of novel species in extreme environments where none could elsewise survive. Mycelia provide the mind as well as the immune system of forests and grasslands, supporting their ecology with a language of biochemical messaging whose development we have barely started to comprehend. In addition to acting as universal allies and neural network of the world, they are its most versatile lifeforms, inhabiting any place from volcano rims to arctic icepack, from the highest altitudes to the deepest depths; they are first to colonize areas sterilized by radioactivity; and some will even endure space travel – all of which are ambitions of humanity. Moreover, the fungi respond to attenuate our pollution, by mineralizing heavy metals or digesting toxic waste. Within the span of my existence, these intrepid organisms have found novel metabolic pathways to break down substances that scarcely existed for as long, ranging from the polymers of plastic to an arsenal of chlorinated biocides unleashed by industrial agriculture.

Yet humans are still the only earthly beings of whom we know able to intentionally heal their own evolutionary destiny. We may become victims of history, passively committing suicide by inactivity; or we may choose, here and now, to revision our relationship with the environment. If we should seek instruction from our surroundings in designing a novel future, let us do so in the fungal kingdom; hence I think it fitting that the agent whereby we shall attain entheogenesis tonight is a member thereof. Behold psilocybin, your endophyte of consciousness and guide to the all-encompassing, primordial magic better known as god."

Aeiolus opened a jar of mushrooms submerged in viscous honey, inhaled their earthy aroma, then passed them around the circle, shifting the concoction he had been simmering on the fire aside to cool. "Civilization distinguishes itself with religion, an institutionally-imposed mentality that would locate the divine outside ourselves; yet the quest for entheogenesis is an inclination shared by nearly all other cultures, and is among the defining influences in the unique phylogenetic path of our kind. The Kogi shamans used years of sensory deprivation to elicit epiphany in light of our mundane. Tribes of the Amazon rainforest brewed ayahoaska, a purgative tea of magical neurochemistry by which they cured illness and learned the medicinal applications of myriad plants. In Mexico, indigenous Americans ate mescaline-containing cacti to gain metaphysical insights. Natives of the lands currently known as the United States fasted and resisted sleep during their vision quests; conducted purification rites in sweat lodges; or mutilated their skin with piercings and dances to connect with the creator if non-endogenous sources of inebriation were unavailable. Indigenous Siberians drank the urine of their shamans, made hallucinogenic by the digestion of fly agaric mushrooms; while those of equatorial Africa took the bark of iboga for information from an overarching non-human intelligence; and although we have not fully confirmed what it contained, ancient Greeks imbibed a sacramental elixir called kykeon amidst a series of rituals to encounter their mysteries at Eleusis. There are many routes, some gentler or darker, but their goal is the same; to gain the wisdom of gods who reside within us. Absent other entheogenic catalysts, people have resorted to more hazardous methods, such as asphyxiation by fumes, ingesting datura, or blind abuse of synthetic psychoactives in pursuit of this eternal knowledge. We are blessed to find a vehicle in psilocybin, whose effects benefit the body, and whose teachings are compatible with human cognition because it is a close analogue of our neurotransmitters; a fortuitous pharmacological conjunction, considering that we have been separated from the fungi for the majority of a billion years' of evolution since divergence from our common single-celled ancestor." He stirred honey from his jar into the pot one deliberate spoonful at a time, handed out turtle shells, then made offerings of incense to the elements: lavender blossoms to the east, dawn, spring, ocean, and emotion; leaves of bay laurel to the south, day, summer, sun, and creativity; rose petals to the west, sunset, autumn, wind, and introspection; pine resin to north, night, winter, earth, and wisdom. Wielding a bundle of sage and tobacco, he smudged us, along with our brew, as we each approached his altar in turn; when mine came I whispered, "Don't go easy on me; I know my way around." Shooting me a sidelong glance, Aeiolus filled my carapace to its brim, then served himself the rest. As we stared at our vaporous reflections, he rolled a sweet-smelling herbal blend in corn husk; after holding the spliff betwixt thumb and forefinger for a while, he lit it off a phragmites stalk from the fire. "By this smoke, we send intentions to psilocybin. I suggest you seriously contemplate what you wish to learn and where you need to invoke power, because if you ask sincerely, the mushroom will fulfill every spell you cast." He pulled slow and deliberately, mingling his exhalation with steam from the brew before passing to his left. Upon receipt, I gave thanks for my life, summoning strength and discipline to claim my place as a man of the tribe. 'Please challenge me to discover how my abilities might best be utilized; help unveil my potential as I strive to be the equal of what life requires; and let Bridget notice me in so doing, if this be your desire,' I prayed. Once it had circled back to him, Aeiolus dropped the roach in the coals. "Now take this, all of you, and drink it. This is haoma, from the chalice of an immemorial and reciprocal covenant, given for you and for all beings so human evolution may continue. Do this in memory of our species." Nodding, he lifted his grail; then we followed suit. The tea tasted sweet with honey and sour from lemon juice, which I later learned was to dissolve the effective alkaloids, thus facilitating their absorption. It had spiciness due to the ginger added for allaying nausea, and a leafy flavor from coca, included to keep us alert. The acrid nuttiness came from harmala seeds, whose monoamine oxidase inhibitors would potentiate the mushrooms that floated in the beverage, imparting to it flavors of earth and must. After we finished, Aeiolus collected our shells. "You are likely to feel a bit strange at first," he warned. "You may get cold, weak, or nauseous; these are all normal parts of the process, but I assure you they will soon pass. My experience has shown, if conscientiously administered and prepared, psilocybin consistently provides a psychonaut the pilgrimage er deserves. When your journey becomes scary or unpleasant, I encourage you to push through, remembering you are not apt to find true wisdom without effort; the best advice I have is: breathe deeply, give thanks, and pay attention. Albeit best undertaken alone, you can ask me for assistance if needed." Oily darkness crept across a clear sky wherein the moon had not yet risen;

I lay on my back, watching stars appear and listening as our blaze crackled. The fungus made its presence readily evident via visceral sensations much more in the foreground than during psychoactive excursions of my past, akin to an internal tickling. I heard Hemlock yawn, and Aeiolus declared, "So it begins." Initially my eyes watered; then their focus became sharper, clearer, and brighter. My surroundings seemed saturated by weird energy; the nervous fluttering within, not unlike lust, intensified until it threatened to split my brain apart. I curled into a ball, orbital sockets buried by fists whilst pulsating four-dimensional matrices dominated my sight; finding next that these persisted before my open eyes. Closing their lids again, I was immersed in an illuminated stream of mythic icons and images from my former life metamorphosing faster than I could process them. I felt the gazes of people I knew upon me; although I had hidden my own from view, I still saw Aeiolus circling us, gesticulating like a conductor to conjure out of thin air a mucilaginous ultraviolet fluid whence our group's visions arose. He wore a shark's head as a helm, his face encased in its teeth, with extra eyes looking skyward and a fin projecting from between his shoulder blades.

"Follow your breath," he advised.

In needed of the reminder, I urged my contracted muscles to relax; they were challenged to do so, since I felt a massive snake coiling wildly inside me and the same alarming weightlessness I could recall from my freefall.

Entering a state in which the position of my eyelids made no difference, synaesthesia coalesced as an intelligible journey. I will attempt to describe my travels and what happened; yet words are bound to prove inadequate because so much that I was told lies beyond my limited verbal capacity.

I met myself cowering behind a dumpster at the dead end of a smog-filled alley in a hot, humid, horribly distorted version of Manhattan. Dark plumes obscured the sky, while flames leapt through the filthy shards of blood and bullet bespattered windows in buildings that loomed malevolently above me. Choking stertorously, I crawled toward the street, drawn there by a roar, but blindly leaned over a precipice, lost my balance, and fell into a mass of sweaty human bodies, writhing like maggots at the chasm's bottom. I caught haunting glimpses of those who knew me as they called out, only to be shoved down, climbed upon, or elsewise submerged in the sea of flesh. Looking across, I realized we were moving inexorably, as on a conveyor; ahead of us, people tumbled into an enormous meat grinder at its far end. A mushroom beckoned from atop the opposite side, and I steeled myself to traverse the abject horde. They grabbed my ankles, wailing as I passed, though I could not help them; focused on the goal, teeth gritted, I inched forward one limb at a time and reached the far wall. After scaling this, I rolled on my back, nauseated by the ordeal, where the fungus emerged from pavement. I knelt down before it, wondering how such an organism could survive in that hostile place; then a voice spoke to me telepathically.

What have you done? psilocybin asked.

I haven't done anything, I responded, startled.

Why? Was there nothing you could do?

I didn't know what to do; it all happened so fast, I thought, as if I was representing all humanity for judgment by an emissary of the gods.

You had everything you could desire; a world of infinite beauty, prosperity,

and diversity, the envoy said. *If you honored these gifts, they might have sustained you forever, yet you carelessly destroyed them instead. I came here to stop you from destroying yourselves as well, but fear I am too late.* Grievous screams emanated from the abyss below, and I began crying also. *It cannot be too late,* I begged. *Surely there is another chance? I cannot change what has been done, and regrettable events are in motion that now won't be stopped; all you can save is the seed of what remains. How?* I wondered, wiping my tears. *Do you accept this responsibility? With everything I am, or will be,* I swore gravely. *Then you must promise to prevent this from happening again. On all that I hold dear,* I declared. *What shall I do? If you look from my perspective, I will show you.*
Bowing down, I felt compelled to carefully bite the cap off the mushroom, and as I chewed violent vibrations erupted; I wanted to vomit from the pressure of an inexorable liquid coursing through me, yet I was turned inside out instead by the fungus assimilating my body. I drew into a ball atop the concrete whilst mycelia crept over my organs, transforming and digesting them. My mind dissolved; in its place grew another mushroom; then my point of view shifted to that of a spore clinging to the underside, whence I observed my own dematerialization. A breeze sent me adrift, floating up through smog clouds and into the stratosphere, separated from me by a hermetically-sealed spherical bubble of transparent membrane. I watched as the fireline ate steadily outward, consuming whole continents; oceans blackened with ash, then vaporized, leaving scorched crust behind. To my dismay, the harder I yearned, the further away my world receded. *Be patient,* psilocybin urged. *You must wait until this storm has passed, and protect the treasures contained within so that spring may come again. You are the future; when the time is ripe, I will help you find your way home.* After it was fully burned, the distant globe began disintegrating and collided with the moon, whose orbit had decayed. Spewing molten fragments into space, Earth formed a revolving disc of debris, then split apart completely to join a flattened dust cloud that reached past the asteroid belt. A faint haze extended beyond this, formed from the atomization of Jovian planets as the sun dimmed, slowing its spin and losing definition in a dispersion of plasma. I gradually became aware of other voyagers traveling beside me: Hemlock, Diomedes, Idomeneus and Aeiolus; Bridget and Airmed; but also deceased heroes such as Judas, Gandhi, Vavilov, and Terence McKenna. Although I called out to them, the space between us transmitted no sound. Suddenly the nebulous remains of our star exploded, throwing us apart into vacant reaches of the galaxy, except for Terence, whose trajectory coupled with mine in a dance akin to binary system orbiting a shared center of mass.
"How can you still be here?" I exclaimed, perplexed by his presence.
A prescient grin spread over his face as he pointed at a supernova shock front hurtling toward us, across the Milky Way. "Everything is changing into something else. Nothing is wrong; everything is on track." Raising his hands, he grabbed the crown of his head, then split his skull in twain, wherefrom a mushroom emerged, covering his limbs with its hyphae. Upon being struck by the radiant blast wave, this fungus and my ethereal

vehicle both evanesced like a plume of spores; whilst dissociating into tiny particles myself, I listened to the bard calling, as from the bottom of a well, "Nothing lasts....but nothing is lost..."

My perception persevered absent physical form, and I realized what I had seen, albeit destruction on its surface, was just the formation of my solar system depicted in reverse. Entering a transpersonal void, I comprehended ineffable lessons about the nature of universe in direct communion with the sacred forces that animate matter and overcome entropy, known as life, love, or god. I understood there is no real ownership, even of our bodies; my soul comprised a mere droplet amidst an ocean of consciousness, which borrowed a handful of atoms and bonded them with sunlight to incarnate the fleeting avatar my ego would inhabit for one lifespan before rejoining an infinite realm. After my cataclysmic vision of our world, this grasp on my own insignificance gave me solace. I knew with absolute confidence I had the ability, as well as the responsibility, to accept impending events; I felt the intrinsic ambition to do so surging through me; and I gave thanks for the opportunity to collaborate in whatever destiny might hold; then found myself being pulled downward, as if by the bucket once tied to my ankle whilst crossing a riptide, but in a sea of twinkling stars this time.

I landed lightly on a beach, where I heard a soft breeze stirring dry blades of grass, punctuated by waves lapping gently. Inhaling, my spirit reentered its corporeal vessel, facing the risen full moon. Pleasant ripples of purple, blue and green ebbed across my vision as I returned to the support of sand beneath me, at peace due to my awareness that I would not be required to get up yet. Aeiolus' squeezed my ankle, and the sensation was comforting.

"Are you back?" he whispered.

"I am," I replied, then added with neither premeditation nor doubt, "Terence didn't die; he went to be immortalized in a psilocybin mushroom."

"Indeed," the shaman agreed. "The Palmer Eldritch effect."

I sensed him moving around the circle and listened to murmurings of my fellow psychonauts. During the decompression, I ruthlessly purged cultural programming from my psyche, amputating extraneous baggage still clinging from childhood but not serving me. I negotiated with my subconsciousness, whose thematic maze unfolded imagery of sex and children, thus accepting reproductive urges, as well as the nostalgic desire to redeem my parents' marriage by creating the family environment we never had. Aeiolus built up the fire later, until it roused us sufficiently to sit up from our sandy beds. Gazing at each other through the flames, there were no words necessary; wide-eyed stares and smiles of recognition revealed the lessons learned. He invited us to recapitulate our visions; judging myself as relatively lucid, I began, with the inevitable omission of my lustful musings on his daughter. Talking proved to be another tryp entirely, in that the telling of it became my journey for a stretch. Presuming to describe eons of cosmic experience with such clumsy abstractions as the phonemes I could form seemed futile; yet in the process I grokked my mouth as an instrument of symbolic magic - our specie's first, in fact. Whilst my fluency increased, the witness in me left its home to join hominid ancestors, early in their exploration of psilocybin. Seeing my modern-day self render the entity therein from the distant past, we shared a common fascination with the future possibilities of linguistics.

Whereas he had not visited urban settings in his mortal life, what Diomedes depicted verbally conjured the uncanny impression of an opulent America from the turn of the century. He portrayed its crowded shopping malls like livestock farms, whose populace reeked of fear; wallowed in their own waste; consumed diets devoid of real nutrition, more akin to fuel than food, which could bring no lasting satisfaction; and hid their faces behind masks. "As I walked among them, the people stared ominously, confusing me; then I noticed that I was naked," Diomedes explained. "They followed closely once I moved to flee, but it was only the shadow of my fear chasing me. Realizing this, I turned to confront the mob, who had become machines - noisy, insectile drones of plastic, metal, and flashing lights, seemingly bent on inserting probes into my brain through my eyes, ears, or nose. Soon one reached out to grab me; I struck it down, thus finding myself embroiled in combat, fending them off with severed limbs of their own kind. Although uncoordinated and slow enough to neutralize, the horde came forth ceaselessly. I gained the high ground by allowing their corpses to accumulate, climbing atop them until a mountain had grown beneath me. From there, I could repel them from all sides simultaneously, whilst gravity disposed of the bodies; but looking down from the summit, I saw the mob was as vast as an ocean, extending to the horizons, and I feared I would be forever trapped by this siege. Dark clouds gathered at the sky's edges; then a concentric ring of energy imploded, an electric ripple in reverse, paralyzing the machines on approach. Some of those that still strove for footholds turned toward the pulse just before it struck and were transfixed like stone in apparent disbelief. When the circle finally collapsed upon me I did not feel afraid; after its blinding flash, a beam of healing light passed through my heart, from the Earth's core to galactic center. At last I was transported back here again, with mind and orifices mercifully intact."

"I experienced a similar conflict," Idomeneus segued, "but rather than machines, my adversaries were hirsute, two-legged monsters who looked vaguely like us and ate human flesh. They bound me, amongst many others, in a dungeon for the gratification of their appetites, where I feigned injury, hence lulling its wards into a false sense of security to effect my escape. I somehow knew that they meant to use my organs as part of an execution ritual; seizing the knife after it was drawn, I slashed the beast that held it, then cut myself open and ate my own liver, to prevent them from doing so instead. It made me tremendously powerful; not quite able to fly, while strong enough to leap over buildings. I broke my fellow inmates' chains, smote the guards, and when those who surrendered begged me for death, I gave it to them. Although horrified by the blood on my hands, in the end I remembered our specie was wrought in a traumatic past. I swam from the prison washed by hope that studying our inherent violence might allow us to influence the sway this legacy holds over our fate. Insatiable impulses have left us no predators, and we've been fighting among ourselves for control of resources ever since, self-aware yet enslaved by facile illusions of isolation. I suppose this is where we choose to be extinct, or rewrite our propensity for war, since it has no future here, through conscious self-domestication." Hemlock, who had seemingly gone through the most arduous journey of all, spoke next. "It began with the arrival of strange folk from across the sea,

whose faces were swollen from hydrocephalus, verging on alien," he said. "They came upon a great raft of rusted metal, wracked by terrible sickness. I went with them to bring a cure to their homeland; although I knew not what it contained, the box that I carried seemed important and I worried about failure. Due to an engine malfunction, we ran out of food en route; absent rain, we resorted to drinking our urine; then people began dying off. Thinking we had been stranded for eternity, I passed the time by painting in my imagination with the wind, which would not save us for want of sails. I discovered that by shaping the view ahead I could move the ship toward its destination, albeit without any volition, thereby manifesting worlds of death, disease, and despair involuntarily. Enormous excavators denuded mountain ranges to cover the maggoty corpses filling desert valleys below. Tractors drilled in crops on top of them, tended by gaunt children in chains, yet these turned yellow, then withered, before they bore fruit. I saw it all in the company of fancily-attired, well-fed aristocrats who wore masks for the ubiquitous stench and netting to block the flies, but offered neither, instead looking at me as if to ask what they should do. Having no ideas, I hopefully opened the chest I still lugged, only to find emptiness within. An overwhelming sense of disappointment dropped me to my knees; then I submitted to the purge, regurgitating a completely new reality whence Aeiolus intervened. Cannabis brought me home, thankfully, and the ambience of my experience was completely changed thenceforth."
Allowing an appropriate pause, Aeiolus told us, "It is remarkably unusual for an initiation to be so consistently drastic or traumatic in character." After he hit the pipe to which Hemlock referred, it passed around the circle. "Nevertheless, I often find that the darker realms of psychonautics afford us the most fertile ground for growth. I had a revelation analogous to yours in another life, just before the Exchange, whereby I watched an android army throwing piles of books onto infernal fires deep inside the netherworld. Endless phalanxes of naked people, with their eyes, ears, and mouths sewn shut, marched from a crag above; falling into the flames they screamed, squirmed briefly, then were consigned to the heap of coals. There was a serpent hiding in a crevice, who told me to assemble a library; I did as she said, and a plague of amnesia disguised as machine memory subsequently relegated human wisdom to the dustbin. From what we've seen tonight, I can only suspect the lords of war are mobilizing yet again, and that this time it will be our specie's very subsistence on their pyre."
I had also noted, while each of us reported a uniquely personal vision, underlying threads of confinement, human death, and food scarcity tied them together. Soaking in the afterglow, we relaxed with cognizance that despite the horror, we would survive to see sunrise; as psilocybin rewarded our perseverance through the night with a sense of gratitude and vitality. Standing for the first time since twilight, I walked to the island's terminus, where opposing waves converged on what might have been the utmost end of the earth. Warm air blew off the moonlit water, for which I was glad, as I savored the gifts the gods saw fit to bestow on me. Aeiolus' figure eventually beckoned from downwind; recognizing the odor of the spliff he offered upon reaching my side, I accepted it and inhaled indulgently.
"We've never smoked together before," I observed aloud.

"I'm aware," he replied. "It doesn't happen much anymore, except on nights like these, that I partake of the herb."
"What's your objection in ceremony?"
"I discourage initiates from smoking before the peak because the tryp then tends to take on a recreational atmosphere, which does not in my opinion befit the occasion; and particularly for those with less tolerance, marijuana is so psychoactively potent alone it can render the teachings of tryptamines incomprehensible. However, I find it reliably attenuates psychic crises or distracting nausea if they should arise, and is helpful afterward for returning to earth, during the integration phase."
"I really do just love a good joint, though," I remarked.
"Me too," he admitted, "yet it's such a prodigal use of cannabis. Paracelsus said with any substance the size and frequency of dosage make the difference betwixt medicine and toxin. More often than not, as in the case of herb, less is more; in yours specifically, I'd guess it isn't always serving you."
His feedback was subtly-put and well-timed; were I sober, I probably would have rejected it out of hand, but in that moment I felt receptive.
"I did benefit from the hiatus," I told him, truthfully so; given a mere week of abstinence, my chi and mental focus had increased markedly.
"Whereas it seems like a while, you're still at the beginning," he chuckled, passing the spliff as we admired the moonlit waves, shoulder to shoulder.
Their ghostly beauty impelled to interrupt the surf's rhythm with words.
"This really is a special place," I declared, just because it deserved saying; though endeavoring to be profound, my admiration sounded naive to me.
Aeiolus grunted affirmatively nonetheless. "I love to meditate here at the interface of the elements, whose alchemical interaction begets all life."
"It's a pity we can't appreciate all four at once, in the full splendor of day."
"That may change, if there is any merit to our visions," he noted.
I shivered at the inevitably cruel implications of his premonition.
For nine months since inheriting Mrs. Jefferson's library, I had believed I would bear witness to cataclysm; yet his statement and my intuition both suggested it might come sooner than anticipated. While he never said so, I thought Aeiolus considered me an informal apprentice; he apparently wanted to transmit noesis, thus emboldening me to inquire in this vein.
"Speaking of which, I couldn't help but notice that you didn't share yours."
"My vision?" The question notwithstanding, he knew what I meant.
"Mine is the same as I've had for half of this earthly existence."
"Of what?" I asked, pressing against his reticence.
"How I'm going to die," he replied, hitting the spliff.
"Oh...I'm sorry," I responded, in a voice fraught with awkwardness.
"There is no need to be; I take it as practice, wherefore I'm glad."
"Practice for death?"
"Of course. I may only get one more chance, and I intend to use it wisely."
"Isn't it sort of depressing, to spend your life preoccupied with the end?"
"Why? Life's purpose is to die; ultimately, it is the sole phenomenon in the world that can. We are conceived, we breathe, and we are transformed."
Aeiolus rubbed his head pensively. "Besides, I'm not convinced of the end."
"Nothing lasts, but nothing is lost," I added, hearing an echo of my voyage.

He nodded in approbation. "Thanks be to Terence, for showing us the way. In my passages through the membrane, I've met entities who transcend our boundaries between consciousness and environment. Whether gods, spirits, or extraterrestrials, they shape the fabric of a dimension beyond linear time; whereas we mortals incarnate over and over until we can move on in a manner that does justice to prior attempts, thus allowing our souls to find peace. I know now what I must do for my own, and have enjoyed the privilege of expecting my death for the better part of my life." From Latin, *ex-spectare*, 'to look at utterly', I thought, recalling my perusal of the etymological dictionary. A great sadness welled up then, leaving me reluctant to further probe the depths he navigated with cool resolution.

"I pray that I may be ready," is all I said, passing him the joint.

"At this rate, you will be." He received it from me again and paused, as if contemplating a change of subject. "Since you 'know your way around' psychedelics, I'm curious to hear how the dosage treated you this evening."

I exhaled audibly. "I'd say I got somewhat more than I bargained for."

Aeiolus laughed at this. "So what did you imbibe, whence you came?"

"Everything, especially the phenethylamines; nexus and X, usually."

He trembled visibly. "Frightening stuff."

"Did you take them much?" I asked.

"It was still mostly Adam on the lot back in my day; yet I did enough of the later substitutions also, by design and by accident, to develop an opinion."

"Which is what?" I prodded.

"That I need synthetic psychedelics in me even less than artificial colors, preservatives, or pesticides. They are on the dark side of consciousness; black magic, to my mind." He spoke forcefully, with perceptible concern.

"Psilocybin is totally different from trolling," I concurred. "It strikes me as something people would have difficulty consuming recreationally."

"It's not a drug in the modern sense, but a cure; hence the threat posed to the status quo and why it was the most efficaciously persecuted sacrament, after its agglomeration with narcotics via the Controlled Substances Act."

"Preposterous, because there is no comparison," I went on. "Drug use is passive; this experience, on the other hand, has been participatory, humbling, challenging, and compellingly organized. I've confronted plenty of strange beings and settings before; yet tonight was like living out dreams in worlds as real as ours, interweaving all of my senses."

"Therein lies the distinction I draw betwixt hallucinogens and entheogens. Hallucinations, derived from the verb 'to wander', are phenomena that do not exist outside the observer, constituting distraction; entheogenesis is a process of awareness expansion, whereby what we perceive emanates from and is an inextricable part of reality, albeit subliminal or unconscious at times. In some cases, a specific substance can manifest either effect, depending on how it's used and by whom, the disparity being in mindset or context. As Terence said, the universe is made of language; psychedelics provide intelligent prostheses to remind us; translation and assimilation of the message, however, remains the prerogative of their human vessel. If you were already intoxicated, partying, and happened to eat a handful of mushrooms, you might be entertained for a few profane hours; while if you cultivate yourself diligently, entering the psychonauticon with reverence, willingness, and discipline, you may just unravel the riddles of creation. We reap what we sow in entheogenesis, which is why ritual is essential; attuning us to interpret the lyrics beneath the surface, so we can hear the voices of gods offering sapient advice instead of abstract static."

"This felt like communication with another being...as if the fungus had a mind of its own, conferred to me through cerebral symbiosis."

"And it's a blessing; how else would we learn to administer it properly? The shamans with millennia of unbroken ceremonial heritage are gone."

"Aren't we nurturing a new ceremonial heritage?" I ventured.

"We've come a long way. I was about your age when I committed myself to the reciprocal interaction of our two species; although it isn't easy on me anymore, I have accepted that, and been ever served by the mushroom."

"The shaman is not merely a sick man..." I began, quoting Terence, "...or a madman; he is a sick man who has healed himself."

"So you've read the Invisible Landscape?" he deduced.

"I've started, albeit not as intelligible as his other work."

"True enough," he replied, smiling. "To heal is to make whole, meaning that separation is the only prerequisite; an endemic condition extending fractally from humanity's relationship with the earth to an individual's with ers soul."

A intriguing notion arose as he passed me the burning spliff.

"Terence died of brain cancer, did he not?" I asked.

"So the story says," Aeiolus gravely answered.

"Since he used entheogens as a lens, peering into our evolutionary future, the nature of his disease would seem a portent of his culture's destiny."

"According to rumor, his tumor grew in the shape of a mushroom."

This response confused me. "Are you insinuating psilocybin caused it?"

"If there is any insinuation, it's that the augury of omens is up to you. I tend to believe disease is at least the reflection of a spiritual imbalance; but if Terence's glioblastoma was spawned by something his psychonautic career, I think it would have been the petroleum solvents in his DMT, infused with residues of war, empire, and the petroleum economy."

"Weren't you an advocate of DMT as a politician?"

"Please, I beg you not to ascribe me that epithet! I was a performer then; as far being an advocate goes, I still am, perhaps more devotedly so; I just no longer utilize petroleum solvents, and I only administer it as pneohoaska, in compliance with the deiman's instructions."

"I didn't know you made DMT." The coveted prospect of encountering the elfin entelechies of Terence's transcultural hyperspace excited as much as it frightened me, lest I dare to state this with blasphemous tactlessness.

"There is far more you don't know, beginning with the fact that we all make DMT in our own brains, for the essential purposes of death and dreaming. It is a source of inspiration to help humans heal and reconnect with their origins, which presents itself to us as a constituent of myriad plant species."

"What is it like?" I wondered impetuously.

"A journey beyond verbal language; at its best, beyond identity. I can only concoct futile analogies, whereby I might say it's the gate to eternity, a tool of spiritual pupation, or naked intercourse with divinity; yet words fail to capture its brilliance. Above all, vaporized dimethyltryptamine is the portal to time travel, made navigable by the betacarbolines in our mykhoaska this

evening; the same that told ayahoaskeros of old the secrets of their forest."
"Are you serious?"
"Absolutely," Aeiolus assured me. "Humanity's most advanced vehicle is the soul, albeit still an embryo; ergo, tryps on the time machine are not to be taken lightly. I aspire to compile a new holy text of Terence's scripture, as a technical kit for the frontiers thereof, thence repurposing the biblical template to disseminate purgative medicine instead of placebo profanity."
"But religion is a cancer!" I protested.
"I know it well, and an interesting attribute of most cancer cells is their lack of differentiation, which means the potential to become any tissue in the body lies within the genome of each. Worship of salvationist icons is a creode so thoroughly-worn in the morphogenetic field of this specie that I'd expect us to have more success mutating our cultural predispositions into a psychic immune system than ignoring them or pretending they don't exist."
"And cast Terence as the new savior?"
"Here at the turning of ages, who else could it be?" Aeiolus retorted.
"I'm not sure how he'd feel about that," I contended. "Didn't he say 'ideology is toxic because it's an insult to the gift of human free thinking'?"
"That he did, yet for all the damage it has caused, ideology at its heart is just a science of ideas. Remember, everything is toxic and nothing is toxic, depending on the dosage. Besides, there isn't much free thought going on at the moment to be insulted by the notion; Terence certainly wasn't."
I found this hard to swallow, since the latter's death chronologically preceded Fremont's teenage self-initiation. "How do you know?"
"He had been resurrected to observe his eschaton in a Peruvian cave where I interviewed him and learned DMT extraction via biomass-based solvents."
Although this tale strained credibility I played along. "How did he respond?"
"It was the only time I've ever seen him speechless," Aeiolus said, grinning, "and I daresay the idea amused him. Terence was an explorer in uncharted waters, so he naturally met the concept of recorded guidance dubiously; yet the irony is not lost on he who, most of all, would proclaim that people need to be shown another way, considering their present circumstances."
Recalling the world of my past, whose laws ensured any entheogen would be eradicated or commodified, I realized no alternate path was available, let alone a map therefor. Dismantling my skepticism of their exchange, I conceded that Aeiolus' ostensibly perverse apotheosis of the iconoclast himself during his bardo embodied the logical fruition of his own poetry. All great wisdom traditions begin as cults; and Terence already achieved the externalization of consciousness he prophesied via digital storage.
"Not another way," I argued, "but THE way; I had no idea until tonight. Thank you for showing me...and for saving my life, for bringing me here, for the challenges, for all of this. There is no way I can ever repay you."
I handed him the roach and he reverently extinguished it; then, in a break from the formality to which I was accustomed, wrapped his arm around me. "Thank you for being here; I'm just glad you escaped with your brain intact. Incidentally, repayment is neither expected nor due. Darkness lies ahead, and to help them see the light our descendants will need people like you."

METAPSYKHIKOS TOMOS

A novel future from BRIAN LOVE

"Man's most human characteristic is not his ability to learn,
which he shares with many other species, but his ability to
teach and store what others have developed and taught him."

"Children must be taught how to think, not what to think."

~ Margaret Mead ~

"Those who know how to think need no teachers."

"Live as if you were to die tomorrow. Learn as if you were to live forever."

"God has no religion."

~ Mohandas Gandhi ~

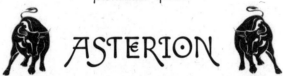

ASTERION

Under Airmed's aegis, four young women were also initiated that night,
whose visions proved psychically analogous to ours at Delos. Spurred by
the collective prophecy, she and her husband brought the tribe together
with the pretense of a feast to honor Ishtar, an ancient goddess of Venus,
fertility and warfare, slaughtering a spectacular black bull calf from Kriti
for this occasion. As venue they selected the outdoor Delphinion theatron,
enclosed by pioneer pine trees with laurel understory, where magnificent
terraced seating formed half of a bowl tucked in the cemetery hillside as if
some deity had removed a titanic scoop of earth via a swipe from the sky.
Spring's first new moon coincided on their agreeably-warm chosen date,
as well as peak blooms of multifariously-colored narcissus lining the paths.
Once everyone in attendance was served and seated, Aeiolus brought the
assembly to order with a short blast from his ceremonial horn. The rest
of the councilors were already arrayed in a semi-circular arc on the stage,
complementing the larger radius of the audience, at the center of which he
and Airmed had positioned themselves. This arrangement permitted any
speaker to be seen by spectators, along with ers fellow representatives.
"Friends and family, neighbors and compatriots, you comprehend, as do we,
the reality of our entheogenic voyages." He looked around to fan flames of
anticipation with his silent, monocular stare. "To anybody paying attention
there has never been much doubt of war coming someday to America, since
it is a law of civilization that one ill turn deserves another; however, insights
of this year's initiates seem to indicate such an exchange is all but upon us."
He briefly related the ambience and symbolism of our visions, previously told
in greater detail herein; then depicted a role for the village by apt analogy.
"We five hundred, amongst the half billion citizens of those United States,
are akin to one seed in a million. Compared to an acre sown with a bushel

of hemp, we are nearly nonexistent; and indeed, our chance for survival through any global military combat rests on hope that this tiny island is not worth the expense of a bomb. Our subconscious minds employ all kinds of machinations to convince us we have a choice in the matter of destiny, yet in this case I'd say our only option is to remain planted where nature has decided; praying for the best, while planning for the worst. We may fail to germinate; we may succumb to predation or pestilence; and we may prove infertile. None of these ends lie within our control, nor should they; nevertheless, the magic of plant cultivation is that a lone seed in a barren field can regenerate an entire crop, or even foster a distinct new variety. If we might someday thus serve the world, then so be it; our avowed quest, now as ever, is to perpetuate the qualities of humanity for this possibility."

Aeiolus next outlined steps to bulwark the tribe against nuclear disaster, which they opined was the likeliest forthcoming scenario, based on lessons garnered from studying the ecological repercussions of what WMD's life on Earth had hitherto survived. Their production plan for the imminent season would shift to bolster reserves of hay and staple foods, with corresponding reductions in spring plantings of fiber or cover crops. He also advocated retrofitting the lighthouses as fallout shelters, given their dense walls were inherently suited to efficacious blockage of neutron and gamma radiation; then he called for construction of the Ark - a climate-controlled gene bank for longterm preservation of the village's collected biodiversity, its most precious resource, which would be similarly shielded from potential fallout. Aeiolus suggested the forestry team disband temporarily, thereby applying all available labor to fortification of old infrastructure and seed production, the latter as indemnity for mortality that might eventuate during storage. When the industrial food supply system was disrupted, a repercussion he expected to arise summarily in such conditions, seed became one of the few tangible assets their tribe had to offer the mainland populace in trade. Lastly, he proposed a year moratorium on conception, because endurance of atomic winter in hibernation would be complicated by pregnancy or infants. In a subsequent round of clarifying questions about these recommendations, several people wondered why the community should rearrange its priorities around our vague visions, or else what seemed little more than a hunch. Aeiolus confessed the augury could mislead them; be that is may, if they adopted this plan its only drawback was a single-year overproduction of seed whilst villagers made permanent preparations for an always-looming eschatological threat; which had, as he argued, facilitated their original settlement. The consequences of not responding to our revelations in the event they were true, on the other hand, would be apocalyptic.

"Why all of this war-mongering?" one of the elder female councilors asked rhetorically at the outset of their discussion. "Have you not said yourself, esteemed father Aeiolus, it is the fear thereof that brings conflict upon us? Have we not purged those infectious influences from our culture by now?"

"My sister speaks my mind," added her neighbor. "Lest it be missed, I notice these visions arose under Aries, an omen of violence; while the ceremony occurred on your brother's birthday by the Gregorian calendar. Perhaps you've channeled him, and this foreboding is merely his restless spirit taking hold; would you bring the entire village down his fearful road?"

As waves of murmuring ran through the crowd, Aeiolus stood stoically, waiting for them to die. "And what do you know of it?" he finally shouted into the void. "Faithless is er who says farewell when the road darkens. If only I could wind rope like you can twist my words, old friends..." His broad grin verged on a snarl, showing a vindictive character as yet unknown to me; Airmed interjected midsentence with a hand on his chest. "Sisters, noble crones, you speak of fear; but you must know, as well as I, my dear brother Areis mastered his as no other who has lived in our midst. Furthermore, what my husband advises here is nothing similar to his path – whereas I still wish, at times such as these, the ethos he inspired might not have been banished from this island along with his personage. How readily you forget it was his defensive systems that twice saved our community."

She stopped deliberately, casting a pellucid gaze over the audience for whom her words were meant, though outwardly addressing the councilors. "Any failure in Areis' crusade is not his but ours, insofar as he was forsaken by this Council to ransom our safety. Yet without aid, and despite being betrayed, by death he achieved what he intended to do – have you? Your reply notwithstanding, I swear on the gods, if I had just one thought more to convey in this world before my final breath, it would regard the way you have desecrated my brother's grave today: for shame, ladies...for shame!"

Hearing shuffling, I turned to see Hemlock, Diomedes, and Idomeneus approaching my bench from above; we quietly exchanged gestures of greeting as the councilors argued among themselves in response to her elegantly elocuted, albeit emotively unsparing, disdainful diatribe. "Now that we've heard from Airmed and her husband, who purport ever to know more about the future than the rest of us..." another speaker began. "This truly is something else, isn't it?" Diomedes remarked, leaning forward so I could tell the comment was meant for me. "Look at Aeiolus; he's eager for a fight, and she's barely able to hold him back in light of her own anger." "I've never seen him like this," I allowed. "Even when he caught me..." I blundered, letting this trail off at the realization of my indiscretion. "Caught you what?" Idomeneus wondered, pressing me.

I was saved from the necessity of a lie by ominous whispers in the crowd, which parted down its centerline to permit the passage of a hooded figure, stooped from age, who descended the theater's steps with the assistance of a staff sheathed in snakeskin and crowned by a sharp-toothed seal skull. "Pytheia," their voices said as she turned to face us from the middle of the plaza, circumscribed by its ring of seated councilors. She bowed to them respectfully, then in an Alexandrine sonnet declaimed:

"The stranger repatriates to bring reminders
that we must admit illness before we can heal.
Whilst new beginnings use death as their disguises,
beautiful futures emerge from trauma and grief.
Have no fear, for all told here already transpires
yet by our imagination shall become real."

Although cataracts fogged her eyes, akin to Mrs. Jefferson's, I felt the oracle's stare burning into my soul during her exit. Those around me must have sensed it also, as they glanced with uncertainty or recoiled perceptibly. I saw Aeiolus scanning faces of his neighbors' to ensure

they understood; then, looking at me, his left eye winked inconspicuously. A town hall-style meeting followed thence, wherein hypothetical deferral of pregnancies proved the most provocative aspect of his presentation, especially for the handful of couples intending to conceive imminently. "Please believe that I am the last person who would want to restrict your choice to have offspring, and I will oppose any social pressure for abortion. I only ask aspiring parents to remember, while you certainly invest most, all progeny are the responsibility of the entire community, which is thus deprived of energy you must withdraw to support your child. Again, these portents may be misinterpreted; yet in your family planning, I implore you to contemplate the difficulties posed both by, and to, newborns in the aftermath of nuclear weapons, contrasted with the potential inconvenience of unnecessarily postponing for a single year." When the stack of speakers for facilitated conversation overflowed, Council moved toward formation of small groups. Although eligible to participate, I thought the format as described seemed agonizingly tedious; because I already felt uncomfortably self-conscious in the public eye and had no valid stake wherefrom to draw an opinion, I quietly slipped away.
"Not staying for the exercise?" Aeiolus chided as he caught up with me.
"I have so much to do," I replied, startled. "Spring has arrived; the first cut of hay is on the horizon; and we're not nearly ready for it in Arkadia."
"It's fine; I'm just kidding since frankly, I've always loathed formal process like these; not how I choose to participate, but if that's what makes some of them happy, so be it; helpful in the long run, I suppose, due to people more eagerly accepting new ideas if they can receive the credit therefor."
Shocked by his arrogance, simultaneously jaded and callous, I said nothing.
"Speaking thereof, how did my plan for the Ark strike you?" he continued.
"Where would we be if Noah had dismissed the voice of god as a schizophrenic hallucination?" I joked, relieved to lighten the mood.
"Or Utnapishtim, by the same token," he added. "I'd like you to build it."
I was surprised that he presumed to solicit my labor before Council even decided to approve the project and uneasily conveyed as much.
"Oh, they'll go along; our initiates have never led the village astray."
"Well, of course, I'll help however I can, once we have a grip on the vegetation at Will's," I offered, with tangible trepidation.
He shook his head. "Not good enough; I meant for you to lead the crew."
"I'm just a laborer," I noted, taken aback when I realized the seriousness of this request. "Surely you could find better qualified candidates..."
"True, but all their lives are much too complicated. You, on the contrary, have no attachments or distractions; neither farm nor family rely on you. I hope, for your sake, that it isn't forever; yet in the moment, you are single as far as I can tell, with youthful motivation to spare. What you might lack in experience is compensated by brilliance, discipline, and desire to learn. A project of this scale requires someone who is inexorably dedicated to its expedient completion. I've spoken with Will and Kristos; I've collaborated with you myself; I know perhaps more about your abilities than you do, which stem from the possession of an essential devotion to your work's quality as its own reward; and above all, you need the responsibility; initiated or not, this challenge will define you as a man of our tribe."

I told him I was intimidated, whereupon he cut me off with a scoff. "If you weren't, I wouldn't trust you; thus, all the more reason you are right for this. View it as a matter of convenience, since the project leans heavily on Amadeus, who will be staying in our house for hospice. Because you also live there, tremendous energy can be saved if you act as intermediary betwixt the engineer's brain and day-to-day humanifestation. In so doing, you may become the inheritor of his expertise, an obligation that someone must bear, and a honor for which you should be grateful." Musing on it as we walked, the prospect thrilled me despite my misgivings; I intuited that psilocybin had answered the prayer I made during initiation. "You hesitate?" he asked. "Do you honestly think I'd say this on a whim? I've considered the matter carefully and you have my complete confidence. Our tribe heard the oracle, while I've seen it written in signs from day one." A sense of dignity inspired me to clear my throat, then straighten my spine. "If you're so sure, I guess I'll have to give it a try." "Try not," he declared, glaring at me through his cyclopean eye. "Do, or do not. There is no try."

As Aeiolus predicted, Council accepted their plan; soon thereafter, Amadeus moved into the guest room. I slept in the library henceforth, since it was where I spent most of my evenings anyway; beyond a table for notes, an etymological dictionary, and my current reading materials, I required remarkably little space. Except for our exchange on the beach, I never really met the engineer, who seemed a legend in his own time after performing at the Pannyxia. Accounts of his accomplishments and technical ingenuity added to a larger than life stature in my mind, so I scarcely knew what to expect in person; yet it turned out that I liked him from the outset. Whereas his illness did not appear as severe as I had been led to believe, I imagined his copious use of tobacco was far from helpful. He approached the habit with a masochistic sort of determination, which Airmed allowed him to continue, astonishingly; while she drew the line at smoking inside. "It's a good thing, too," he told me sardonically, "because that's the sole reason I have to get out of bed. I'll gladly starve or soil myself, but if not for cigarettes, I'd probably just lay down and die." "They can't be good for you health, though," I ventured dubiously. "Hell yes," he argued. "Smoking gives me an edge on the cancer, by making my body an inhospitable environment." "Based on that logic, you might as well seek chemotherapy." "You know how long it extends the lives of terminal patients?" he asked; I shook my head. "Two measly months. You spend your last six, or more, puking, losing hair, wallowing in headaches, to gain two. Smoking tobacco is about quality of life for me; and when it comes to the coda, I'll still take quality over quantity. I'd prefer to die with my vices than from a remedy." He had an unruly gray beard, an oddly full mane of curly, unkempt hair, and an old, black motorcycle jacket he wore almost constantly, even in bed, with leather so weathered it looked ready to disintegrate in a stiff breeze; ostensibly inexplicable apparel for an invalid, in my opinion. On one of the rare occasions that our paths crossed at the shower, I saw the tattoo on his chest, which he said represented his view of modern society when applied.

A decapitated figure with an illuminated tablet in place of ers head sat astraddle a robotic bull, pursuing a fiery whirlwind of dollar bills. The mounted rider was wreathed by a maze of wires and electrical arcs; these faded into Amadeus' own network of blue veins, easily visible through his thin, translucent skin. A broad, mangy-feathered bird skeleton attacked from behind, clutching an assault rifle in the talons of one leg, disemboweling erm with the other, whilst feasting on bloody entrails as they unraveled.

"Is that a vulture?" I asked, pointing to the grotesque raptor carcass.

"Not quite, but close," he remarked. "It's supposed to be a bald eagle; sort of a misnomer, since they actually had plumage on their heads."

"I've heard of them, though not that they also ate carrion."

"They would if necessary; yet as hunters of fish and accumulators of toxins, the American eagles eventually fell prey to oceanic collapse." He chuckled sardonically. "The bird once appeared on the United States' coat of arms, its Great Seal, and all of the printed money via the so-called Federal Reserve emblem, but died out before I took it as my totem instead." When asked what the image meant, he claimed he had forgotten, saying "Figure it out, then let me know." I left feeling uncertain of whether this was intended as a koan. His bent spectacle frames rested askew on his face because he wanted them that way - "Crooked, like me," Amadeus quipped - and golden rings pierced his ears to symbolize his sub-equatorial sailing adventures. He spoke in the distinctive accent of Boston, his homeland; after I told him I had been walking there prior to my rescue, he jeered.

"What a cesspool...you would rather die on the beach."

In our initial design meeting, we enumerated the essential functions and components of the Ark, beginning with its various storage conditions. Orthodox seeds, which constituted a majority of the villager's crop species, would survive longer, with the least genetic deterioration, below freezing. Recalcitrant seeds, like citrus, as well as plants propagated vegetatively, from sweet potatoes to some succulents, would need cool temperatures and controlled humidity. Next came all the perennials that do not breed true to seed; the tribe's collected apple varieties, for example, could only reproduce from cuttings, implying a grow room to cultivate scion wood. This, in turn, necessitated a human resident, to care for the live plants whilst monitoring the climate in other compartments; automatic controls, even if they had been feasible to implement, might be paralyzed by the electromagnetic pulse of nuclear detonation, hence rendering our whole endeavor futile. The occupant, then, would require accommodations – living quarters, stockpiled food, basic kitchen and bathroom fixtures.

All of these parameters pointed to an underground structure, since the soil stayed consistently around fifty-five degrees starting about two feet below its surface. Such environs were optimal for rootstock preservation; acceptable for the grow room, if supplemented with heat hypothetically produced by lighting therein; and tolerable for the curator indefinitely. Most importantly, an earth-tempered structure would conserve power expended to keep the seed room cold, as opposed to above-grade building, which could be exposed to temperatures over a hundred degrees at times. Still, mechanical cooling remained the greatest challenge Amadeus foresaw. "It's going to need a lot of insulation and one hell of a heat pump," he said with a grin, referring to technology that fascinated me because it subverted the laws of thermodynamics. Heat, by definition, cannot move from a cold location to warmer, yet our device had to achieve precisely this effect; ergo, like life itself, surmounting an allegedly universal tendency toward entropy. In his former career as engineer of renewable energy equipment, he worked with geothermal systems using water for the transfer medium. To maintain seventy degrees in a temperate region is one thing; while we planned upon a walk-in-freezer, employing volatile refrigerant instead, and ours would be without access to the grid, thus running on a very limited electrical budget.

The Ark, in its entirety, was fundamentally conceived as a bomb shelter. Resistance to fallout demanded dense wall and roof assemblies, ideally of steel-reinforced concrete, plus interior linings of aluminum and lead, to shield against secondary ionization. A ventilation system would filter incoming air whilst creating positive pressure, thereby preventing inward leakage of atmospheric contaminants through any cracks in its envelope. Standard design practices called for a primary entrance to serve as airlock, along with an emergency exit concealed from the view of potential looters. Amadeus suggested some wise provisions for surveillance and security - "better primed than not, heaven forbid the need should arise," he said - as well as instrumentation to observe weather or radioactivity outside. With this list of features established, we briefly considered but rejected the notion to construct such an edifice from the ground up in favor of the old Omniscion wiring building near the textile mill. When Americans evacuated, Block Island had still been among a few in the northeast lacking any physical connection to the mainland; thus all phone calls to or from its numbered wires were converted to microwave on one side of the water, received by a tower opposite, then translated back to the signals carried along the physical network. Omniscion erected its own 130' pylon in New Shoreham for the purpose, at whose base lay a hub that once contained the company's power supply, terminals, routers, switches, and other hardware.

This structure, serving at the time as a defunct salvage shed, suited our project handily in many respects, being well on its way to a bunker already. The footprint was a 40' x 60' slab on grade, with 14' tall walls of concrete block covered by brick veneer. There were no windows openings and only a single door, fortuitously located on the uphill side, which we intended to backfill for thermal stability. After enclosure by a bulkhead stairwell, this subterranean entrance also functioned as the airlock. Whereas a fully-buried building would have been preferable, hilltop topography at Omniscion's site did not lend itself to this, in exchange for better exposure of wind turbines and less excavation. The best we could do was berm the north side, then cover the roof in soil, leaving the south wall above grade, along with about half of the east and west; a configuration that Amadeus thought a decent compromise, given the constraints imposed by reality. Conduit penetrations were available in abundance for the convenience of our utilities; albeit absent plumbing, we could run drains and supply lines through the bottom of the north wall before earthmoving, making these connections ultimately frost-proof. While hollow, the existing blocks had been laid with a full running bond so the cores of successive rows aligned; once poured solid, the building's shell would have a total 12" blanket of

radiation-absorbing mass comprising our first line of defense against fallout. Its roof, however, was another matter altogether; utterly cheap and nasty, akin to so much else of imperial media beneath the skin. Rusting I-beams held up a flat foamboard deck with leaky synthetic membrane, not nearly sufficient to support heavy mud a foot deep; even if they could, that would be an inconceivable amount of material to acquire, mix, and place - all told, almost a hundred cubic yards, or 350,000 pounds. We next considered a shallow pond upon a thin slab to effectively absorb nuclear decay particles; yet the span proved impractically long for this, by requiring the horizontal concrete to resist potentially heavy snow loads atop its own dead weight. Our ultimate decision comprised an asymmetrically domed roof design, cast via hybridization of ferrocement and pre-tensioned methodologies. At 6" in finished thickness, the vault needed relatively little cementitious material, but due to the inherent strength of arched structures, it could easily withstand an additional two feet of earth, plus a sizable allowance for accumulated ice or moisture. To counterpose the outward thrust, we would retain what remained of the extant flat roof as a shear plane tied to the walls, then thoroughly braced, which eventually became the frame of an insulated drop ceiling. Our soil depth called for a parapet that acted as a bond beam, poured monolithically with block cores and first layer of ferrocement, to reinforce the edge whilst providing a drainage channel. The original deck did afford good scaffold for the formwork, most doubling as reinforcement – an inverted basket of woven steel bars covered in taut hemp mesh. Given proper moisture content, sufficient grout oozed through to permit simultaneous stuccoing over the underlying cage from below.
When the dome's rough coat had set, it would be topped with a matrix of salvaged cables connected to and tensioned by anchors cast in the still-wet forms of our parapet wall, thus incorporating the stiffness of a prestressed slab after grouting. Two layers like this were to be applied over the base, followed by waterproofing, then three thousand wheelbarrowfuls of earth.
For the emergency exit we settled upon a concealed hatch in the ceiling, accessed via a sort of attic left betwixt the flat deck and dome's underside. By making a beveled knockout opening at its summit, later filled by a plug only removable from below, our roof permitted somebody to tunnel out if necessary; soil, sod, and whatever ice might sit atop them would fall into the Ark as its occupant dug, the escape eased with gravity in ers favor.
Omniscion's hub was particularly accommodating because it had once been run on a 48 volt battery, ensuring continuous phone service to islanders in the event of a power outage. Absent regular charging and maintenance, the original lead acid cells did not last long beyond their desertion; but an 80 kilowatt backup diesel generator installed around 12 A.T. survived in operable condition, courtesy of its own small steel enclosure; while the rectifiers that converted AC electricity from the motor to the DC voltage accepted by the battery were apparently unharmed during the Exchange.
This engine sometimes powered the textile mill, a hundred yards away, whose photovoltaic production was prone to the vicissitudes of cloudcover. Comprising 60 modules rated for 200 watts peak output each, its array could afford a power source for the Ark without conflict, since operations there would likely be suspended by chaostrophe, as a matter of course.

However, at this relatively low voltage, the engineer deemed line loss over the four hundred feet required to connect the structures by DC to be theoretically unacceptable, even employing 1/0 stranded copper salvaged from the Block Island Power substation; furthermore, amid nuclear winter or just a weather event comparable to the Superstorm, inundation by snow drifts would render the low-lying ground-mount ineffective, regardless of whether we circumvented the limits of distance. Hence we resolved to shift its panels toward the Ark, installing them two stories from the earth on the Omniscion pylon, and thus above the deepest foreseeable accumulation. Conceptually, we had the perfect option, minimizing our wire lengths whilst still able to send the mill their current, on the same existing cable used by the generator. Practically, though, it posed a serious challenge, given the modules' combined surface area exceeded a thousand square feet; after sketching the 25' x 50' rack, inclined 45 degrees and attached to the tower, I felt overwhelmed by the structural necessities of supporting, bracing, and restraining what had become, in essence, an enormous, dense, fragile sail of glass with only the random materials on hand.

"If there is no solution, then it is not a problem," Amadeus decreed. "Besides, I've seen worse."

Trusting that a mounting system could be imagined, our attention turned to the interior. Assuming a modest continuous output from wind turbines, we sought a battery capacity of over three thousand amp hours to store enough power for the heat pump and what minimal lighting the grow room required during consecutive days of overcast weather; beyond then would necessitate charging with the generator. This was one of the components we had to import; yet when I asked Aeiolus about a budget for the project, he simply said, "whatever it costs." The engineer recommended an obscure, expensive, non-toxic nickel-iron cell that predated the lead-acid variety, reputedly long-lived and far more tolerant of discharge, abuse, or neglect. Once our electrical components were established, Amadeus focused on the mechanicals while I attended to construction sequencing and schedules. We tentatively intended to finish before Skorpios, in time for fall seedstock, because so many trades would be encumbered by frost. Looking backward, I determined we should have all the concrete complete by summer solstice; thus leaving us about a moon to shuffle the panels and do utility rough-ins; another for materials acquisition, formwork, and reinforcement; plus a few weeks of mixing and placing mud. Our itinerary seemed tight yet possible; since Aeiolus promised as much help as might be efficaciously delegated, this alignment with the calendar proved auspicious in several respects. Early phases were backlogged by management and technical labor, lacking potential to benefit from extra hands; but we aimed to pour in Dioskouri, thereby begging the bulk of such assistance when villagers tended to be less than fully employed: largest cuttings of hay would be stored; spring planting and poultry brooding over; calving, kidding, lambing, and shearing done. The difficulties of that season lay largely in enduring its heat, as our most strenuous jobs coincided with the least amenable conditions, which further complicated the endeavor by accelerating cement's initial set. Seeing no way around them, I fervently prayed to have clouds on the appointed days.

By the arrival of Beltane my surroundings thrummed with fertility like I had not yet seen, making the beauty and sheer intensity of each day tantamount to psychedelic experience for me. Villagers spoke of that spring as the most prolific in island memory; but being from the city, I suspect my experience was on another level entirely. Rapidly-accelerating plant growth, pupating insect populations, and frequent thunderstorms all contributed to a sense of time compressed by virtue of activity therein. I never knew nature at her finest before, which is to say as she swelled with uninhibited reproduction; in appreciation of her flourishing fecundity, I invited it to fill my life as well.

Due to my responsibility for the Ark, I regularly discussed our logistics and timeline with Oulixeus, a man of twenty-seven who was among Aeiolus' preferred sailing crew. Their frequent absences had inspired the name, conferred during his participation in the tribe's first native-born initiation. Whilst not at sea, he had mastered artisanal food preservation by smoking to create delicacies like authentic bacon, and helped his gorgeous wife Penelopeia as he could maintain a modest but prosperous homestead.

When I returned to work, fraught with stress, after dinner amidst the waning moon, Oulixeus convinced me to join him in a climb up his favorite tree instead. Hammocks were suspended from the upper limbs, whence we listened to mating calls of frogs, discussed metaphysics, and watched the dancing moths drawn by his pipe. At sail, many hours on watch afforded ample opportunity to distill the classics of philosophical literature, whose greatest volumes he commended to me. By my unqualified assessment he was both a scholar and sourcerer in training, though a while passed ere I noticed his expertise since he had neither need nor motive to broadcast it. As indigo spread over prismatic twilight above the treetops northeast of us, I spotted a satellite, albeit mistaken at first for a plane. Oulixeus told me that private jets would not fly over Block Island for fear of radioactivity, whereas military aircraft did appear on rare occasions, without incident. By way of orbits, the conversation meandered toward physics and relative motion; thence my wise friend, who had not suffered compulsory education, began teaching me calculus and its applicability to the observed behaviors of astronomical bodies, which I was learning to identify in my evenings on the porch with Airmed. Scholastic peers deemed me anomalous for choosing to do multiplication or even long division mentally, rather than on my iTab; yet I developed these skills naturally, unlike the rest of my class, through extensive dealings with dosage, weight conversions, and various prices. They translated to design as well as building because, for me, figuring was automatic; Oulixeus, on the other hand, elevated mathematics to magic.

"I apologize for trypping out on it," he noted, punctuating a digression.

"I'm studying celestial navigation as part of my arkhos pragmatos."

"You've got my interest, so tryp away...but what did you just say?"

"It's a research thesis, bringing new knowledge to the tribe, whereby my kuriator will decide whether I'm ready to guide others in hyperspace."

"Hyperspace? As in pneohoaska and the deiman?" I blurted impetuously.

He nodded. "I must be proved pragmatikos before I may administer."

"Well, what is this calculus, then? An arcane art of some kind?"

"Not in the traditional sense, though it occurs in apparently infinite realms of imagination – it's a sort of meta-algebraic language, a method beyond

just solving equations, of nesting them inside one another to study their relationships...how to explain...you're familiar with Cartesian coordinates?"
I was not, since the math taught in school merely distinguished betwixt integers and operation keys; aghast, Oulixeus extricated a sweaty grid-ruled notebook from his pocket, rubbing furiously with an eraser as he explained how disciplines such as algebra or geometry were based on a conceptual two-dimensional plane, divided by numeric measurement on both axes in a manner akin to city streets, except uniformly square 'blocks' resulted; thus any point on its surface could be addressed as an ordered pair of values.
By the rising gibbous' light, he drew their intersection on a sheet of paper.
"Let's say we wanted to represent daylength, over the course of a year..." he began, marking ticks along the bottom edge to show equinoxes, solstices, and cross-quarter festivals; on the page's left side he simply wrote 'hours'.
"It's one period of a sine wave, repeated for every orbit around the sun," Oulixeus continued, gracefully tracing a pattern that seemed to comprise three arcs; then he jotted down the symbolic variable function thereof.
"A vertical line indicates a moment in time; where it intersects the graph, we find a date, and the horizontal line through that point tells its length."
"So it's like a map," I ventured cautiously.
"Indeed," he agreed, "but the secret is that it's a holograph as well, permitting more data to be encoded beneath the surface. What would you do if asked to tell me, for example, how much daylight is in all of summer?"
Peering at his graph, I puzzled over this question until finally realizing the coordinate plane showed the totality of time; the penciled curve delineated light from dark; space above embodied night, while what lay below was day.
"Count the squares in here?" I said, gesturing to identify a region bounded by the wave, between vertical lines defining the equinox and solstice.
"That is certainly a way to estimate," he remarked, "though it ignores the issue of our curve passing through some of them."
"Split the difference," I suggested, as Will was often apt when contending with the vicissitudes of rough lumber. "Add half of the number it crosses."
"A reasonable idea," he allowed, "yet a convex section of the graph tends to enclose over half the total area of blocks it intersects; a concavity, less."
Following a hesitant pause, I glibly replied, "Then get a magnifying glass, divide each into a finer grid, and count the smaller component squares."
Oulixeus shook his head. "Hence you will achieve an additional decimal place worth of accuracy, a tenth as significant as its predecessor," he said, completing my clever idea in anticlimax, "and the next iteration would be a hundredfold more laborious." We lit up the pipe before continuing.
"When inhabiting a grid mentality, you are ever limited by your ability to make only successively less efficient approximations. Calculus, conversely, takes the problem to a new dimension, wherein the area under the curve is ascertained via its own algebraic function, which emerges from the first after integration. If you do the inverse, differentiating the original graph, you can define its slope, or rate of change, at any moment along its length; the best geometry might do, alternatively, is to determine the angle of the shortest line segment you can draw from two points upon a curve."
"Wait...you discovered this on DMT?" I wondered with astonishment.
He laughed vigorously. "No, this was discovered by Isaac Newton and

Gottfried Leibniz, kuriators of the scientific revolution; yet like their work, pneohoaska practice intends to shake fundamental assumptions of reality. The deiman does not just transport us across the membrane and back again; it demands the concrescence of novel paradigms, whereby we may explore the possibility that our proverbial plane is not flat, but curves around the sphere of earth; whose grids are not square and whose surface areas span more dimensions than we can see from our perspective. My thesis concerns the forces increasing earthly day length infinitesimally from one to the next as tidal deceleration slows our planet's spin to the tune of about a second every sixty thousand years; meaning that the pitch of its revolution, if we equate astronomical motion with sound, is falling very slowly over time."

"It sounds like you might have a bit too much time on your hands at sea," I joked, head whirling, and my constricted chuckle grew to a ticklish cough.

"Perhaps, although mine cannot be sold," Oulixeus replied. "In the end, what is time? And if we ceased to count it, what would become of our perceived existence? These are among the mysteries DMT begs of me."

I felt inspired then to recite, "There has been no progress in sixty thousand years in reducing the psychedelic experience to a known quantity. It is as terrifying, as awesome, as ecstatic, as irreducible to us as it was to them."

By sunlight reflected off the satellite whose eccentric orbit caused the same tides he studied, I observed Oulixeus cocking an emphatic eyebrow at me.

"Terence McKenna?" he guessed with some suspicion, or else surprise.

"Evolving Times," I specified. "Anno domini nineteen-ninety-five."

"Oh, I know; I'm just surprised that you do, too...a fellow time traveler, who theorized not only on evolution of hominid consciousness, but also temporality itself, with a computerized model of ingression of novelty."

"Maybe you'll help me unravel The Invisible Landscape," I began hopefully. "What I do see now is how concurrent use of tryptamines and computers for predicting his singularity would lead to analogies of prosthetic intelligence."

"Or intelligent prostheses," Oulixeus clarified.

"I noticed Aeiolus calls the Apple as such," I said. "What's the difference?"

"If you have to ask you'll never know," he elided with a sly smile, "but upon meeting the deiman there will be little doubt of whose prosthesis is who."

"Let's take a tryp to hyperspace," I suggested eagerly.

He scoffed in response. "You will, but not like this. As Terence teaches us, psychonautics are an art; we don't necessarily get to surf the eschatological timewave our first time offshore. You've seen trance shows, I suppose?"

"More than I care to recall." A shudder of disgust accompanied my answer.

"Follow me if you want a hold a seance for him," he replied, going down.

"Wait...we're climbing in the dark?" I asked apprehensively.

"Unless you want to stay all night; besides the moon, I didn't bring a light."

Descending the tree by feel was actually instinctive; when I mentioned this Oulixeus told me, "Of course it is; we've done as much for millions of years." The bag he left at the tree's base contained an iTab from a lifetime previous, its design similar to Mrs. Jefferson's, thick with memory and power supply.

Whilst curious, the taboo on such devices had been so deeply engraved by the incident involving Aeiolus' Apple that I stepped back reflexively.

"Afraid of breaking the rules?" he teased. "Don't worry; as sailing crew, I'm exposed by default to machine consciousness, and thus receive special

technological dispensations. Pay attention; this is DMT in musical form."
Before I could respond, the iTab sprang to life, reverberating at low volume
but high resolution; it drew me irresistibly with an ominous wind, like the
bard's psychedelics "whistling past the graveyard", mechanical whirring,
then electronic crackling; these metamorphosed into an eldritch screech,
howling, and next, the songs of insects. I felt transported to the origins
of humanity, as during my initiation, whence came Terence's enunciation,
his voice steeped in the sacral ambience of a tryp simultaneously vibrating
in the background. Electronic waves rose and crashed; from the ripples
of distortion emerged intricately overlapped rhythms, synchronous with
either the chanting choruses or ecstatic glossolalia of some tribal ritual. ·
In its electronic twists, this composition faintly resembled the synthetic
frequencies to which I was accustomed by trolling, yet became far more
complex. Whilst listening, synaesthesia conjured the intertwining dance
of mutating nucleotide strands that begat Kristos' new vegetable varieties.
Acts such as *Hypnotyze* produced tones meant to reward certain areas of
the brain, like narcotics; while here I heard creativity, stimulating and alive.
Oulixeus only nodded, shushing me, after I made a comment to this effect;
then Terence spoke again, his voice distant amidst a storm of psychoactive
sounds, as if from the Amazonian cave wherein Aeiolus had once met him.
"Everything is machine-like, polished and throbbing with energy, but that
is not what immediately arrests my attention. What arrests my attention
is the fact that this space is inhabited. And so like jeweled self-dribbling
basketballs these things come running forward and what they are doing
with this visible language that they create is they are making gifts for you!"
The transmission hence unfolded into instrumental oscillations, fading out
alongside frog calls, until I noticed the track was over, its denouement
blending seamlessly with the noises of wildlife from a pond to our north.
"Whereas Terence's orbs of verbal entelechy were akin to alien entities,
I meet mine in stars themselves, which teach me in the archaic languages of
math and physics," Oulixeus explained. "The laws of thermodynamics still
claim that all things degrade via entropy; however, my mortal experience
resonates with his, of a trend toward greater complexity, organization, and
connection in the heavens, brought forth by the logos, or consciousness,
singing in harmonic matrimony with khaos. When it comes to duration of
Earth-days, a single second in sixty millennia may be insignificant; but our
ability to observe this increment is not, because wisdom gained therefrom
disillusions us. Why do we perceive linear time? Except without it we would
not have stories, journeys, or music. Like Terence's ingression of novelty,
I find in astrology or wobbling orbits the elements of a cosmic orchestra."
"Methinks we just heard them celebrating," I added, nodding to the iTab.
"I can imagine. At sail, we get close enough to shore for pirating American
data channels, just out of morbid curiosity; and I must confess they leave
me deeply aggrieved. What the nation has now is an inhuman commodity
absent any authentic merit, yet another symptom of their cultural affliction.
People once used machines as tools to make art, which is at heart an act of
thanksgiving; when you remove that intent, media decays to a commodity
with human mascots, solely concerned for its own infectious perpetuation;
then the dominion of artificial intelligence is complete. No wonder those on

whom it is inflicted don't think straight; they're constantly bombarded by
noise pollution and subliminal advertising, atop the other digital plagues."
"What a shame to lose such potential for lack of computers,
since we could be creating with them instead," I lamented.
"To us it was never lost," Oulixeus amended. "We are blessed by Apellon,
and they will play at Ayakinthia next moon. If math intrigues you, consider
studying music, especially theirs, where you may encounter fractal patterns
emanating from infinity, upon application of calculus to psychoacoustics."
The foliose canopy closed in overhead as we walked north, out of Akhaia.
"How did you get into all of this?" I inquired at the Arkadian gateway.
"I wanted to impress a woman; how else?" he quipped; we both laughed.
"Perhaps you could help me in that respect," I hinted.
"You've found your muse, eh? Well, good luck to you, and I will if do so
I'm able; just please don't tell me who, so I won't inadvertently meddle."
"My desire is simply to know how I can attract her interest."
"In truth, did any other aspiration ever motivate men to improve ourselves?
Whilst pursuing Penelopeia, I made a rival of Menelaos, who'd likely defeat
me in combat, and contrived to stand out in her eye via my arena of talent."
"Which is?" I asked, with earnest curiosity because his wife was a goddess.
"Her father often joked nobody could court his daughter who had not
first beaten him in a race along Lakedaimon, and I took the challenge."
"It would seem to come with a high risk of embarrassment," I observed.
"Indeed; but I thought the prize worth my gamble nonetheless.
She motivated me to train diligently every morning I was home;
a habit that has fortunately stuck with me until the present day."
This struck me as an excellent idea. "Could I join you sometime?"
We were approaching the bustling, illuminated community hall,
and paused at the fence where woods met a pasture dotted by cows.
"I heard about your beach adventure," Oulixeus told me. "Although you
have good legs and an inclination toward endurance, given your build I
expect you've better chances of becoming a champion fighter than runner."
"Against Will?!" I exclaimed. "The man is a beast!"
"Or Menelaos, depending on the outcome of future Olympiks."
"You're crazy; I don't know the first thing about fighting."
"I'd bet you know more than you would suspect," he contended.
"I just meant to do some conditioning...to get in shape for the work ahead."
"Yes, I grok; summer is near, and you hope she'll notice you on the Ark.
If you're serious, meet me an hour before dawn to run Concrescent Beach.
With honing you may even find a guide who'll introduce you to the deiman."
"What about you?" I wondered aloud; he shook his head prodigiously.
"I'm still a kurios mystes; besides, by seeking, you forestall the encounter,
because the kuriator will determine when you are ready, not vice versa."
"Who is yours?"
"Airmed, who has probably forgotten more astronomy than I'll ever know,
despite being a doctor by trade. I'm honored to have her hierophantikos."
He stopped to face me, his features solemn under the brilliant moonlight.
"Beware the yearning to devour your entire life at once, my friend; in haste
you'll waste the journey, or burn out; if you pace yourself, you may learn to
enjoy it all - love, loss, health, sacrifice, and the mystery of our divinity."

"Give me a long enough lever,
and a fulcrum on which to place it,
and I shall move the world."

~ Arkhimedes, 2287-2212 B.T. ~

"Let him that would move the world first move himself."

"I desire only to know the truth, and to live as well as I can...
To the utmost of my power, I exhort all other men to do the same...
take part in the great combat, which is the combat of life,
and greater than every other earthly conflict."

"I was really too honest a man to be a politician and live."

~ Sokrates, 2469-2399 B.T. ~

 # DIOSKOURI

I managed to drag myself from bed to meet Oulixeus for our first run
at the next new moon, and gave all I had to keep his pace, which lasted
through about half the distance; but after developing a cramp in my side,
I watched him get progressively further away until he disappeared amidst
the rocky coast of Ithaka. Dawn was peeking above the horizon by the time
I reached the jetty, where he left me a message scratched in the sand:
'The race is with yourself; what matters is that you finish strong.'

Early months on the Ark offered the steepest learning curve yet in my life,
and I loved them for this. In the beginning, I spent my evenings pouring
over plans with Amadeus; during most days I worked beside Aephaistos,
the kuriator of metallurgy, who had allegedly learned his trade from direct
experience, a lack of formal education evident in the simplicity of his speech.
Perhaps out of self-consciousness therefrom, he tended to stand back and
observe among large groups; but when his mouth opened, not a word was
wasted in proclamations as terse as they were profound. The man himself
had a thick frame of average height carrying robust musculature, despite an
age underscored by his snow-white ponytail and sternly creased face, clean-
shaven for the sake of welding sparks in flight. He had earned the villagers'
esteem by helping almost everybody out of a quandary, or a few, at some
point or another, repairing machinery and replacing parts without which
they would have been impotent. His repute notwithstanding, Aephaistos'
shop left me appalled. Whereas the structure looked neat and well-cared
for from outside, this ambience did not translate to the interior. A chaotic
jumble of metal covered its floor, except for convoluted aisles betwixt pieces
of equipment, positioned even less ergonomically than in Aegipan's barn.

ENTHEOGENESIS · Origin of the Divinity within Us

His wall-mounted storage racks gave a semblance of organization, but were inaccessible without stumbling over the mess in their way. His main table bore a mountain of tools, scraps, paper, unfinished projects, and foodstuffs; thus he had to shove aside a vast swath of the pile just to liberate a corner whereon he would awkwardly clamp a workpiece, then proceed to make cuts or welds with apparent disregard for fire hazards abounding in his vicinity. I eventually discovered that, beneath its disheveled façade, the metal shop contained a meticulously kept inventory, albeit in Aephaistos' mind alone. When asked for a specific profile, he typically hobbled toward an ostensibly random junk heap, dug blindly into the bowels of his collection, and soon emerged holding precisely what was required. Left to my own devices, I might never have found the piece I sought, unless it lay in plain view; while Aephaistos seemingly remembered the last time he had touched every object therein, because he did not need to search for anything. Although slow and methodical, his hands moved with unflagging efficiency, even as villagers came asking for assistance; on such occasions I noticed he could be gregarious one-on-one, always willing to set down his labor for conversation. He inquired about the details of each visitors' family life and health out of genuine curiosity; after they grew obviously uncomfortable with the interaction's duration, nervously shifting from one foot to another, or gesticulating subconsciously toward the exit, he would then often launch into an obscure anecdote from the deep recesses of his memory. Clients were too courteous to tell him they had elsewhere to go; while Aephaistos' productivity permitted him to take advantage of their visits, drawing out his words with perverse satisfaction. These tales begged the question of whether he intended to convey unspoken lessons about haste; yet despite propensity therefor, he evaded explanation of his limp when I queried him, sharing only that he blew out his knee by refusing to tap in a jiujitsu match; "The stupid pride of an angry young man dueling over a woman," the smith mumbled wistfully, then asked me, "Have you ever played chess before?" Reminded of my failed advance toward Bridget by this, I nodded dejectedly. "Submission grappling is like chess with limbs instead of pieces," he added inscrutably. "The irony is I sacrificed my queen for a game I'd already lost." Beyond this lameness, he had better coordination than any else I have met; his steady grip left weld beads always straight and consistent, the molten lapmarks of his electrode's arc as evenly spaced as those of automation. Along with most people, I cannot draw a circle freehand to save my life; but from four punched indentations for guidance, Aephaistos' torch cut curves that could have been drawn by compass. He would watch me struggle with a dull drill bit in his peripheral vision for a while; silently bringing it to the benchtop sander, he then established its cutting angle by feel, sharpening freehand and engulfed in blinding plumes of sparks via a few quick twists of his wrist so nonchalant I might not have thought them effective, except that their symmetrical bevels passed through steel like softwood afterward. Senescence aside, the metallurgist proved to be a bit of a reprobate, whose late wife Kythereia was regarded as the loveliest woman in Lakedaimon. "Yet such beauty has a price," he confessed. "Hers was a wandering eye;" hence the fight that crippled him, I surmised. He had an immoderate habit of connoting sex by repeating elsewise prosaic remarks in a lecherous tone, preceded with the phrase "I'll show you"; e.g. "how large to bore the hole", "the length of my brazing rod", "some spatter in the crevice", and so forth; whilst cutting on the wet saw or grinding chisels, he eagerly conveyed the importance of lubrication, winking lest I miss his vulgar, unsubtle innuendo. In a few instances, what he fabricated from plans I drafted with Amadeus did not match the original intention. Partially out of my deference to him, partially due to perceived sensitivity, I exercised mindful circumspection in addressing errors. To prevent them, I covered drawings with redundant dimensions, as well as extraneous notes clarifying what I thought should have been obvious, frequently to no avail. Upon hearing of my frustration, Amadeus said, "Being dependent on Aephaistos is a challenge and a gift. Given something broken, he will typically fix it with his first attempt; once a problem is defined, he can cut the parts and make the welds based on schematics in his head; but if he didn't design an assembly or doesn't have the underlying reasoning, he may just put it together in the manner he finds easiest or best. You must either accept this limitation or relinquish control, leaving room for his ingenuity to astound you. After all, this is the artisun who forged everything from the kiste of the Apple to the armor of Areis."

I had gone to great lengths with efforts to detail our photovoltaic rack, becoming rather attached in doing so to my calculations; yet in the field I reluctantly submitted to Aephaistos' authority, privately fretting over his evident carelessness of geometric accuracy as he barked orders at me.

My job was dicey, with the majority done via harness, rope, and pulley; making matters worse, in stressful moments he would mutter suggestions like, "We should get a crane," which I found far from helpful. Meanwhile, Bridget harassed me about power shortages at the mill and circuit breakers popping during the system shift as if I meant to sabotage her purposefully. Ultimately all my fears were laid to rest, since the array ended up straight and true. Hovering two stories above the ground, with cantilevers as long past both sides of the pylon, our edifice looked ready to take off in flight. "Not bad," Aephaistos announced. "I guess now the real work can begin."

Provided clear sky, midday had by then grown dangerously bright, so it became my habit to do all of the farm chores in a single stretch lasting from dawn until I could no longer endure the rays, usually just before noon. After a cold plunge I had a lunch of salad and smoothie, recovering from exposure with a nap in the shade if absent interior work. Once the sun fell enough for the outdoors to be safe again, I would plug away at the Ark past twilight with some coca or mate to extend my energy. I paused on such an evening to mop my brow and hydrate, admiring the crescent moon as it set in the crack between the worlds; later igniting lanterns so I could finish the vault layout. The song of frogs, insects, and lambs bleating was interrupted by the clatter of somebody climbing the ladder that led to the roof. To my pleasant surprise, Bridget appeared unannounced at the parapet, hypnotically vivacious as she danced across I-beams in the dimness with a basket balanced atop her head. She stopped in front of my pile of tools, candlelight flickering on her fine feline features. "Sorry for giving you grief about the power. Although its no excuse, I had my own issues to work out, and hope you'll accept this token of my apology."

Bowing skillfully, she let the box slip into her hands and reached toward me.
"No worries," I replied, with a feigned yet evidently convincing nonchalance.
The basket felt unexpectedly heavy as I accepted it, while her visit had a
gravity more significant. A pie of glazed raw blueberries and nut-stuffed
phyllo pastry lay inside, topped by cumulous piles of fresh whipped cream.
"This is decadence," I exclaimed, nibbling on a sprig of the mint garnish.
"Seeing how you like to work late, I figured you might get hungry up here."
In truth, I was ravenous, and grateful she had foresight to bring a fork,
which saved me the embarrassment of eating off my fingers or pliers.
"Mmmm," I moaned, savoring the sensuous flavors of my first taste;
with my mouth still full, I gracelessly murmured, "You're a goddess."
"It's easy to make when I have the ingredients," Bridget said. "Everything
is so abundant this year, as if nature is equipping herself for a long winter."
In the context of my responsibility for the project on whose roof we sat,
I felt important next to her; genuinely empowered by my training beside,
or behind, Oulixeus; and thus inspired, without noticeable nervousness,
to inquire whether I could reciprocate by rubbing her back. I had observed
other young men employing this thinly-veiled courtship to express interest
in sex, experiencing various levels, albeit some certain measure, of success.
"A massage, eh?" Her dubious drawl intimated she saw through my charade
but enabled it anyway; promising, I figured. "If you want to I won't refuse."
Dangling her luscious, coppery legs over the edge, Bridget leaned against
the bucket betwixt my legs. Kneading her taut back, I unwittingly glimpsed
down her blouse to a heart-shaped pair of dolphins suggestively tattooed
upon each ilium. We quietly watched stars emerge, enjoying the sea breeze
as well as its relative dearth of biting insects. Following a bowl of cannabis,
she alternately helped herself to the pie and fed me bites over her shoulder.
I have not forgotten the fragrance she wore, honeysuckle mingled with rose
blossoms, in which she caught me indulging as my face grazed her mane.
"Are you smelling me?" she asked, her voice ing a hint of indignation.
"Oh, no...I think it's congestion from all of the pollen," I lied, sniffing again.
She grunted skeptically, yet did not move away, so I changed the subject
in haste. "I was wondering what can you tell me about the time machine."
"Not much," she declared firmly. "Why do you suppose, despite ceremonial
tradition of almost two millennia, the Eleusinian Mysteries remain as such?
Those pilgrims didn't go lusting after the gods so boldly as you do, while the
hierophants diligently guarded secrets thereof. Even Diagoras the Atheist,
who desecrated the rituals by invoking them outside those settings, failed
to divulge the unrepeatables, and fled into exile with a price on his head."
"Is that a threat?" I replied, half-joking to disguise my discomfort.
"The topic is not to be broached lightly, though if it will slake your curiosity
here's a piece I can convey, on second thought: the deiman often shows how
tenuous our conceptions of time truly are. Whereas we witness a flow from
past to future, the nature of cause and effect could as easily be its opposite.
Upon consideration of a universe wherein that which hasn't yet happened
creates whatever we remember, anything becomes possible, by our ability
to conjure it through conscious awareness of the present moment."
"Wow..." I began, fumbling fecklessly for an erudite response; none readily
came, but channeling Terence saved me from an excruciatingly long lapse.

"Really, isn't time only experienced by the events which occur within it?"
"Final Earthbound Interview." She twisted around, fixing her gaze on me.
"You've tasted the Apple, haven't you? How did you open its case?"
My mute mouth opened as Aeiolus' stern instructions echoed in my mind;
then, in a tone that was probably unintentionally, yet painfully seductive
nevertheless, Bridget hissed, "Oooh....you're baaad," with mock reproach.
From my position this epithet sounded auspicious; very much so, actually.
In response, I told the story of my unrequited interest in the computer,
and Aeiolus' censure when he caught me. She laughed mellifluously as
I described our awkward interaction; when I sought her opinion on its
coincidence with the new year, she shrugged ambivalently, declaiming,
"The machines, by allowing us to model, calculate, and simulate
very complicated multivariable processes, extend the power of the
human mind into places it could never dream of going before."
"Shamans Among the Machines," I remarked. "A.D. nineteen ninety-nine."
"Well done; though cataloging Terence quotes is a far cry from time travel."
"Just lead the way," I propositioned indelicately.
Turning again, she stared with intensity that both criticized and enticed me.
"What is it?" I demanded at last, breaking the stalemate.
"Nothing...I was distracted by the pie on your cheek."
As I rubbed my face self-consciously, Bridget said, "Hang on; I'll get it."
I froze whilst she wiped off the glaze, and my jaw dropped involuntarily to
lick her finger, which lingered long enough for me to question her motives.
"I'd remind you of Eleusis and Diagoras, but you men don't seem to learn,"
she went on, glancing at her clock. "Speaking of time, mine is gone for now."
"How was the massage? Did I do something wrong?" I called as she went
down the ladder, listening amid my confusion for her invisible midway pause.
"You have strong hands, and do not want for enthusiasm or effort;
given practice, I daresay you may be adequate in days still to come."
I felt disappointed, since I aspired to much more than adequacy; yet glad
that at least she had sufficient respect for me not to spare her judgment.

Immediately after we completed the Ark's power system, installing our
massive hydroxide battery thereupon, Amadeus shared unfortunate news
regarding its bermed walls. "They're far too tall; albeit stupid to overlook,
I did so nonetheless, to make our endeavor extra challenging, I guess."
He explained that the fourteen-foot stack of blocks, once held in place at
top and bottom by the roof vault and slab, respectively, would be subjected
to a bending stress in the middle from the earth berm pushing against it,
whose weight the concrete was too brittle to resist. I wondered initially
if we could simply add rebar; as it happened, however, our limiting factor
lay in the fixed interior dimension of the existing cores, hence requiring
our steel to be centered just to have minimal grout coverage all around.
"In 12" block we'd get thrice as much space at the back of cells; but even
with number six bars in every one, this span would still be questionable,"
Amadeus retorted. Of course, we had naught for 12" block; yet if we did,
it would have demanded construction of an additional wall, when the sheer
volume of fill materials was already astronomical. I estimated upward
of fifty cubic yards for the first pour, plus fifteen for each of the others;

and felt disinclined to increase this because I knew not then how we were physically going to put it in place. Forming a solid vertical slab behind the existing block could take another twenty yards; adding a series of internal buttresses proved unfeasible since any concrete in the seed room needed insulation to prevent thermal conduction, thus eating excessive floor space. We next discussed reinforcement from the outside, by a series of buried cables connected in tension to satellite footings beneath the northern fill; this seemed impractical, inelegant, and risky. The engineer had told me, for our poured eight-inch block, eight feet was the maximum unsupported height he could countenance; ergo, the optimal solution would introduce a horizontal diaphragm midway up the wall, breaking the strain into two smaller segments. He became tenaciously adhered to the concept of a floating slab; I consequently found myself repeatedly pointing out that with the necessary insulation on both sides, as well as the floor and ceiling, his solution consumed nearly half of the interior headroom available to us. Moreover, it entailed additional cement, while Aeiolus balked at my original estimate of eighteen tons each fly ash and magphos for the walls and roof. These ingredients were to be transported from Boston aboard the *Kismet*, equating to as many trips thereof. Given favorable weather, it was still a push to have all materials onsite by aestival solstice, the generally-accepted date when insolation might prohibit such work by midmorning. Grasping at outside-the-box options, I asked whether the job could be done with wood, which is both structural and relatively non-conductive. After momentary rumination, Amadeus said, "I can't believe I didn't think of that myself." By creating an elevated floor system, twice sheathed in diagonal lumber like the *Wyrd*'s hull - locust in this case, for strength as well as durability - we would achieve precisely the desired effect without a thermal bridge.

We elected to locate our diaphragm a foot off-center, allocating six feet of ten total to a tight, though efficiently-stockable, refrigerated gene bank. In the remaining four feet above, roots, tubers, bulbs and so forth could be organized by an adult crawling. These required separation from the warmer living quarters or growing space, but not the stable temperatures of their below-grade concrete shell; therefore, a split-level configuration reduced the total area of insulated assemblies to build in our remodeling project.

As its floor plan coalesced I attended to logistics. The extant entrance was fortuitously located on the northwest corner, hence readily isolated, whilst permitting the walk-in-cooler to be a contiguous aisle along the north wall. Because the magphos and fly ash arrived in totes, a pair at a time, we had to store them inside, where it was relatively dry, until ready to pour. Oulixeus laughed at me during the first delivery, upon discovery that one-ton pallets did not fit through the door; I consequently had to remove its frame, then cut away half a block from each jamb, leaving corbels to support its lintel; a dreadfully loud, dusty travail laden with plenty of cursing. Aside from my embarrassing oversight, this method of handling cement worked beautifully. Employing a drawbridge ramp hinged on the pier, we expeditiously unloaded the *Kismet* via jigger and winch, thence drove the totes to the Ark on Will's tractor forks, depositing them just beyond my neatly-widened threshold; once inside the building they were easily maneuvered by pallet jack again. As cement accumulation soon began a race with reinforcement, Aephaistos made a 15' drill from a carbide-tipped bit and iron pipe to dowel vertical steel into the slab, which thereby became a simple matter of feeding the unwieldy apparatus down cores. Bending excess rebars over, we tied these to the parapet curb, thus interconnecting with an inverted basket of woven metal that looked like, and accordingly took the name of, the Turtleback. This phase compelled me to manage labor at the scale of a crew instead of duet collaboration; it felt odd for those with far longer tenure in the village to pay me deference, yet they exhibited no qualms with the arrangement, presumably because I stayed past twilight, departing last on a daily basis. I participated among the revolving cast of laborers, ostensibly for quality control, though I also wanted to project that I was not above grunt work; an artifice more for my own psychic comfort than anyone else's, in fact. I saved strictly mental effort for my time alone and undistracted, if possible. After the skeletal long bars had all been fastened at their ends, I engaged eager youngsters of the tribe for the tedious tasks of tying intersections and subsequently covering them in hemp mesh; chores disguised since they comprised climbing on an enormous, miraculous trampoline. Meanwhile Amadeus interfaced with Aephaistos regarding the heat pump design to alleviate my stress, as I felt stretched thin already by pour preparations. The seed vault would receive a canopy of copper tubing that conveyed refrigerant through a compressor in the mechanical room, followed by a buried exchange coil to dump heat, before returning inside, passing through an expansion valve, and cooling the chamber in a continual cycle. During this busy period, I indulged a compensatory coca habit, courtesy of Oulixeus, who cultivated the plant to aid staying awake on late watches, "So you can borrow from tomorrow what you need for today," he noted. Its leaves were immensely helpful at work, as for our runs in the wee hours; with a quid thereof stuffed in my mouth, I could last longer between meals, get through the day on less sleep, and maintain my focus amidst blistering conditions, an impediment to progress looming as high as the sun in the sky. Like phenethylamines, the coca did promote sweaty insomnia, but nothing a night swim failed to fix, whilst absent the jitters of X-analogues or even caffeine; in hindsight, my intensifying excitement as the fateful concrete pour drew near may have been to blame for my sleeplessness anyway. Our motorized mixers handily produced quarter-yard batches, containing a bucket of both magphos and fly ash, plus a barrelful of aggregate mix, from coarse deposits of sandy gravel dug high on the beach, leached of salt by the rain, sifted through diamond mesh to remove large shells and organic debris. During a trial wherein we cast the stairs along with their bulkheads, I figured we could produce eight loads per hour on average; it took two minutes to handle ingredients, four or five to mix them and measure another round, then one more to empty and rinse the hopper, preventing the next batch from being accelerated by leftover hot residue. The big pour constituted upward of two hundred, which meant it would take twelve or thirteen hours total if we ran two machines concurrently – an epic day, albeit doable, with some daylight to spare. A tractor would stay at the sediment mine whilst a pair of trucks traveled back and forth, loaded in rotation to keep the mixers supplied. Aephaistos set up a drum tipper for the purpose above our staging area, whose swiveling ring clamped

ENTHEOGENESIS · Origin of the Divinity within Us

around the sifting barrel's center of mass, hung from an articulated boom. This mechanism allowed folks to shovel directly into screens from the bed, then swing it over the hopper and dump a quarter-ton of sand singlehanded. We would lift wet concrete atop the Ark by pulley, placed with pails that were to be refilled three thousand times during the first pour alone. The operation employed two dozen people at any particular moment; half as many again had volunteered, for the sake of regular breaks, while others less physically vigorous graciously committed to serve refreshments. I arrived before dawn on the chosen day after a restless night to reconfirm that I made every possible provision. Considering our collective investment, failure was not an option I could entertain, and for longterm stability the pour had to be monolithic from the bottom of cores to its dome's omphalos. Oulixeus met me early; next came rosy tendrils of morning, bringing clouds and with them a sense of relief. Will led the crew in a sunrise yoga session, followed by my orientation; amidst general levity and the obligatory jokes about the scale of our enterprise, we began. The first batch left its mixer at six; the mud was soon flowing smoothly; all present looked invigorated; and my head swelled with pride as I walked along the block wall's top edge, admiring the long-anticipated fruition of prodigious groundwork. I dashed around constantly, checking water content, pitching in where bottlenecks appeared, troubleshooting, and issuing suggestions on efficiency, if due. When spectators happened by to offer their appreciations or moral support, I greeted them but neither stopped, nor cared to; as the cumulus thickened my thoughts were only of finishing before heaven let loose a deluge upon us. What I welcomed at dawn as comfortable shade had become a suffocating blanket of humidity; lost in the routine, I neglected to drink water until the concrete reached two blocks below the vault, which I previously deemed our halfway mark. With the sun obscured, I asked if anybody could tell the time, expecting to hear about noon; yet in fact it was well past two. Remaining outwardly composed, I panicked, as perhaps the single person who knew our progress, or lack thereof; nauseated by uncertainty of how to inform the rest that I had grossly underestimated the duration of our task. Given a full crew moving at its then-current rate, the job might not be done by eleven, assuming the rain waited as long. Turning to take stock again, I came face to face with Bridget, who held a jar of vegetable juice, eggs, and a strong dose of honey with an unusually amicable expression, as if she understood my predicament. "Get out of the sun for minute and drink this," she urged. "I promise it won't be the end of the world." I complied, feeling an immediate flood of vitality, since stress coupled with coca had enabled me to push my organism toward a state of hypoglycemic heatstroke. "Now, how do I help?" she asked in a tone of earnest magnanimity. "Lights," I whispered, so as not to be overheard. "I thought we would finish by nightfall, but I was wrong; we could use any you can find." Nodding compassionately, she left; I resumed work with my energy restored by her elixir, as well as the motivation evoked by her attention, keeping exigencies of time to myself until we had poured the parapet and began creeping up the Turtleback from all around its perimeter. "I have a regrettable announcement to make," I hollered over the din. "My ambition to complete this before dark now appears untenable.

Although I don't expect anyone to remain later than they intended, I'll be
here to see it through regardless, and am obliged to those who will join me."
From the surface area remaining, even eleven o'clock seemed unrealistic;
yet sunset conspired to assist, as falling temperatures permitted us to pick
up our pace under the pressure of pregnant thunderheads, drawing from the
reserves we previously denied ourselves, which no longer needed rationing.
Upon return, Bridget compelled me to eat some solid food; I felt grateful
she did, since adrenaline had banished my appetite. Her presence proved
invaluable for contributing illumination and initiative; but more so because
I would not willingly submit unless I first went the distance in her eyes.
Despite comprehension why vain desire to impress a woman may be an
unhealthy impulse, I chose to harness what I had available in the moment.
Oulixeus gave me a sapient nod at twilight; seizing the opportunity to
distinguish myself, I surpassed and set new limits for my endurance
by deciding that I stood equal to the challenge looming in front of me.
Crew members began abandoning ship at nightfall, per anticipation,
with cordial farewells wishing the rest of us luck; it had already been an
inordinate effort by most accounts, and the vault's summit was getting
crowded. The core group, all of whom participated on the Ark previously,
plus Phaedo, who lent his troweling expertise to the underside of the dome,
found a third wind in the darkness, impending storm, or a sense of duty to
take up the slack, thus rescuing the project from my overzealous appetite.
"I'd say you've got this about sewn up, boss," Will hollered from below,
the last man still standing, as he washed his hands beside Bridget.
"Thanks for the push; you know I couldn't have done it without you."
"Likewise; but I'm saving my favors for later," he replied; then to her, "You,
sister, are a true champion; can you make him quit before you go, though?"
"I reckon so," she laughed, and proceeded to stay with me till the very end,
cleaning tools whilst I applied a rough texture to bond with the next layer.
When it felt my arms might fall off, I said at last, "I'm calling this a day."
"Congratulations," she sang in her lovely voice, coiling the electrical
cords amidst spectacular thunderclaps. "It's quite an achievement."
"I don't know how to repay you," I admitted, regretting that after all
of the lights were extinguished we could no longer make eye contact.
"Repayment is neither expected nor due, but I'm open to surprises."
This interaction was as inviting as any we ever had; I climbed down blindly,
shared her pipe in exhausted silence, and watched a solitary shaft of rain
pass through the somber chamber, akin to an etheric umbilical cord when
the yellow lightning flashed. My fervent hopes of walking Bridget to her hut
aside, I think it best in retrospect I did not ask. I was filthy, smelly, spent;
blitzed out of my mind; and given the torturous ambiguity of her reception,
could easily have said or done something offensive. The shower intensified
throughout my soggy solo trek, yet I went slowly, letting it wash over me
between thunderbolts showing the road. Upon return home, I met Aeiolus
and Amadeus in the kitchen, whose absence from the pour I did not notice
during the activity thereof; frankly, I felt surprised, and more than a little
disappointed, they never visited the scene. Nonetheless, they had waited
up for me, judging from their expectant stares as I dripped on the doormat.
"You got it done?" the engineer asked. Albeit an innocent enough question,

his laconic manner mocked the scope of my ordeal, which I suspect he knew. "Yes," I announced evenly; a single syllable that for an instant reverberated to the root of my existence. "We got it done." "In the nick of time, by the sound," he remarked, glancing upward. To hear hail pounding the roof was wondrous indeed, precisely because it had waited; I thanked the gods for granting this mercy, despite my hubris. "Well, I must confess my expectations were obscenely optimistic. We should definitely have used a concrete pump instead," I sighed. Aeiolus chuckled. "But then you would have been deprived of the chance to orchestrate the greatest single-day concerted labor project in erstory." Suddenly the wear on my body hit me, with its sunburned skin, torn fingers, peeling blisters, and aching back; since I had just endured the equivalent of two days' hard work in one, I failed to appreciate his compliment until later. "I'm sleeping in tomorrow," I groaned, causing them to grin in unison.

Enshrouded skies poured for days thenceforth, though that was fine by me; I needed several to recover, and the weather provided excuse for reprieve. They cleared the next week for a partial eclipse, wherefore we gathered in the afternoon at Athenai; Aeiolus led the subsequent new moon ceremony, coincident with his birth, billed as 'Apologues of Alexander the Apotropaic.' After a succulent feast of daylily soup and mint-infused pork, I realized the audience lingering to hear him speak comprised largely those of my age and younger for once. The elder generations, I presumed, were better versed in his story than I, having lived through it; whereas the natives, or children who arrived on the island in tow of their parents knew him only as Aeiolus - brilliant, charismatic, intrepid, enigmatic, but of a legacy confined to the island. His tale, which I have heretofore cited and will not yet reiterate, followed the approximate outline of Ariadne Jefferson's biography, except his wistful review focused more on the personal journey toward communion, mentioning famous achievements as mere milestones therein. He described New York City to the wide-eyed youth of the tribe, and a crowd one million strong, adding with visible satisfaction that his exceeded the audience of presidential inaugurations; then, with palpable grief, he told how this rally would be dwarfed by concerts, sporting events, or some celebrity funerals. "Given your campaign's purpose was theatrical," I began, interrupting him out of my unrequited curiosity, "what would you have done if elected?" The question evidently caught him off-guard. "Wouldn't you like to know?" He took a drink, adding, "I'm afraid we must save fantasy for another time." The most glaring discrepancies between his telling and the published book stemmed from details of his death; these he elided with cryptic references to resurrection bodies, ayahoaska, or the scripture of Terence, thereby planting in my mind the recurrent notion that perhaps, like Kristos' Jesus, he had planned his passage from the start. As I gazed at his scarred side, however, the willful endurance of such anguish was still beyond reckoning. "When facing death, we are utterly naked and alone, save for what learned lessons our awareness can bring to bear. As long as I'm able, I will thank the gods for revealing this to me early, as I thank them for the gift that is an authentic existence, whose direct knowledge comes with the necessity and responsibility to make our fleeting life a sacrifice in service of creation.

By striving thus, I've enjoyed much more of the experiential spectrum than most could hope, in spite of all that I had or was being torn away from me. Now you have the chance to build upon wisdom your progenitors diligently sought, and I pray you will find inspiration to perpetuate our heritage. Above all, you must forsake material wealth as a futile, soulless pursuit, because we humans possess nothing in the end, not even our own bodies - 'dust thou art, and to dust shalt thou return' - but by the grace of the stars, we are permitted to borrow these substances for the incarnation of spirit, which is what we are at our core. Regardless of how hard you cling thereto, it cannot be taken with you; attachment in this world can detract from your transition to the next, since these human organisms may only be dreams of the psychonauticon. They enact incredible beauty or terrible pain through our consciousness; and trust me, suffering exists you would not believe. All that matters in the end is the love you bring via your piece of this vision."

He spoke of what it meant, in his life's arc, to return from the other side; of the ambitions he left behind; and of his "most important attachment, which might, if I let it, compel me to dwell forever in this dimension" - his marriage to Airmed. She snuggled against him, smiling nostalgically as he recalled their extremely-extended honeymoon adventures, hiding at sea, exploring foreign countries, and engaging in countless illicit activities. "He was so vain," she interjected, "that whilst accepting the beast in his mirror as too hideous for romance, he never noticed me falling for him." The mood lightened when they finally reached the island, as the audience could readily relate to his story; for a while, the tale became a pleasantly clamorous collage of laughter, private jokes, and fond childhood memories, wherefrom I was excluded. He poignantly editorialized community erstory, recounting tragedy as well as triumph; paying homage to friends, opponents and pioneers who had passed on; then the ambience grew solemn again.

"I have more to tell than we have time tonight, so I'll leave you with this," Aeiolus said, particularly to the native-born villagers seated in front. "Those of us who saw the world as it was will soon all be gone. The rest of you might not know, but this island is far from alone, and future generations will have neither the benefit of our experience, nor our protection from the civilization beyond your horizon. We are blessed with a momentary peace; yet paradise will inevitably confront forces hostile to its survival, which is, after all, an exception to the rule of extinction. This tribe must choose to fight for its existence, or else join so many others at the gates of Aides."

Perhaps reading about the man before I met him gave me a different insight into his personality, because I connected especially with my projections of the character flaws making him uniquely human. While he wore them well, beneath the surface lay a labyrinth of frustrations with a reality even his formidable intent could not change; resentments toward a culture that heard, but did not listen to his message; grief for what had been lost as a consequence; and a streak of the avenging angel, which would have begot outright vendetta, were it not subdued to a perennial discontent by his wife.

"What advice would you give to accompany this warning?" Diomedes asked. The hall was silent, except our breathing, until Aeiolus said, "Look to him." I thought at first he nodded to Oulixeus, who sat by my side; then noticed all eyes had rather fixed on me. Aeiolus raised his left brow, gesticulating expectantly; in the taut pause that ensued, I grokked and rose to my feet. "Behold, my dear friends, he who has arrived to serve as your future guide." Amidst inscrutable applause, I recollected the journey leading there from my prior life; nine months unplugged, equal in duration to human gestation. Ruminating on how I had grown, what I had done, and who I had become along the way left me no less intimidated by the challenge he set forth, yet an indisputable urge to meet it rose also, since I was the one who could, given my intimacy with American empire. Under my peers' attentive gaze, I felt the weight of an uncertain duty; admittedly, I even felt uneasy pride.

When the clouds finally parted I visited the Ark, cheered to discover that its vault still had a rough texture, recent hailstorm notwithstanding, hence providing a strong key for the next coat, and devoid of visible cracks. In haste, or hindered by night, I forgot to check the anchors for subsequent reinforcement; miraculously, all were cast in their appropriate locations. Our second pour, compared to the first, went downright leisurely, working atop the hardened base rather than clambering on planks scattered over an elastic cage in the darkness; so we took our time, filling in voids until the dome was uniformly convex. Absent half of the original crew, we still finished by early afternoon, whereupon the meme of Turtleback took hold, referring to its shape as well as Iroquois oral tradition. Seneca told the myth of their homeland, created via mud smeared atop the carapace of such a reptile, which swam amid Earth's primordial waters, much like our island. We celebrated with a vigorous game of disc golf in the Arkadian forest; but by the third coat we had mastered the program, whose conclusion seemed almost a shame, though the momentum and expertise our crew thus gained would be readily applicable to remodeling of the lighthouses. The better skilled among us leapfrogged across the vault on kneeling pads, ensuring that its entire surface was troweled to a dense, water-resistant sheen, whilst the remainder packed up tools or loaded excess materials. After they departing I savored my solitude, straddling the escape hatch, soaking in a sense of accomplishment with blazing sun on my bare back. Hard labor, plus my diet and calisthenics, had transformed my body; I came to love the invigorating tingle of exhausted muscle fibers as they knitted themselves back together, along with the security of an abundant source of energy, available if I needed to draw from it instantaneously. "Hey there," Bridget called, standing across the road at the textile mill. I turned toward her, drew myself up straight and tall, shading my brows under one hand; even from a distance, she was so gorgeous I could cry out of desire. We regarded each other for a loaded, electrified moment, wherein I felt as though we were the only two people left in the world. "Looking good," she said, breaking the silence. Realizing that she might have been talking about me or the Turtleback, I hoped her statement was intentionally ambiguous. I nearly replied, "Speak for yourself," but hesitated, then choked, for better or worse, managing just an underwhelming, "Thank you," instead.

"The essence of all beautiful art, all great art, is gratitude."

"For art to exist, for any sort of aesthetic activity to exist,
a certain physiological precondition is indispensable: inebriation."

"One must still have chaos in oneself to be able to give birth to a dancing star."

"Ah, women – they make the highs higher, and the lows more frequent."

"What does not destroy me, makes me stronger."

"The 'Kingdom of Heaven' is a condition of the heart –
not something that comes 'upon the earth' or 'after death'."

"Let us beware of saying that death is the opposite of life.
The living being is only a species of the dead, and a very rare species."

"There are no moral phenomena, only moral interpretations."

"It is my ambition to say in ten sentences what others say in a whole book."

~ Friedrich Nietzsche ~

 # KARKINOS

Whilst the Ark predominated in my life, other islanders were busy elsewise.
For morning and evening hours when the sun was tolerable, they harvested,
weeded, or mulched crops, gathering seaweed as fertilizer therefor at night;
due to our seed saving initiative, the fields employed more hands than usual.
The village's production of rope, fabric, paper, charcoal, turpentine, alcohol
and biodiesel, along with preservation of its voluminous produce, continued
as usual under shade; in addition to the covert labor of retrofitting both
lighthouses to accommodate hundreds in a case of indefinite hibernation.
The five buried fuel tanks at the old power plant, whose cumulative volume
approached a hundred-thousand gallons, were scoured, then refinished
by a nontoxic process, hence serving as centralized potable water storage
protected against fallout and freezing. A robust crew known as The Grunts
ran almost ten miles of buried polyethylene pipe therefrom, connecting this
reservoir to the emergency fortresses. They utilized a motorized ditchwitch
of antiquity to trench the easy runs, but busted through old pavement with
jackhammer or explosives; digging by hand, exercising surgical precision,
under and around existing utilities. The lighthouses themselves received
minimal electrical systems, designed for ventilation, task lighting, laundry,
and refrigeration; while anaerobic digesters installed in the basements of
each would process solid waste once they had enough input, thus providing
methane for cooking or, given excess available, judicious water heating.

Most of the underground space would be devoted to livestock housing, primarily for poultry, which required daily feeding, might lay some eggs in those condition, and could be readily processed for eating if necessary; plus a few of the best-behaved pigs to aerate their bedding, a handful of sheep and goat breeding stock for the worse-case scenario, as well as half of the tribe's lactating cows, all of the above adding manure to biogas production. The expectation was that rising heat from this biological activity, combined with the bodies of their human residents, would warm these structures sufficiently; their masonry walls were insulated by stacks of hay bales, to be eventually used as animal feed. The remainder of ruminant flocks would take shelter in existing structures, left to cope with the shielding afforded by metal roofing, or whatever precautionary upgrades farmers could make. Accordingly, Aeiolus and Aephaistos developed a prototype self-feeding fodder rack of welded wire panels, extending from floor to ceiling on the walls of his own barn. Livestock had their hay replenished from above; as unpalatable stems accumulated in the bottom of the hopper, bedding grew deep on the floor, letting them reach fresh meals. The trick lay in balancing population density with the amount wasted, such that their stalls might not be fouled too quickly in absence of husbandly intervention. Ground levels of the lighthouses were repurposed as cooking, dining, and living spaces, with sleeping quarters located in the acoustically-segregated upper stories. Both buildings had around a hundred bunks, hence requiring residents to share beds in rotation. I knew not about plans for amorous relations therein, but assumed someone thought about the matter; since I was not expecting to have any myself, I did not ask. Rumors indicated that ten gallons of water per week had been proposed as the personal ration for drinking and bathing, which I guessed would at least reduce interest in sex.

Although onerous, I heard no complaint concerning workload; folks seemed invigorated by the coordinated, collaborative effort; proud of their ability to rise to the challenge Council had set forth; and by the arrival of summer solstice in an ostensibly abundant year, spirits were high across the island. To celebrate the season, initiated adults partook of Ayakinthia, a mystery festival of art, music, poetry and dance at the Telesterion, atop Parnassos, whose posts were delightfully festooned with vines, wildflower blooms, and luminarias; whilst its potluck buffet presented an edible array of astounding variety, mouthwatering sensuality, and delectable presentation. Villagers spared neither effort nor expense in sharing their prosperity, as if the night might be the last of its kind, since that distinct possibility had been planted in the tribe's mind. The global economy notwithstanding, I knew no place else where a person might have spring rolls with lime-cilantro peanut sauce; feta-pesto lasagna; marinated oyster ceviche; wineberry flan; and lavender baklava, to name just a few of my favorite offerings, at once. Cannabis was proffered freely, but in contrast to the Pannyxia, we limited our libations to entheogenic tinctures. By twilight, the plaza pulsated with psychedelic jubilation from the sheer extravagance of it all. Risqué tattooes ordinarily hidden by attire of propriety were revealed in their full glory, whilst masks and ornament reserved for the Aestival finally appeared after a year retired. Nearly everybody attending wore a provocative costume; yet the younger initiates stood out especially, their scantily-clad figures decorated in bright paints, some of them like extinct species; others mimicked ancient warriors ranging from Pyktes to Polynesians, with so much flesh exposed that evening I thought it might have been an overt fertility rite. Our bonfire comprised cement pallets, sawmill slabs, and whole trees uprooted by Elysian waves, standing twice my height above the ground before the musaeum; an exodus of mystai emanated thence at sunset, once Apellon's players gathered upon the Telesterion balcony with their equipment. The participants encircled this pile as Estia doused it in turpentine and walked away, spilling a trail of liquid on the ground behind her. I saw the drummer in back nod toward the shadows in which she waited; then a burning stream ran through our ring. Reaching its omphalos, an eruption roared and deep percussion evoked the prorrhesis of music akin to such as I had only heard once prior, via Oulixeus, courtesy in this case of a digital sound synthesizer, alongside electronically-amplified live instruments. The event thus bore a superficial resemblance to trance show in the urban arenas of my past; albeit here the power of an intelligent prosthesis our tribe traditionally stigmatized was conjured by artisuns rather than marketing executives, whilst Melpomene projected her soprano voice far into the night, singing in foreign tongues and feral cries. Shifting logs threw upward plumes of sparks to join the constellations, visible by a clear sky devoid of moon; soon dancers converged on the agora, stamping and swaying to the intricate, ever-evolving rhythms of Apellon. A trio of women marched onto the gallery next - Terpsikhore with a hoop; Thaleia bearing a staff; and Bridget, the last, held poi hanging from brilliant silver chains, like a burnt pair of shrunken heads Kali might wield as flails. Estia ignited an arced stripe of fuel laid across the masonry before them to form a pyrotechnic delineation of their space, wherefrom they lit wicks of their incendiary implements, which were saturated with the same solvents, recovered after ceremonial exorcisms of the deiman in the time machine. I stood at the crowd's edge, playing the role of awkward neophyte initially, but watching Bridget's performance, I allowed myself to be lured closer. She wore a mercilessly small breechclout, baring her flanks from ankle to clavicle except for a girdle of cordage that left just a slight indentation in the luscious flesh of her hips. A narrow strip of dark fabric wrapped behind her neck and diagonally over each breast, intersecting at her throat chakra, then tied around her back under the shoulder blades, thereby revealing the sleek skin of her torso from firm mons to soft, cloven expanse of her chest. By the flames, I could have counted the delicate crenelations of her ribs; her gorgeous mane swept up, arranged like a crown with barrettes of bone; her face was painted as a skull, its ghastly jaws covering her voluptuous lips; while her bodily display proved more than I had restraint to discreetly bear. Euterpe and Erato, attractive initiates of the year previous with whom I may have tangled during Pannyxia, approached my side. They made eyes at me, plans seemingly in their minds already, when I cast my gaze about, which was not often; despite any thrills implied, I only had eyes for Bridget. Her poi spun between outstretched arms like the two blades of a propeller, forming a perfect golden halo that passed through the cleft of her breasts, tantalizingly close to her chin. Striated abdominals quivered as she bent backward, and I could have given my right arm to be one of the wicks licking her navel. After extinguishing their incendiary instruments, the trio bowed toward the crowd, whose sounds drowned out those of Apellon momentarily. The mug of mykhoaska I imbibed earlier had me feeling giddy, though not yet overwhelmed; once Bridget's dance ended, I shared a pipe with my female companions, relaxing enough to enjoy their sensual caresses. "You should come home with us," Euterpe crooned, nibbling on my ear seductively. A surge of icy anxiety broke over me, and I stepped away. "Don't worry," she added quickly as Erato giggled. "It will be fun..." This scenario, perhaps the most popular fantasy among all the heterosexual males I have ever met, was one with which I first became versed via Varian and virtuality. Part of me found the proposition to be deliciously appealing; nonetheless, the rest craved an intimate connection of emotional depth. "I honestly would love to," I sighed, "yet regret that I must decline." This seemed to catch them by surprise. "Are you serious?" Erato asked. "I'm afraid so," I replied remorsefully. "I'm sorry..." "Don't be; we'll have a good time whether or not you join," she assured me, but with noticeable confusion. "Since when did you take up celibacy?" I hesitated, unsure of how to explain my reluctance. "I'll bet it's someone else, whom he admires from afar," Euterpe intuited, "putting her up on a pedestal, so he can strive for the unattainable." "How utterly noble, and what a pity," Erato said; noting for my benefit, "Well, you know where to find us, if your decision changes." Swiveling to embrace her friend, she shot me a sidelong glance as they kissed, lustfully. Unresistantly watching their tongues mingle, I realized my tryp had arrived in earnest; then excused myself on the mumbled pretense of urination. With racing heart and pouring sweat, I surreptitiously escaped to prepare for what I imagined lay ahead, panting heavily in brush beside the agora. Upon return, I saw that a circle of torches had formed around two men – Will and Menelaos, a native farmer I knew by reputation alone, who lived in Lakedaimon. The music transitioned to a simpler, relentlessly driving beat, embellished by the twangy resonance of stringed gourds, synchronized with their movements whilst they stalked each other in a sparring ritual. Wearing just trunks, their mesomorphic musculature rippled in the firelight, exemplifying excellence of human anatomy through both its pale and darkly pigmented ethnicities. Their capoeira game constituted a challenge for the championship belt of Olympik martial arts, which Will defended thrice prior. Although I still had yet to witness a fight, I gathered that he trained for the combat sports, when not indisposed by his family life, work or yoga, in what he called the Areian tradition. The match at hand comprised feints, parries, light strikes, and a spellbinding flurry of takedown attempts; by continuous maneuvering, their overlapping volleys and acrobatic attacks occupied the same volume of space, dislocated solely in time. Defying gravity with an impressive twisting frontflip over his opponent's round kick, forcing Will to follow through or else give up his back, Menelaos landed on his feet in a bow and the song resolved abruptly. Will reciprocated this gesture of deference, indicating acceptance of his contest, as the spectators roared. Reverberations of Apellon resumed, synergistically intertwining intonation, electronics, and animal vocalizations, whilst the sandy, ecstatic free-for-all began anew. The visual acuity induced by psilocybin led to dizzying trails;

essentially my simultaneous apperception of multiple moments, I observed. When I found Bridget again, she was dancing with the challenger; whereas being tall or handsome were not valid reasons for me to dislike Menelaos, I certainly disliked the sight of him grinding against her backside, his chin tucked over her trapezius, her mouth facing toward his, exchanging breath with parted lips nearly touching. Frankly, he did have better moves than I; thus lacking confidence to advance on the object of my ardent worship so aggressively, I allowed jealousy to get the best of me, and turned to leave Parnassos, my originally celebratory attitude becoming suddenly sullen.

A hand on my shoulder stopped me; it belonged to Oulixeus, enjoying the rare luxury of an evening's childcare with his lovely wife Penelopeia, whose pregnant womb was on prominent display, decorated as if transparent.

"Looking for somebody?" he asked, arms betwixt swollen bosom and midriff.

"It's these mushrooms," I spluttered. "There is just
too much going on for me to handle them right now!"

"Happens from time to time," Penelopeia said breezily, proffering a spliff.
I reached instinctively, then withdrew my hand upon further consideration.

"I think I've had enough," I told her, as Aeiolus' voice counseled me.

"Suit yourself," she replied, adding, "We'll be here if you need help tonight."

"What I need is to get out of here," I gasped, disoriented by all the masks.

"Home is that way," noted Oulixeus, spinning me around. "Just remember
to give thanks and you'll do fine. May the source be with you, brother."

My frantic exit, amidst escalating waves of psychic intensity, quelled panic; I had no particular objective, except to avoid the sight of Bridget writhing erotically with Menalaos. Given distance, the music's volume diminished, restoring my sense of coordination along the luminaria-marked pathway. Vicious thirst drew me off track, through a patch of turgid touch-me-not, toward the Pytheian fountain, where I encountered the blind, aged sage, alone other than a vitreous bong sitting beside her. Folklore said she could tell future events by vapors of the salvia it contained blown across her pool, though lessons of the diviner's mint were thought inapprehensible for most; and I smelled upon approach that another supplicant had visited recently. Despite singling me out before the villagers in the theatron of Delphinios, not three moons earlier, my presence on the eve of Ayakinthia was entirely unremarkable; the seeress outwardly did not know or cared who I might be.

"Have you also come to learn how you will die?" she inquired eerily.

Albeit an intriguing prospect, psilocybin had different ideas for me.

"No, I haven't, because I believe the manner of my death is indeterminate,
and to put faith in your prophecy would be to give up my volition therein.
Even if it all is already written, I would rather not ruin the surprise."

"You speak with wisdom beyond your years, child," the oracle replied as her
hand dipped in the spring. "I give you then a hermetic message in its place:
Whilst we ingest our teachers, they to us do the same.
Beware how you present your soul to hyperspace,
for this ride of ours is now bound with the allies' fates."

Seeking higher ground, I strolled among gravestones, which were befitting to my mood; the fireflies had emerged, and I felt glad for their fellowship. Climbing atop the tallest of tombs, I laid my spine against its warm granite, gazing at the emotional mess in my mind, projected upon star-studded sky.

I did not want to negate my yearning for Bridget; yet I had let it become covetous and self-destructive, when I rationally should have accepted her as either out of my league or plain disinterested, then continued my journey. After all, would it not be best to find my personal fulfillment individually? Musing thus on romantic love, I realized the female complement whom I idealized, or idolized, could never find my breed of adulation attractive. The partner I aspired to be was an empowered, actualized adult, such that I might enter my next relationship ready to grow and contribute, instead of carrying childish needs in front of me, primed for codependence. With this intent, I resolved to go about my life as though solitary by choice, focusing on the cultivation of my unique qualities for their own sake whilst divesting my expectations of being consequently noticed by a woman. Many people, perhaps more than not, neglect to find their fabled soul mate in this life; if I went through mine pursuing a naive infatuation that did not bear fruit, I would hence deprive myself of so much else our precious existence offers. From my cemetery perch, I both heard and saw the aestival evening's songs drifting uphill, like the externalization of spirit predicted by Terence, until they were released, musical abeyance giving way to a chorus of cicadas. A barred owl hooted eight times in the emptiness, then Melpomene called, "Sistren and brethren, please welcome Linos to the stage!" Joyous ejaculations of the dancers brought an unwitting smile to my face; somebody struck a handful of notes on the piano, presumably Aeiolus, and pandemonium ensued. Airmed's voice came next, clarion albeit remote. "I was introduced to the Gospel of Tool during my first earthly encounter with the mushroom, and we share this scripture especially for those of you who are in communion tonight..." An orgasmic howl from the crowd interrupted her, but abruptly yielded to reverent quietude as Amadeus began plucking his cello. A low, insistent bass line soon echoed the melody, followed by a soft drumbeat, their volume billowing; upon the crash of cymbals, fiddle, viola, and piano joined in also. After their anticipatory prelude of mathematically-precise power chords, the orchestra diminished; then an alchemical chant issued forth in Bridget's mezzosoprano, alongside the harmonic tones of her mother and Melopmene, to which the audience responded with decorously brief yelps of ovation. Complex patterns of Aeiolus' dozen fingers tied the symphony together; not until later did I get to witness a recording of its accompanying imagery, projected at the time onto a bleached hemp backdrop by an appendage of Apellon's computer, aptly showcasing universal miracles in cellular mitosis, astral collisions, time-lapsed germination, incubation, and vaginal birth. My own synaesthesia, however, seemed comparably impressive, wherein an origami architecture of DNA strands unfolded new galaxies with each change of metrical signature. Recalling superficially-similar trolls during hologrammatic stadium shows, characterized by hallucinatory disintegration rather than coalescence of thought and imagery, I realized the fundamental contrast betwixt them and Ayakinthia was commodification, or lack thereof. Our tribe cultivated psychedelic sacraments instead of synthetics for profit, while its concert was a celebration of mutual love, not a product to be sold; try as societies might, their money can never buy the basis of an authentic existence, namely free choice and gratitude. Overawed, I missed the lyrics

at first, but managed to hear when the chorus started anew, discovering in so doing that they epitomized my tryp, from whose egoic concerns I had detached enough to explore a visionary tapestry mapping the origins of art. Distance notwithstanding, I felt as if their song went straight for my heart.
"Over-thinking, over-analyzing separates the body from the mind, withering my intuition, missing opportunities and I must feed my will to feel this moment, urging me to cross the line; reaching out to embrace the random, reaching out to embrace what heaven may come...I embrace my desire to swing on the spiral of our divinity and still be a human..."
Whilst they sustained the last syllable, Amadeus' put his bow to the cello, filling the vacuum left by their vocals with a compelling solo, despite illness. A round of applause delineated it from the final crescendo; Aeiolus carried the energy, playing the keys as he also sang in poignant duet with his wife. Regardless of my unrequited affections for their wondrous daughter, I had an amazing life, for which I gave the most heartfelt thanks I could muster; moreover, I paid homage for the surrogate parents who had both nurtured and challenged me in precisely the ways I needed, as no one else could. The coda verse concluded triumphantly, then faded out, punctuated by theatrical rockets fired high into the night; villagers laughed or cheered enthusiastically at their bursts, giving it a Dionysian sense of déjà entendu. Comforted by the void of infinite firmament, indifference of the fireflies, and silence of the dead, I was able to appreciate the remainder of the Aestival's mysteries without returning physically to their venue.

"I need the room," Airmed said, rousing me amidst the night of the full moon with a firm squeeze on my leg whilst I slumbered in the library. I snapped upright in response to the urgent tone of her voice, noticing through the open door that the main house was brilliantly illuminated. "Help me move this," she commanded peremptorily, and I groggily helped her slide the oak table into a corner, shoving my bed and clothes beneath. Stumbling wearily toward the living room, I met a gurney bearing a prone, pregnant figure in plain robes, with Elithyia and Oulixeus standing still behind it. Although frequently absent from the island, or devoted to his family when at home, he had by then formed a fellow brotherhood with me through our running, as well as snippets of philosophy. I felt for him a loyal willingness to go to the ends of the world, which I suspect he reciprocated; thus my heart sank heavily at the sight of his distraught facial expression. Penelopeia, who lay breathing stertorously atop the sweat-soaked sheets, ranked among the village's greatest fiber artisans, and her young son had been the first child of its second native generation. Their family came for dinner periodically, often before Aeiolus and Oulixeus set sail, whereby the tender affection they enjoyed imprinted a subconscious template for my own domestic dreams. She was a sophisticated woman I knew mainly by reputation, with whom I would eagerly have grown better acquainted, since I worried, probably excessively, about her esteem. To my regret, as the primary parent of an energetic toddler, and such a highly-sought artisun, she lacked incentive to invest much in new friendships beyond her childcare cooperative. She treated me affably during these visits but tended to converse with Bridget, who doted on her son, while sharing the concerns of their common work at the textile mill. In general, the hormonal glow symptomatic of women who were expecting appealed to me; nonetheless, I thought pregnancy looked especially becoming on youthful Penelopeia. In light of her imminent birth, Oulixeus had been particularly motivated to finish acquisition of the cement ingredients, working tirelessly to keep our project on schedule however he could; in fact, he brought a load the night of the big pour, yet helped for the entire next day without more than two hour's rest, a superhuman ability developed by keeping watch on dark seas. I admired the diligent efficiency of his efforts, despite an athleticism that would have allowed him to get by with carelessness, easily; this, he said, extended precepts of sailing and his jiujitsu practice to the rest of life.

I wished them well as they passed, joining hands with him in solidarity; the library door closed firmly; and then I collapsed in the living room unto restless dreams, dozing on the couch until disturbed by it shutting again. Elithyia emerged, wearing the ceremonial gown of priestesses, with a small bundle in her arms. Rubbing sleep from my bleary eyes once the kitchen lights turned on, I watched her lay a baby on the table and place a mask over ers face, attached to an artificial respiration bag. Squeezing every few seconds, she seemed to fall asleep on her feet, yet noticed me stirring. "I really should be with the mother; can you lend a hand?" she asked.

At her request, I fetched Aeiolus' metronome, which she set for twenty beats per minute, not missing any of her own. Leaning over the newborn human being whilst receiving her instructions, I swooned. Whereas I had never seen one close, ers head pained me immediately, frightfully enlarged with an extreme case of hydrocephalus that complicated Penelopeia's labor, ultimately requiring Airmed to make the delivery via caesarian. Her tiny child inhaled fluid in the process, hence the necessity of a bag valve mask. Although it obscured ers face, I could tell there was only a single eye, whose socket aimed grotesquely downward as a consequence of skull deformities. This baby made sounds unrecognizable to me, part gasp and part squeak, prior to my realization that they constituted ers piteous efforts at crying. "Oh, you poor thing," Airmed moaned as she came out to wash her hands, removing her surgical garments upon completion of Penelopeia's sutures.

I continued pumping the ventilator through her examination. Unwrapping the fabric and turning the child on ers side, she revealed what appeared to be a huge, violet wound on the back, albeit actually nervous tissue protruding through lumbar vertebrae, still unfused due to spina bifida. When she pinched the skin on ers shriveled, atrophied legs, the newborn did not react, indicating paralysis; issuing a sigh, she returned to the library. Because the house was nearly silent I unwittingly overheard enough of their discussion to grok the situation. In a voice both sympathetic and detached, Airmed explained to the parents that she could surgically close the grievous lesion; yet even if their child evaded meningitis, er would suffer from lifelong paraplegia. Pressure from excess cerebrospinal fluid might be relieved by surgically opening the skull, then compressing the cranial bones until they eventually reconnected; though associated swelling had already obstructed ers brain development, thereby causing irrevocable mental retardation.

The remaining conversation was limited to murmuring between Oulixeus and Penelopeia, with occasional remarks from Elithyia. After a few minutes

the parents arrived at a decision; Airmed confirmed that they were certain, leaving the chamber without questioning it twice. She quietly went upstairs, then laid out vials and syringes whilst I continued pumping the ventilator. "They've asked for euthanasia," she told me needlessly. "You're welcome to stay if you wish, but once the injections are loaded I can administer solo." I hailed from a culture wherein talk of death had been stigmatized, whose medicine sought to prevent it however possible, rather than enhance life. In a society measuring human welfare by infant mortality statistics and actuarial notation, the very idea of dying well comprised a blasphemous contradiction in terms; thence its prevailing dogma conceded the moral high ground to prolonging earthly existence, regardless of cost, sense, or mercy. Considering my own consternation about ethics of the scenario before us, Airmed's serenity intrigued me; so I chose to stay, though with reluctance. When the syringes were prepared she took my hand in prayer, declaiming, "Naked came I from my mother's womb, and naked I shall return thither; the gods giveth, and the gods hath taken away. Blessed be their names." She bent down to kiss the engorged forehead of deformed newborn, who stirred in response, crying again. Finding a tiny blue vein in the translucent skin of ers arm, she inserted a needle full of anesthesia and depressed its plunger; the tiny frame struggled briefly, and soon fell limp. "There is no need for that now," she whispered, stopping me, then the metronome. With my resolve wavering, I looked away as she removed the breathing apparatus and administered the final injection, which induced cardiac arrest. Turning around, I saw a tear running down Airmed's cheek; this time, my hand held hers until I felt the child's spirit had left the room, listening to muffled wailing in the library. At her instruction, I hauled wood from behind the house, whilst she carried the fabric-swaddled corpse to its fire circle. By the glow of the setting moon, we built and lit a funeral pyre, watching sacred flames of transformation amidst palpitating cricketsong. Elithyia joined us near dawn to say goodnight; having been awake with the parents since the evening prior, she sought her own bed, noting they were sufficiently at peace, in spite of the circumstances, to fall asleep together. With our silence broken by the doula's departure, Airmed explained that it was customary for those stillborn, or given defects warranting such intervention, to be neither named nor buried, unlike other children.
"What causes this...kind of...mutation?" I asked uncomfortably.
"The fallout, I suspect," she replied, a plaintive note in her tone.
"Didn't you tell me when I arrived it wasn't so high anymore?"
"Indeed, I did; optimistically it seems, since I hoped to be free therefrom; but these illnesses are prevalent among those exposed to nuclear reactor meltdowns or the United States' depleted uranium munitions; because she was born here so early, Penelopeia's ova have been exposed to some of the higher total radiation loads in erstory; thus I must entertain this diagnosis."
"You've seen it previously, then," I observed with curiosity.
"Once," she whispered, following a pregnant pause. "My son, actually."
Before I could apologize for inadvertently broaching a sensitive subject, Airmed began recounting her long resistance of maternal urges. She made Aeiolus wait until she was forty, and the village on its way to concrescence, only willing to raise children in a world with the possibility of future healing.

"His congenital disorder foreboded ill especially, as the tribe's first birth; unnerved by its implications, we fought viciously over our fateful decision. Although it caused us great pain, Aeiolus maintained he had not been meant for this plane; akin to the cases of crops or livestock wherein we would have culled without a doubt. Our community must adapt to a rapidly-changing environment, an ethos that, as well as his anatomy, bound our son never to procreate; hence he was genetically dead already. Even if surgery might have furnished him life, it would be an abomination and burden to the tribe. I agreed on principle, yet couldn't bring myself to euthanize my own son. Aeiolus did so instead, allowing me to build an irrational resentment of him in my postpartum depression. Tormented by our baleful sacrifice, I wanted not to get pregnant again; and soon thereafter, lost my brother as well."

"Areis?" I asked. "I heard mention of him in Council, after our initiation."

"A disgraceful charade," she scoffed. "I'm sorry you didn't get to meet him; a man of real integrity and perhaps the greatest martial artist in his day, whose fierce autonomy our leaders could neither comprehend nor contain."

"What happened to him?"

"He left the island, long ago; before you were even conceived."

"Why?" I wondered, observing that people always seemed to talk around, but not of his deeds; rubbing her temples, she inhaled deeply from memory. "In the beginning a disease afflicted this community, commonly called fear, to which he proved immune. In spite of contributing immensely during his tenure among the pioneers, his destiny ultimately lay in another sphere. He would be ruled by no person or institution; eventually, his attitudes toward propriety and authority cast him as antisocial. At the end many of us still held love for Areis; yet he could not live with the community any more than it could live with him; hence, he accepted ostracism."

"Not like the infamous mechanic?" I clarified.

"No, this happened to be legitimate," she avowed; "his idea, in fact."

"For what reason, if I might intrude?"

"You're not intruding at all," she said unequivocally. "He was willing to commit murder for the sake of justice, defined solely in his terms, and preferred to ask forgiveness therefor, rather than permission."

I observed that my programming prevented me from readily admitting thoughts of killing human beings, whereas the culture it spawned did so with brutal efficiency, by military, penal, economic, or unconscious agency; nonetheless, to openly discuss homicide felt disconcertingly inappropriate.

"Truthfully, he had already decided to leave us in pursuit of his doom; Aeiolus, ever the politician, simply conspired beside him to achieve his own ends through my brother's departure; yet upon learning of their collusion, I accused him of manipulating Areis, then grew so upset that I left him, continuing my medical practice whilst living alone. The sorrow brought by helping others through gestation and childbirth became unbearable, until I disappeared from the island in hopes of finding the joy I had lost. I didn't tell anybody because they would have argued for me to stay when my mind felt made; except on the eve of departure I went to say goodbye to the one who understood, and in our zygote Bridget's soul incarnated. As far as I knew, I was infertile, setting sail without a second thought. Leaving liberated me, and I reached the Caribbean before discovering our conception. The flood of emotions that came from this knowledge, however, could not be denied. Albeit locked away behind walls of grief, my desire remained for family; no matter how far I traveled, my love for Aeiolus stayed with me, since no other man can even hold a candle to him. Realizing my mistake, I returned in crazed haste, via the riskiest, most gut-wrenching solo passage of my life, beating upwind on the Gulf Stream in early spring for over a thousand miles; a frenetic epic of terrible waves, squalls, and morning sickness, concluded by a nightmarish freak blizzard. After contending with two torn sails, I ran out of fresh water; delirious from hypothermic exhaustion, I finally accepted that I couldn't make headway in the storm by jib alone, lying down in the cabin on an outbound tack to take what might come; but then the wind shifted west, and a fair zephyr carried me home. Despite my debilitation, the sight of Aeiolus standing there as the *Wyrd* limped into the harbor made the ordeal I endured worthwhile. Although Bridget's conception had been unplanned, it was no accident. The choice to euthanize our child tore us apart; yet that separation gave our relationship a depth thenceforth we may not else have attained."

Allowing a respectful period of silence, I eventually asked, "Do you think Penelopeia and Oulixeus will fare as well as yall, in the wake of their loss?" She sighed with a weariness I had not seen previously. "I daresay they'll do fine. As on the morning of my ill-starred birth, the moon will be eclipsed an hour after our sunrise, attesting to its influence on the tides of change; and their tragic night notwithstanding, a new day is dawning as we speak."

"What a burden," I mused compassionately, "to have the power of curing illness or forestalling death, but an inconsistent rate of success in so doing."

"I'm long past the time when I presumed to choose who should live or die; if I can, I leave that responsibility to entities more powerful and wise than I will ever be. To do otherwise in a vocation like mine is emotional suicide; which if why I differ from my husband, if it comes to the concept of try."

"How so?" I wondered, amidst momentary confusion.

"For him, life or death is a matter of pure awareness. How can I attach to outcomes of events that began long before and will go well beyond my brief existence? I see, with time, what goes around comes around, whether in ghosts of Aries, unfinished business, or a restless soul needing exorcism, so I just do what I can for those I love. Since the world is of me as I of it, this circle extends to infinity; and the rest I leave in the hands of the gods."

I noticed then, at the corner of her eye, despite her brave words, she had let herself cry. Burgundy sunrise broke over the bluffs as the pyre burned down to ash; hearing a cough at my back, I turned to see Aeiolus squatting against the south wall of their home. Elithyia's exit had apparently left its entrance ajar, permitting him to sneak out for eavesdropping undetected. He and Airmed rose in tearful unison; as they gazed at one another, I could only guess at the scope of nonverbal communication passing between them. Aeiolus crossed the yard, gently took her in his arms, and said, "I know." Choked up myself, I quietly slipped inside, closing the door behind me.

In hopes of defusing my attraction to Bridget, I focused on the job, then came to love it; perhaps a bit more obsession than love, actually, but helpful regardless. Unlike her, work never acted fickle or capricious;

albeit frustratingly difficult at times, the Ark remained steadfast and reliably there for me. Soon after solstice, Aephaistos finished piping the heat pump condenser; once our underground plumbing, drainage, waterproofing and grading were completed, everything left to do was indoors. This came as a relief, partially because summer had grown inhumanely hot; moreover, I would be spared the sight of Bridget's comings and goings from the mill. Although she shared dinner with her parents once per week, I managed to avoid the awkwardness of overlapping these visits by putting in late hours. When our paths did cross, I behaved courteously and respectfully, training myself to admire absent desire, rather than pretend to ignoring her beauty. Construction of the Ark's partitions and floors proceeded quickly, thanks to the elegance of its layout, as well as our reprieve from weather-related challenges. Upon entrance at the northwest corner, the seed vault would be on your left, running to the building's east end, with cool cupboards above sharing a full-height internal wall at their common southern side. Straight ahead, along the west, you would find the mechanical closet, then storage compartments containing largely soil amendments and provisions. Quarters for the Arkonaut, accessible via a ship's ladder, had been fit in the narrow space above, whose design drew inspiration from the compact cabin of the *Wyrd.* All open floor area in the southeastern quartile was reserved for the grow room, divided from floor to ceiling by multi-tiered racks of potted trees, for optimal utilization of space and illumination, whilst passively creating a temperature gradient that permitted plants to be arranged in accordance with their microclimatological preferences. Most of the indoor work came down to mud and insulation. Hempcrete, made from the woody hurds constituting the bulk of cannabis stalks, has about 40% the heat resistance of polystyrene foam per unit of thickness. Limited by his electrical allowance for the heat pump, Amadeus specified a staggering two-foot layer around the seed vault. The total volume for the project exceeded two hundred fifty yards, or thrice that of the concrete, yet weighed only thirty tons, tantamount to the yield one might expect from ten or fifteen acres in a season. However, this was more than the storehouse had in inventory, which presented us a sequencing problem, since insulation preceded all other work on the project, but the stands still growing in fields of Arkadia and Attika would not be harvested until Astraia; unless we sacrificed their textile fiber by putting the whole raw crop into the walls, thus making field-dried stalks available soon after Lammas. "I'd hate to do so," Aeiolus lamented. "If we had better equipment…" Ethos averse to waste, he proposed to pull Amadeus and Aephaistos' away from the Ark long enough to take another stab at a decorticator for unretted hemp; I felt comfortable with this because electrical and mechanical work had slowed down substantially by then. "We'll harvest early in any case; if our design fails, you can have it all," he promised. The standard application for hempcrete was exterior wall construction, wherein resistance to the elements became a builder's overriding concern; these dictated the use of hydrated lime as a binder, albeit slow to cure. Given that the Ark's envelope happened to be uniquely protected by its masonry shell, I suggested a mix utilizing gypsum plaster instead, which is fast-setting and does not cause chemical burns on exposed skin, as calcium

hydroxide is apt to do. Aeiolus seemed thrilled by this idea, since the coal-fired power plant whence he obtained fly ash also produced plaster of paris via filtration of its exhaust through a sulfate-absorbing limestone slurry. We still needed some quicklime as retarder in the hempcrete mix, then later as a desiccant for orthodox seeds; but compared to the traditional version, our gypsum formula consumed far less embodied energy, while simplifying materials acquisition substantially. The hempcrete crew was accustomed to erecting many shutters at once; these required tamping and had to stay in place until the danger of slumping passed, whereas our new mix enabled more convenient formwork, thus requiring them to mold just what could be placed by lunch; afterward, the boards were moved to their next area and refastened using premeasured spacers without concern for the previous lift. To avoid delaying Aephaistos amidst his completion of the cooling system, they insulated the seed vault first, working so efficiently that our progress stalled temporarily for lack of ingredients. At the cusp of Leon's dark moon, I came home to see Aeiolus preparing his signature quahog chowder with a sack full of hurds sitting on the kitchen floor beside him.
"So it works," I guessed optimistically.
"Not quite," he replied. "The fiber is inferior; somebody needs to be there constantly unclogging the machine; but at least we're on Schlichten's tail. Someday we may catch up to where he was a century and half ago."
"Where's Amadeus?" I asked. "We should celebrate."
Stirring intently, he said, "It's been a long day, and he went to bed early." As it happened, the engineer's singularity was near; from then on, he did not often leave the guest house. If I knocked on his door for consultation, he feebly told me to return another time. When the 'Please Do Not Disturb' sign appeared on its knob at last, I resolved to answer my own questions. The only people who entered his space with any frequency were Airmed, bringing food, medicine, and fellowship; or Bridget, who would read to him on the evenings she came to dinner and sing in mellifluous dialects.
Although I kept my distance, if I chanced upon a window open to the courtyard I did not deny the opportunity to listen. Her voice touched the divine, reminding me of a theory invoked by Terence in Food of the Gods; that the development of verbal language had been the province of women, because as omnivorous foragers, the ability to describe plants and their locations would have conferred on them untold evolutionary advantages. Men, conversely, were naturally selected by mates for hunting prowess, which consisted primarily of observation skills or patient waiting for an auspicious moment to strike; a livelihood wherein oral communication was of conspicuously less utility. Savoring Bridget's ineffable mezzosoprano, I acknowledged that her words still sounded more practiced, and precious, than mine, wishing only to hear her singing go on until the ends of time.

"...along with the other animals, the stones, the trees,
and the clouds, we ourselves are characters within a
huge story that is visibly unfolding all around us;
participants within the vast imagination,
or Dreaming, of the world."

~ David Abram, The Spell of the Sensuous ~

"The world is indeed full of peril and in it there are many dark places;
but still there is much that is fair. And though in all lands,
love is now mingled with grief, it still grows, perhaps, the greater."

~ J.R.R. Tolkien, The Fellowship of the Ring ~

LEON

Grace gave birth at the new moon, with Will at her side and under the
expert aegis of Elithyia. Their daughter, named Hekate, would be the last
child born on the island for quite some time, due to the Council-prescribed
suspension of procreation. I felt deeply pleased by my subsequent receipt
of an invitation for the ceremony whereat selected men assembled to honor
Will, known as a papow; a portmanteau of 'papa power' that lent itself to
humorous puns about popping; while the intention of the event afforded a
masculine counterpart for traditional blessing ways, since birth may leave
Dad with a sense of alienation or even abandonment, if only unconscious,
especially by the brethren for whom parental duties do not permit him time.
During pregnancy the tribe's attention, as well as his own, tend toward the
mother, to ensure her health and comfort; after delivery, they fixate on the
infant, who is such an incredible gift to behold. The maternal flow of milk
and hormones can become a communion whence the father feels excluded;
hence any romantic consideration he might hope to receive from his partner
is necessarily diverted to formation of her new emotional and genetic bond.
Dad gets to participate intermittently in their shared adventure by holding
the child, changing diapers, or caring for Mom; yet knows subliminally that
he became biologically superfluous at the moment he ejaculated; then the
reality of the intimacy and autonomy he has given up truly begins to sink in.
The papow served as our tribe's consolation prize for him, marking a man's
entrance into parenthood, in appreciation of what he, and he alone, brings
to his family. This ritual revolved around deliberate preparation of a wine
unique to each novel soul, whereby the magic of the occasion was captured,
embellished by fermentation, and preserved for painstaking dispensation,
once the respective child came of age. Will's evening invoked his tale of the
birthing process, including dramatic anecdotes preceding it, which a vow of
confidentiality prevents me from repeating here; nonetheless, I can say that
he added some of her placenta to the cauldron of tea constituting the mead,

along with a prayer for his daughter's healthy and spirited development. Oulixeus spoke next, assuaging any concerns about his tolerance of the celebration; he seemed in possession of an uncanny ability to dissociate his own grief from happiness for the fresh parents, though he did not elide the tragic subject, contributing ash from ers funeral pyre to honeyed brew. Continuing around the circle, every man related a relevant story, provided counsel, committed support, issued warning, or paid homage to Will, whilst placing ingredients of medicinal and metaphorical significance in the tea. Other fathers were apt to pour libations from bottles of their own births, thereby signifying the childrens' intertwined destinies as they inoculated Hekate's with not just the gravity of those ceremonies, but of the papows that went into them, then into those, back through an unbroken lineage reaching to the origin of the tradition. The childless among us tendered herbs, roots, and fruit; because I am not at liberty to repeat our sharings, I suppose you must manifest such customs in your community to grok what can happen if upstanding males gather together in a heartfelt manner for feats of emotional maturity. I especially noticed the solidarity between the martial artists with whom he trained, begat by jiujitsu practice wherein they literally entrusted one another with life and limb amidst submissions. When my turn came, I reflected on never meeting my father, then on how I could have been affected, mentioning his specter's enigmatic appearance to teach me of leverage in my moment of crisis. I was interested to find, through Will, that I had ended up working in construction, also his arena of professional expertise; and felt as if his restless spirit might requite bygone dreams by guiding my vocation, which better embodied the little I knew of my dad's morals than his own. Near the end I realized, though did not say, I sought somehow to redeem the home life he, my mom and I were denied. "Admittedly, this is awkward for me because I suspect you know me least of all in attendance; but am grateful nonetheless for the chance to be present in such an exemplary circle. Growing up, I was usually ashamed of my own gender, and it's a privilege to now live among authentic peers. Your wisdom enables me to prepare for parental responsibility, should I ever have that adventure; while I trust you'll be a spectacular father, based on paternal guidance you've already offered to me, wherefore I thank you sincerely." Will laughed presciently; I doubt he would mind me excerpting his response. "I do know you, more deeply than you may suspect, and we have the rest of our lives still ahead. I've wanted an opportunity to invite you to join us in the dojo, or imbibing my ally, *la purga*, as you have much to learn from martial arts and regurgitation of new universes, perhaps even of your dad, whose truth is out there, awaiting discovery. Regarding your own future, I expect family will come without rushing; you're young, yet already exhibit and cultivate the qualities a man offers his wife. I pray you find one as fit for you as mine is for me to the inevitable storms of this winding journey, so I may look forward to giving fraternal advice at your papow someday." I put retted hemp in the cauldron, fragments saved from our first meeting, when he introduced me to work. They represented gratitude for his support, as well as Will's tolerance of my youthful overzealousness; my intention for his progeny to reap bountiful harvests; and my wish to partake in the labor of sustaining our tribe beside him, and them, for many years thenceforth.

Once we had reclaimed the Ark from our muddy maelstrom of hempcrete, Aephaistos welded sheets of aluminum to line the seed room; then, whilst he ran coils of copper tubing on its ceiling, we plastered interior surfaces. On the momentous date whereat all for which we had diligently worked was connected and pressurized, our heat pump failed to function; the refrigerant would not condense properly, returning to its chamber still above freezing. For hours on end we wracked our brains, yet the apparatus lay so far beyond my expertise that I deemed myself unqualified to diagnose the problem. In the evening, I went to see the engineer, who did not answer initially; at a loss for options, I reluctantly knocked again, with greater urgency. "Later, please," came a hoarse whisper I barely heard through his door. "Sorry, but I really need your expertise," I begged, "with the heat pump." An uncomfortably long pause passed ere he bade me enter the guest house. Although we lived next to each other, almost a month elapsed since I last visited Amadeus, and I noticed the drastic metamorphosis immediately. Even reclining in bed, I could tell that his former verve had diminished to a withered and seemingly fragile remnant beneath the sheets. The skin over his frame took on grayish cast; while his eyes, closed when I arrived, flicked open briefly at the latch strike, revealing the deep yellow film of jaundice. He coughed weakly into a kerchief, amid a stertorous struggle for breath. "How are you?" I asked on impulse; this seemed an indelicate inquiry, yet I could not think what else propriety permitted me say in the circumstances. "Dying; isn't that obvious?" he wheezed, and his sardonic chuckle progressed to wracking expectoration; then he extended the rag toward me, as if to show the piteous results thereof. "No thanks," I replied, averting my gaze. "I don't blame you...better not to ruin the surprise." "How do you mean?" I wondered. "I never believed the decay of my physical body would be so disgusting, and those damned cigarettes are going to serve as nails for the coffin." "I figured you'd quit," I remarked, judging from an absence of tobacco odor. "Only because I began coughing up blood; evidently mine doesn't clot anymore. Now I have pneumonia and can't even smoke at the end." He panted heavily as I took a seat by his side; hearing him talk of his death with such simultaneous nonchalance and brutal honesty unnerved me, but with the ice already broken, I stayed present for the encounter. "Is Airmed giving you anything?" "Opium, which is about all she can," he said. "I wish she'd let me take more; she claims I might die of heart failure." He heaved again, so violently I averted my gaze. "It's funny, since I'm going to die and that appears to be about the best way. She's cured cancer with cannabis oil before, albeit ineffective against my breed of leukemia, regrettably." I remained silent, lest I speak irreverently in the face of his terminal illness. "Well, what about this alleged heat pump?" Amadeus prompted me at last. Eager to change the subject, I reported on all of the pressures, flow rates, and heat differentials we observed at the Ark; he went through a logical series of questions, indicating puzzlement in response to my answers. "Wait just a second - did you backfill the condenser?"

It was that simple. Our heat exchanger had been submerged in a water bath still sitting above ground, thus exposed to daytime highs in excess of a hundred degrees, rather than the subterranean Fahrenheit fifty-five wherefore he designed it. Of course we were unable to cool the seed room; despite prayers to the contrary, heat could not move against the gradient. "I thought your job was to catch my mistakes," he added with a raspy laugh, which provoked another fit of coughing. I waited until his spasms subsided, and when he slipped into semi-conscious exhaustion, moved for the door. As I reached for its handle, he mumbled something that sounded like 'hell'.

"Beg your pardon?"

"Hellen," he repeated, loudly enough for me to hear.

"My daughter...I wish I could see her once more."

"Where is she?" I wondered aloud.

He issued a slow sigh. "I honestly have no idea; she left, years ago."

"I'm sorry," I began, but the empty apology hung in the air. "Why?"

He swallowed, with difficulty. "As rumor has it, she was taken prisoner."

I suddenly understood the previously-related rape tragedy to a much fuller, evil extent; Kastor, who sacrificed himself to save the village from pillagers, had been Bridget's lover, the victim's brother, and also Amadeus' last heir.

"If you ever happen to meet her, I need you to pass a message on for me."

In his sickly delirium, he begged the impossible of me; wanting neither to dash vain hopes, nor to deceive him, I uttered an ambiguous grunt. "Please tell her...tell her she's not to blame, and did nothing wrong...what occurred is my fault alone. Tell her...I'm so sorry...can you do that for me?"

"If I see her, I will," I promised solemnly, though if sounded like a lie.

"Thank you," he whispered, closing his eyes again. "I'm very tired now..."

Relieved by this break in the tension, I left quietly to let him rest.

I crossed Bridget's path as she exited the mill on a misty evening after Lammas, whereupon we both worked late and no one else was in sight. She casually offered me her pipe, opting to ignore the precedent distance between us; then we silently watched the sun set through a narrow strip of sky below the western clouds, atop the Ark's freshly-planted roof garden. Once it had fallen beneath the sea's surface she invited me to join her on a walk through the hollow in Akhaia; naturally I accepted without hesitation. The road she selected was initially of sufficient width for occasional gaps in the canopy; yet as we descended the ravine its foliage closed overhead, affording little visual guidance through the fog. I followed the sound of her walk when if I could hear it, groping for the trail's roots and rocks with my feet when I could not, sensing as I went off track by understory branches raking my face. At such junctures, she waited quietly for me to catch up, sometimes inadvertently bumping into her from behind.

"Can you not see?" she hissed at first, impatiently.

"Not at all," I admitted, amazed that she could. "I'm sorry..."

"No, it is I who should be sorry," she whispered, in a gentler tone. "Living in the city must have desensitized your photoreceptors."

"Do you think it's reversible?" I asked.

"Perhaps, though you'll need to spend much more time in the darkness."

Whether in my haste to catch up, or lured by her pheromones, I know not;

but I eventually stumbled into an abrupt collision with Bridget's back. "I'm starting to think you might enjoy this," she teased, catching me, still balanced, leaning firmly as I steadied myself rather than recoiling. "Sorry," I said disingenuously, lingering for an inhalation of her delicious fragrance prior to stepping away, chagrined. "I still can't see anything."
"Why do you do that?"
"Do what?" I asked uneasily, with my heart racing from the expectation she saw through my ruse and would accuse me of smelling her again.
"Apologize," she clarified, allowing me to relax slightly.
"It's always 'sorry' from you; are you really so fraught with regret?"
"I suppose it's my ignorance and my clumsiness I regret," I confessed.
"You need not be sorry for those, so long as you strive to surmount them."
Kneeling down, Bridget declared, "This must be the spot"; then, sweeping aside an armful of damp leaves from the forest floor, she revealed a bed of embers, illuminating the fragrant ground via their ethereal blue glow.
"Let there be light."
"How did you do that?" I wondered dimly.
"I did naught," she replied. "This is fairy fire...bioluminescent fungi."
The gleam thus cast permitted me to discern my companion's silhouette; crouching next to her, I leaned attentively over the area she had cleared. Beneath the debris were countless slithering worms, prowling spiders, and industrious insects crawling across radiant fragments of decomposing trees, which ordinarily passed my notice.
"I had no idea such a phenomenon existed."
"How would you?" she asked rhetorically, albeit absent condescension. "And yet, despite your ignorance, it has been here, transforming wood into soil for millions of years, fostering a world where the two of us might live."
She lifted a palmful of the magically incandescent debris to her face; by this improvised lamp I could just make out the curve of her lips, and speculated hopefully on whether they were beckoning mine.
"What do you think of that?"
Under her scrutiny, I fervently wished to say something clever or profound; the words, "There is more to reality than meets the eye," came to my mind.
"Indeed," she agreed, holding a fragment of fairy fire before me betwixt thumb and forefinger. "Imagine - our entire galaxy could be as this, a tiny speck in the hand of some god, while we are minor characters in her dream."
"Well, I wouldn't go quite so far," I argued with naïve self-assurance. "It's well-established that there is a vacuum beyond our atmosphere..."
"Thanks professor," she interjected brusquely, "yet you forget I've read the books, too. Truthfully, neither of us have gone out in space to check; thus, your guess, based solely in what you've been told, is as good as mine."
"But the evidence for an expanding universe is overwhelming," I argued.
"As it once was for the geocentric paradigm," she quipped. "You expect me to believe humanity has defined reality by what we can see of its surface?"
This gave me pause, in which a territorial buck snorted on the slope above.
"Even ignoring the possibility that your evidence is created by observation," she went on, then switched to a familiar nasal impression; "It's just the limit case for unlikelihood that the Universe would spring forth from nothing in a single instant for no reason. It makes no sense; in fact, it's no different than

saying, 'God said: Let there be light.' And what the philosophers of science are saying is, 'Give us one free miracle, and we will roll from that point forward, from the birth of time to the crack of doom; just one free miracle."
Feeling myself blush, I admitted my logical error, grateful for the darkness.
"Terence?" I ventured.
"Eros and the Eschaton," affirmed Bridget.
"I must have missed that part, since Aeiolus caught me in its midst."
"Please don't mistake my meaning; I love science dearly," she amended, "though I've found its greatest service to us is the revelation of how much humanity does not know about the Universe, instead of how much we do. When science relies on coincidence; when it denies the consciousness, logos, or divinity infusing everything by insisting we alone comprehend, and should manipulate their workings, it falls prey to the most specious practice of all."
"Which is what?"
"The creation of data to support a conclusion, rather than vice versa."
She let this critique of syllogism lie for my consideration in the subsequent void, filled with nocturnal sounds of the Akhaian forest.
"A coincidence is what you have leftover when you apply a bad theory," I added, quoting from the same scripture to break the silence and simultaneously demonstrate that her point had been well-taken.
"You've come a long way from the city rat I first met, yet still have plenty of deprogramming ahead, my friend."
She was correct; "Perhaps some time travel would help me, then," I suggested on impulse, with echoes of 'Eros and the Eschaton' in my ears.
Laughing, she patted my hand ambiguously. "Always rushing, you are."
"Only because we might be running out of time," I said in my defense.
"Time?" Bridget asked dubiously. "Tell me, what is time? Moreover, in this endlessly expanding universe of yours, how will we ever run out?"
Mystified by my own paradoxical reasoning, I stared at her quizzically, and remembered in so doing that she had night vision far superior to mine.
"Assuming it survives us, life on this blue orb has a billion orbits remaining before the sun's luminosity drives away all water, thereby making biology as we know it potentially impossible - a duration longer than terrestrial evolution to date, or the whole tenure of multicellular organisms hereon. I suspect in forthcoming ages this planet may engender intelligence with sufficient self-awareness to humbly pursue the prospect of an alien home, if or when the adaptation of our Earth proves untenable," Bridget argued.
"Makes sense to me," I agreed conditionally, "but how would you persuade civilized humanity? My own best friend, like our culture, upon discovery of worlds beyond this, inveterately lusted to conquer them by projecting imperialism into infinity, absent foresight, introspection, and trajectory."
"Because your concepts of cosmic travel stem from unsustainable models, constrained by physical bodies and fossil energy; motivated by narcissistic, expansionist fantasies; coupled with the desperate appeal of escape amidst cataclysmic resource depletion," she noted. "Now our gods enact the myth of Phaëton, watching a puerile culture rush for power and fall poignantly."
"Phaëton?" I echoed. "I only know the eccentric asteroid, of the Geminids."
"Named for the sun's progeny, from Ovid's Metamorphoses who doubted his divine parentage, and as proof desired to drive his father's chariot for a day.

When he up took their reigns, the forces drawing Helios felt Phaëton could
not restrain them; careening out of control, his ill-fated flight evaporated
the seas, caused ice ages, and forged deserts. Angry oceans rose to drown
him but did not quench the fire; inevitably compelling the gods to intervene,
and hubris smote his ruin upon the sky, whence he plummeted to Eridanos,
the smouldering river that leads to Aides. As quoted by Terence at the end
of 'Eros and Eschaton', the grateful dead say, 'You can't go back and you
can't stand still; if the thunder don't get you, then the lightning will.' "
    "Sounds like a demise befitting the American empire," I remarked.
    "Indeed, and I trust we must have time, since his epitaph was writ
at the height of Rome's, contemporaneous with its alleged Christ:
    'Here Phaëton lies, who in the sun-god's chariot fared;
    and though greatly he failed, more greatly he dared.' "
I sensed a warning in the allegory. "What does this have to do with me?"
She grunted dubiously. "Beware the urge to harness unknown powers."
    "You mean with dimethyltryptamine?"
"I mean in any realm, though the deiman is a relevant example," Bridget
elaborated. "It's not all rainbows and unicorns in the psychonauticon."
    "I have no illusions to that effect," I declared firmly.
"Then you should not enter innerspace as our specie has the interstellar.
Unlike your society across the water, I have no fear that if it's right to leave
the life of this planet will do so; our responsibility in the interim is to prepare
for such a challenge, wherein our participation is predicated upon survival.
Like yours, my mentation resides increasingly in the future; yet I'm learning
to let it come instead of striving toward it. May you someday understand
no exertion is required; events arise when they are ready, regardless of our
efforts to the contrary. Focus on being present, rather than yearning to
meet the deiman; we have plenty of time for travel therein, by definition,
as for space exploration, but only if we can someday manage to approach
those frontiers with an attitude of curiosity, gratitude, and peaceful intent.
"Not necessarily, according to Aeiolus," I said, referring to temporal limits.
    "My father..." Bridget began, then stopped with eerie gravity.
    "...sometimes prefers to inhabit a different future than the rest of us."
I struggled to unravel this as we listened to the treefrogs, katydids, and
continued perambulations of the deer, leaning shoulder to shoulder on
the base of a grandfather locust. Collecting a handful of woody debris,
Bridget ran streams of the fairy fire from one hand into her other.
    "Tell me a story," she demanded suddenly.
    "About what?" I asked with a halting trace of dread.
    "That's up to you; just make it interesting."
    "Interesting?" I swallowed under the pressure.
    "Yes...pretend you're trying to impress me."
While no pretending was required, I hesitated to say anything about it,
concerned that my life prior to the island might be a bore to her.
    "And if I have no stories?" I stalled.
"I shall not be impressed," she told me flatly, then prodded, "yet I suspect
you have more than most. To start, what brought you to the whale grave?"
I opened the tale on Nexus, atop my former roof, realizing mid-sentence I
would need to go much further back for it to make sense, and ultimately

restarted several versions, becoming less articulate with each iteration.
"I'm sorry; this is sort of a long explanation."
"Stop saying that!" she jeered playfully. "I requested it."
Beginning anew, I described the circumstances of Kerberos' death, which
led me to the library in Mrs. Jefferson's studio; I did my best to translate
concurrent ordeals of addiction, discombobulation, isolation, and escape.
During my dehydrated, delirious, mosquito-ridden trek across Burbarus,
Bridget tugged on my shoulder; thus I found myself reclining, head cradled
by her warm lap in a single smooth motion. Due to my nervous excitement
therefrom, augmented by her cannabis, I momentarily grew faint; when
composed again, I spoke of my extended haunting by her would-be father,
Alexander Fremont, culminating in our corporeal meeting on the beach;
how his biography first awakened me to the very shaky basis of my reality;
and of the anger I had borne toward civilization thenceforth, its authorities
especially, for ignoring the ubiquitous evidence of our modern predicament.
"What about your scars?" she wondered.
"Oh yeah," I groaned, surprised I omitted my suicidal near-misadventure;
yet in hindsight I can tell my subconscious deemed it not exactly flattering.
"Do you remember what you were thinking?" she asked once I returned to
my initial introduction, conversing with Aeiolus' phantom on the rooftop.
"That I couldn't figure out whether he was an actual person,
but jumping off would provide an answer of some sort."
"And...?" Bridget coaxed expectantly.
Her simple question startled me. "I'm here now, aren't I?"
She laughed auspiciously. "To the degree that I can see."
"I had heard our memories flash before our eyes when we die," I continued.
"It's a form of time travel," she remarked, "via DMT from your pineal body;
the third eye, or ajna chakra, deep inside your brain on its sagittal plane,
is a mysterious secretory gland believed by some to be the seat of the soul."
This theory resonated with me intuitively. "It's hard for me to say for sure,
but the impression left from my coma is of the future; as if enacting my life
is a process of recollecting, since I've foreseen all this in unconsciousness."
"Not all," she amended, resting a hand on my head. "May I touch them?"
"If you want to, I won't refuse," I replied, though it was needless to say so.
Whilst I explained my craniotomy, whose gruesome details appealed to
the witch doctor in her, Bridget's electrifying fingertips slowly traveled the
full length of incisions that had been made in my scalp, perusing the slight
coronal bulge where titanium of my reconstructed skull met the original.
"Does it ever hurt?" she asked.
"In the past, terribly...not anymore."
"And you did this to yourself to ascertain whether or not my dad existed?"
"I know it seems crazy, yet in the city, for me to get lost became so easy.
I had no connection to whence my food, water and energy came; where in
the world my waste went; what the hidden cost of my drugs was, or how
the effects of my consumption were felt. In a seething cesspool of media
overdose and drug-induced delusion, that book provided a thread tying all
these weird events together when I had lost track of which might be real."
"You were willing to die for this information?"
I reflecting thoroughly thereon to ensure the truth of my response.

"As the epitome of my society, I had nothing to live for besides addictions."
She allowed a pause, listening to a remote pair of barred owls converse.
"Despite your facile paralogy, you've come a long way, and may now
be among few from our generation who can grok what he knew."
"Somebody must remember, after all...if the record of his life dies,
the system that attempted to assassinate him wins," I concluded.
"How else do you expect us to shed all these neurolinguistic pathways and
morphic creodes worn by ages of algorithms based on faulty premises?"
She stopped stroking my scalp, lifted a glowing piece of wood,
and employing it as a torch to see by, examined my face.
"Very strange," she determined finally. "Still an egg;
yet an interesting specimen, unlike any of the other men."
Potential insult notwithstanding, I felt thrilled to be thus noticed,
and moreover, to learn she considered me an adult; assuredly green,
but a man nevertheless. I groped for a cautious response; although my
experience made her statement true, any agreement I might concoct struck
me as self-serving; while to claim else, strictly for the purpose of feeding
our conversation or appearance of modesty, would have been dishonest.
"Thanks..." I began awkwardly, then recovered with, "and you are utterly
unique among all the women I've ever met, and my absolute favorite,"
summoning as much sincerity, intention, and empowerment as I could.
Her fingers stroked my sagittal crest again, with a conspicuously
unnecessary tenderness, causing my entire organism to tingle;
therapeutic attention was a step in the right direction, at least.
"Sorry if it feels like I'm inspecting you," Bridget whispered.
"No need to be sorry," I teased gently, hoping she did not
mean this entirely in the medical connotations of the word.
"You can inspect me any time...I don't mind one bit."

I went to find Ovid later that night, discovering the Metamorphoses had
been checked out of the library by Oulixeus months earlier, and my decision
to rouse him in the wee hours exhibited an admittedly myopic lack of tact.
Exasperated, he told me the book was aboard the *Kismet*; despite staying
up for the rest of the night with this epic, preternatural motivation literally
surged through me as the solar corona came tangent to the horizon during
our run the next morning. At the rocky section of shoreline on which my
training partner typically put distance between us, I kept his pace easily.
The resolution of my perception seemed enhanced, and my cognition was
accelerated, as if I had just upgraded to a better processor; my feet knew
where to plant themselves in advance as I juked through the cobblestones,
abruptly observing, for the first time, his stride had fallen behind my own.
Our trips along the beach were never meant as races, yet at last I realized,
as he once wrote upon the sand, that the competition truly was inside me.
I pushed, and ran faster; finding the speed doable, I strained even harder,
wondering how swiftly I could go; then the beach's terminus at the Argolian
breakwater compelled me to stop, still accelerating with capacity to spare.
When Oulixeus arrived, I was already breathing normally again; the ruby
sun stood halfway above the horizon, our run delayed by what he called my
'inconsiderate nocturnal interruption'. The morning throbbed with vitality,

the waking symphony of birds and insects, overlapping pulsations of surf, as well as the magnificent all-permeating magic whereof we were a part. "Guess I need a hiatus from the herb...I may be tired and grief-stricken, but I'm used to running like the wind," he gasped. "Did you even sleep?"

I paused to shake my head whilst washing off in the sea.

"What in god's name are you smoking? I thought you might take off flying."

"It's Bridget," I told him proudly. "I'm falling in love with her."

"Whoa now," he exclaimed, wide-eyed. "Slow down there, my friend."

"I'll do no such thing," I declared defiantly. "She's a goddess incarnate."

"Oh, I know it well," Oulixeus remarked, wiping his brow with a sleeve and giving me a stare indicating that he had been down this road before. "One of the finest ever conceived, which is why you're in such grave peril."

"Or rather, I must strive that much harder," I argued glibly.

"Don't reach too high," he warned. "Didn't you read the Ovid?"

"Most of it," I replied.

"Then remember Ikaros."

His advice aroused my insecurities, and I slashed back as if attacked.

"Oh, and I suppose you would make of yourself Daedalus? I've escaped the labyrinth on my own before, sir, and having done so, I already know the chance to pursue her is worth the risk of death..."

"Listen to me," he implored, putting a sober hand on my shoulder, which I shrugged off. "You sound like a crazy person. You bring danger and despair upon yourself. If you're so obsessed with a woman that you're willing to have your heart trampled, then you probably will."

This barely registered; jumping on the granite blocks, I shouted, "So be it!"

"All right...you spent last night with her, I suspect?" he asked.

"Yes, we talked for hours in the Akhaian ravine," I said. "It was beautiful."

"Uh-huh," Oulixeus grunted patronizingly. "You talked. About what?"

"Everything...my past, science, Terence, space exploration, time travel..."

"Hold on," he interrupted. "What did she have to say about time travel?"

I smiled at our evocative moment. "Oh, mainly that I shouldn't rush."

"Precisely. You should read betwixt the lines; I doubt it's all she means."

"What else could she be talking about?" I scoffed.

He stared mutely at my dumbfounded expression until I saw the obvious.

"Really?" I squawked, and he nodded in response. "You think so?"

"Believe it or not, infatuated men, including you, are shortsighted idiots."

"But...then...why would she have invited me?"

"She's still investigating, you fool," he exclaimed. "I know how you are, as I was the same way...it's all or nothing, and you're ready to dive in."

"Yes; fully committed," I vowed, clambering restlessly on the granite blocks.

"Hence you do yourself a great disservice. Bridget, on the other hand, went there with a partner already; you'd best look at what it brought her."

The wisdom, or plain awareness, of his suggestion suddenly hit home.

"I'm not saying your cause is lost," he consoled me, "yet if you want a shot, you can't pressure her; let love come and unfold as it will, if it is meant to."

From my stance atop the jetty, overlooking the harbor wherein Kastor had sacrificed his life, I noticed her Korinthian hut; and also that our runs were likely visible by dawn, given the vantage thus afforded. Focusing thereupon, I thought her curtains waved, though it may have been just my imagination.

"No, there's one thing the Bible makes clear:
The biblical God is a sloppy manufacturer.
He's not good at design; he's not good at execution.
He'd be out of business, if there was any competition."

~ Carl Sagan, Contact ~

"...Man said, 'Let us make God in our image, after our likeness:
and let us have dominion over the fish of the sea, and over
the fowl of the air, and over the cattle, and over all the earth,
and over every creeping thing that creepeth upon the earth...' "

from THE FIRST BOOK OF AEIOLUS
commonly called The Life and Death of Alexander Fremont
by Ariadne Jefferson

 ERIGONE

After managing to make my way home from work without a lamp, beneath
overcast skies amid the moon's void of course, only to find an empty house.
I fixed a plate of leftovers, noting a faint glow inside the guest room; then
Aeiolus entered the kitchen, though I never heard him cross the breezeway.
"Have you ever seen a person die before?" he asked gravely before I could
even greet him. I had been present for livestock, the child of Oulixeus and
Penelopeia; near Andre Geos' final moments, and just after Mrs. Jefferson's;
yet not for the passage of an adult soul, let alone that of somebody I knew.
"If you intend to be ready, so you can do it well when your turn comes,
I recommend seizing this opportunity; Amadeus wants to speak to you,"
he said, gesturing for me to follow. The chamber was dimly lit by candles,
filled with shallow rasping, and smelled of his death, mingled with incense.
The engineer squinted at me, barely lifting his head as I entered.
"Well, did you get it to work or what?" he murmured.
I choked up, eyes watering, in the presence of a man who faced his
end with utter courage, concerned for the completion of our project, which
would never benefit his mortal organism. Standing beside him, on the verge
of crying, I felt cowardly in comparison, and steeled myself to respond.
"It works perfectly. The seed vault is down to thirty, and still dropping."
Exhaling with a rattle, he asked Aeiolus, "We picked a good one, eh?"
"As I recall, you proposed to euthanize him on the beach."
"That's right; I almost forgot," Amadeus wheezed, grinning at the memory;
and then to me, "Seriously, I'm sorry for underestimating you. I meant
no offense; only mercy, rather. We had no idea who you might be."
"Me, neither," I croaked; fixing his gaze on me, he seemed to grunt
approvingly. "I probably would have done the same in your position."
"I'm glad we didn't follow through," he added. "Can you forgive me?"

A novel future from BRIAN LOVE   249

"Completely," I whispered, with my throat closing up. "No hard feelings."
"You turned out all right...just like him." Turning toward Aeiolus, he spoke
quietly, as if sharing a dark secret; "Not many of us left, are there now?"
"No, not many," his compatriot agreed.
"If I could collect, I'd bet you'll be the last to go; always so damn healthy."
His feeble laugh became a hapless hacking fit; he gasped between spasms,
slowly drowning in his own hemorrhages and mucilage. Aeiolus held a
basin for him to spit in one hand, supporting his back with the other,
until the engineer's respiration was calm again, albeit erratic.
"Fucking show-off," he grumbled at last.
"Any regrets?" his fellow pioneer inquired forbearingly.
"Ahh," Amadeus groaned, taking a deeper breath. "You know
how it is...far too many to recall, yet none I can take with me."
"Anything you that would like to take along?"
"Finally," he replied; then, whereas it did not need saying, "A cigarette."
"Are you sure you can still smoke?"
"Hell yes," he declared, winking in my direction; "to the bitter end.
I know its against the rules, but hoped I could have this one indoors."
"We might be able to accommodate that, just this once," Aeiolus told him.
He ceremoniously rolled some cured tobacco, adding enough opium from
Airmed's chest to prevent the engineer from coughing; blessed and lit it;
then offered me a hit. The aroma evoked the evening on which I met them,
masking the harshness of nicotine, though it still caused my head to spin.
Amadeus kept the spliff betwixt his lips, savoring long and slow pulls as
Aeiolus periodically caught the ash in a shell, until burnt down to a roach.
"Well, I guess I'm ready now," he drawled, noticeably detached.
"You've lived well and fully, my friend. Blessings on your journey,"
Aeiolus said, smiling wistfully with a hand on his chest, whose rise
diminished as intervals between inhalations grew. There were no words
for almost an hour; I could see him slipping away therein; yet when Airmed
and Bridget arrived, attired in the headdresses and gowns of priestesses,
the engineer stirred slightly, mumbling, "Dear god, the angels are here."
They charred bundles of cedar and sage over the candles, smudging each
other, the space, then Amadeus, followed by offerings of the appropriate
incense to the elemental directions. Sitting on either side of the mattress,
they both took one of his hands in theirs, and began to sing in a mellifluous
language unintelligible to me, mother providing the melody, daughter the
harmony. Although tears streamed down Bridget's cheeks, that lovely voice
of hers I would know anywhere never faltered; nor did she release his hand
to wipe them off, instead letting them fall on the lap of her ornate dress.
Their ikaros went on quite a while, another hour or more toward midnight,
by which point his breaths were weak, shallow, irregular; frequently ceasing,
for long and longer periods of time; until at last they stopped permanently.
Perhaps I just observed the subliminal hemostasis; yet I could swear I bore
witness to his soul's departure from its mortal womb, hovering above the
room as a sigh of relief extinguished the fire within him. Whatever might
be the qualitative difference betwixt person and organism, I maintain that
his transition from life to death was distinctly beyond biology. The women
continued singing; a moment later his eyes snapped wide open, whilst

the body began convulsing; albeit certainly disturbing, they held on with sober resolution. The nervous spasms continued for about half a minute, yielding as his jaw dropped and head tilted back, issuing a hiss; only when all went limp again did their lyrics break down to plaintive wails. Forming a sign of peace, Aeiolus pulled down his eyelids soon thereafter; he placed a twentieth-century American quarter, eagle side up, on the lifeless tongue "for the ferryman"; then ushered us out. We left the body undisturbed the next day, wherein a few villagers came to share last words or pay respects. Rather than its annual Olympik games, scheduled to coincide with the final episode in a triple conjunction of Jupiter and Uranus begun some seven moons earlier, the tribe held a funeral, whose ambience felt as if we had naught to celebrate, with spirits subdued by a dismal sky, threatening rain. Amadeus wished to be buried near the Ark, just below the hillcrest that provided its backfill; I joined Will, Musaios, Phaedo, and Diomedes for the somber excavation of his precisely rectangular tomb, no small feat of geometry in such sandy soil, whereat we each took a turn lying down upon completion to embrace the inevitability of our doom. In the interim, Airmed and Bridget cleansed the engineer's body, dressing him for the occasion in his favorite motorcycle jacket; a crown of feathers from his extinct totem, an animal archetype of freedom and leadership long before its cooptation by the United States, complemented his proud, aquiline nose. At noon, I helped carry a locust casket that, according to Kristos, they had once crafted together, from the first timber-sized trees cut by the pioneers. Concentric rings of villagers surrounded his tomb with their hands clasped, sharing nostalgic memories of the man they knew as Amadeus. In absence of direct offspring, Aeiolus led the closing prayer, nodding in conclusion to those of us who served as pallbearers. His corpse was lashed to a board, which we removed from the casket so it could be used again, lowering him in with ropes whilst the women began singing in rounds, unearthly music akin to what I heard the night he died. Fine drizzle commenced; after sprinkling a solitary shovelful of soil over him, Aeiolus handed his spade to Airmed, who did the same, then stepped outside the quiet circle. One by one, attendees replaced the earth in a wordless, unbroken chain, tamping the loose tomb with their feet as its level rose, adding flowers or embedding mementos if they were thus disposed; Bridget stolidly strewed locks of his son's golden hair, while Aeiphaistos spread metal shavings from their shared projects. Rather than a shallow monument abstracted from the deceased's identity, our community traditionally placed a symbolic tree atop ers gravesite; a white oak had been selected for Amadeus, emblem of his archaic namesake, long-lived like him, and multipurpose, offering shade, mast for wildlife, as well as durable wood that might shelter or warm the tribe in its forthcoming incarnation. As his grave filled, the sapling was transplanted without a beat missed, watered in by an abruptly intensifying shower, subsequently beaten by hail, and heralded by portentous thunder. Upon awakening from my convalescence, Aeiolus told me funerary rites were an artifice for the benefit of the living; yet not until the engineer's burial did I realize he had not meant this judgment to be derogatory. The only such ceremony I attended in my childhood, at my mom's behest, struck me as a counterfeit affair whereby members of her far-flung family expended inconceivable amounts of energy for the sake of appearances, meeting in a sterile Floridian retirement home filled with fluorescent lights, polyester carpeting, noxious fragrances, and its other inmates, lying in wait. A pubescent priest for hire officiated the momentary observance, crammed between death and cremation, of a life belonging to someone he never met; convincing us nonetheless my maternal grandmother would be welcomed into a heavenly kingdom, ruled by a vindictive God who metered out justice and redemption as part of a fable epitomizing the character of our culture. Those present for his extraneous sermonizing seemingly sat through it with their minds occupied by the free food or alcohol to follow; then disbursed dispassionately, as estranged after from each other and mortality as before, while my unconsoled, disillusioned mother swore off of religion forever. The young oak on Amadeus' grave was mulched at last with broad leaves from the new season's tobacco crop. His place of timeless sleep had been dug in the same ground whence his nourishment came; his corpse would nourish the tree that, in turn, nourished his homeland. Rather than an anthropomorphic deity or false hierophant thereof, the divinity presiding over his interment was the inextricable interconnectedness of all beings. Our ritual strengthened ties of fellowship, offering cause for sententious contemplation of our own impermanence. Life is ephemeral, a finite and precious gift, to be cherished for its brevity, not squandered in anticipation of eternity. The ceremony reminded us to make the most of it, since we may get just a single chance. Gratefully remembering his contributions, I celebrated that the engineer's legacy would go on in works he left behind. The song ended; hands still entwined, we raised them to the weeping sky, releasing in unison with a forked bolt of lightning. Our circle was finished, and his kindred remaining moved on toward the rest of their lives.

Given decent conditions, I preferred the weather mast at Pylos, among the island's five lookout posts, whereby I conquered acrophobia. This slender pole swayed like rubber in stiff winds, while rain or ice could render the crow's nest highly unpleasant, if not altogether inaccessible; yet I elsewise deemed it to the most interesting, thus jockeying therefor whenever my turn for sentry duty occurred in the rotation. Taking the position required an invigorating vertical climb of about two hundred feet, via rope and ascenders, hence yielding the longest views, its watches made exciting by perpetual response to changing winds. Descent was by rappel; albeit frowned upon, I enjoyed testing my reflexes near freefall, arresting myself as close to the ground as possible. Despite a few miscalculations, injuries did not deter me from pushing the limits of friction and gravity. I had an early shift, from sunrise to noon, on a gorgeous day two weeks before the equinox, with a slight hint of incipient autumn on fresh breezes from northeast; the western vista obscured, as usual, by ocher haze over New York and New Haven. I was reading the library's sole surviving copy of The Three Stigmata of Palmer Eldritch, which I located during an exhaustive search of the _Wyrd_, in an effort to discern what Aeiolus meant by reference to Terence McKenna the night of my initiation; and I performed cursory scans of the horizon with my binoculars for every brittle page flipped. Around midmorning, as the waning gibbous sank into the smog, I spotted

ENTHEOGENESIS · Origin of the Divinity within Us

a nondescript blur bobbing on waves to the north. Expecting it to be some barrel or piece of garbage, I notified the other sentinels via VHF codes per the dictates of protocol; yet within half an hour, I had confidently identified the anomaly as a johnboat; and by the time a team of Lakedaimonian women at the north light broadcast their corroboration an occupant was visible, propelling the tiny craft with oars. I held my position until the mideastern sentinel had a clear view, then dismounted, since mine would be readily evident from the coast. Whilst unable to raise Aeiolus on the radio, I did reach Airmed at the house, who supposed he might be on Arkadian farm. Being closest, I rode there to find him beside Aephaistos, tinkering with their self-feeding hay racks, and interrupted to explain the situation.

"Rowing? From the north, you say?" he replied, suddenly vigilant.

I followed him home, where Airmed and her apprentices were bottling herbal tinctures in the kitchen. She shot her husband an inquistive glance; "We may have guests today," he explained obliquely; she responded with a discrete nod as their conversation resumed. Beckoning me upstairs, Aeiolus retrieved a hunting rifle from its hiding place and slung it over his shoulder; a handgun, which he holstered in the small of his back; as well as two magazines for each; then we left through the side door. The north sentries reported that the johnboat seemed intent on continuing down the western shore; he asked me to accompany him up the Korn Neck to keep an eye on their landing, and whether I knew how to use firearms. Although unpracticed in riflery, I had spent hours at a basement range with Beamer and a nine millimeter, thereby considering myself a fair marksman, at least to thirty yards in an artificial environment.

"But I don't want to shoot anyone," I protested.

"That's comforting," he replied, handing me the pistol and clips.
"I still want you to carry this...just in case of the unpredictable."

I could sense his anxiety as much by telepathy as his intense silence or brisk stride. Updates came at regular intervals on his VHF handset after the boat passed Delos, apparently on a trajectory toward the salt pond. We stalked it along Kretan fields, just inside the forest buffer; when he judged the craft abreast of us, we crept through the windbreak to dunes on the waterfront. Peering above the shadbush thickets holding them, Aeiolus through the scope mounted on his rifle, me with my binoculars, we saw that the prodigiously-rowing man wore his long, greasy gray hair tied back with a rag and matched by a thick beard. Getting our first good look at his cargo, we realized he actually had a passenger curled beneath a blanket in the stern; either a woman or child, based on ers tiny stature.

"We need to block them by the breech cut, up ahead," Aeiolus urged. Because the coastline comprised only ankle-rolling cobbles and no cover, he indefatigably bounded across the hellacious shrubbery, permitting me to trample in his footsteps. We crouched at the reedy edge of the narrow estuary, sufficiently swollen by the lunar syzygy for such a buoyant craft to cross, wherein the johnboat veered, per anticipation. He bade me freeze, putting a finger to his lips as they approached; once within shouting range, he fired a warning shot over the stranger, who stopped and turned around, evidently surprised by our invisible presence as he bobbed on a choppy tide.

"Wait there, and state your business," Aeiolus hollered.

Due to the wind we heard mere noise, whilst the rower gesticulated toward the figure lying in the boat. Aeiolus cupped a hand behind his ear; in sign, I indicated that I could not understand either; then he shouted, "Disease?" Albeit mute, the stranger's head shook in vigorous negation. "Anyone else?" he asked, receiving the same response. "Where do you think they're from?" I whispered. "That is the question, isn't it?" he growled. "I'd like to know the answer, and am not happy about them being downwind." "So what are we going to do?" I pressed, regretting my words immediately. "WE are doing nothing," he snapped, gaze aflame. "I intend to let them land and ascertain how, or why, they've found us; you are going to draw your sidearm, release the safety, and silently await further instructions." Stunned by his curt demeanor, I hesitated. "That means now!" he ordered. I shakily did as he commanded; sweat had begun rolling down my temples. Aeiolus fired a second round; fumbling clumsily in the bilge, the stranger retrieved a white plastic bag and waved it as a flag of surrender, looped on his oar. Covering him as he stood, I watched Aeiolus extend his rifle overhead, directing the rower southwest to the ship channel with a black bandana flown from its muzzle. We waded across expeditiously; yet the boat gained a lead near the harbor, whence we took a shortcut to its strait, thus walking out on the cape unnoticed until Aeiolus caught the stranger's attention again with a third shot. Making eye contact, he pointed down the canal and toward Korinthian marshes opposite, one arm maintaining his aim whilst he reported the situation to other sentries on his handset; "Be sure they can see you're armed," he instructed, keeping his scope fixed on the water. To witness his territorial instincts, unmitigated and unleashed, had me struggling to remain composed despite my empathetic trepidation. Sporadically switching frequencies, he told those at the lighthouses to look for pursuers, bidding old Nestor of Pylos, atop the pylon in Argos, to meet us at the Hellenspont, since his post was closest. When the johnboat had drifted out of range, he gave me permission to use safe mode; relieved, I holstered the slippery Glock. He took off along the salt pond's north shore, whose curvature lengthened our trip to its far end so the rower stayed abreast of us. We splashed through the Lakedaimonian lagoons emptying into the harbor, running upon vast flats of short, sharp grasses that lacerated my shins and ate away even my calloused footsoles. Pace notwithstanding, Aeiolus held the rifle ready across his chest except whilst fording the deeper inlets, and then, never losing sight of his quarry. Finally emerging from the vicious marshes with a coating of their fetid mud, we sprinted to the Korinthian isthmus, where Nestor had respirators for us. "While I don't know what they're doing here, I aim to find out," Aeiolus asserted as he passed Nestor his rifle. "When they land, I'll search the pilot; I want yall here for deterrence. After he's been checked, you'll guard him, because I'll have Nestor's gun on her next," he said austerely. "Don't touch them, or their boat, unless I tell you elsewise." The rower advanced, glancing over his shoulder regularly, and ran his hull aground. I saw several inches of putrid liquid sloshing in its bilge, mixed with what might have been vomit, feces, blood, or all of the above. "I trust you know the drill," Aeiolus bellowed. "Put your hands on your

head and slowly stand." It was not a request he issued, but an ultimatum. "I'm here for help...don't want no trouble," said the rower in a jittery drawl. "Then you'll be quiet," my benefactor barked. "Now turn to face me, walk up to the tideline, and stop there, keeping your hands up."
Once the stranger complied, we closed in with guns drawn until Aeiolus signaled for us to stop, about a dozen paces away. Although downwind, he reeked appallingly of alcoholism, malnutrition, and absence of hygiene. "Hold your arms straight out to your sides and do not move."
Unarmed, Aeiolus quickly searched him, taking a knife off the man's belt in the process; then he lifted the tangled mess of hair from his neck, examining the scarred, imprecise incisions left by removal of an ID chip. "So you're a fugitive. What brings you here? Who's after you?"
"She's hurtin'..." he stammered. "I thought maybe there's a doctor..."
"You thought? Why? How did you know about this place?"
"Please...you gotta help her...it's real bad..." he went on evasively.
"If she survived the ride across, I suspect she'll endure another moment; besides, we'll get to her sooner if you'll answer my questions truthfully."
Circling to the front, he leaned threateningly close, heedless of body odor; the stranger glanced to us, gaze averted from his inquisitor's mutilation. "Look at me," he demanded, staring into the rower's eyes; the men were about the same size, while the visitor appeared somehow devolved, with one socket set grotesquely higher than the other, amidst scaly eczema.
He looked to be middle-aged, and cowered before the much older man who grabbed him by the collar, putting his own blade to his throat. "I said look at me!" he roared. "Have you been here before?"
A growing patch of moisture crept down the stranger's thigh to validate his bewilderment, along with the sour stench of fear. "Ize just lookin' for help," he replied, trembling. "I aint never come here..."
His body recoiled, unbalanced, as Aeiolus made a short feint toward him, took a prolonged, invasive stare through the rower's persona, then grunted. "Keep your gun on him," he ordered Nestor, motioning for me to follow him to the boat, wherein the woman still sat doubled over, hair hiding her face. "Can you look at me, miss?"
Whimpering, her head rose. She was so young; I would guess fourteen, or fifteen at most. Her pallid skin had a greenish tinge, pouring rivulets of sweat, and her eyes, surrounded by dark rings, seemed to beg for pity.
"I'm going to get in," he warned softly. "I promise I won't hurt you."
Dropping her chin, the girl shrunk back from him and turned to the bilge, clutching her belly. He laid a hand on her forehead, then lifted the soggy blanket, revealing an enormous stain on the clothes she wore beneath it. "She's not just injured," Aeiolus announced in a low tone. "She's in labor."
He hailed Airmed again by VHF, incited to anger by social traffic on the air; "Switch to a different channel!" he reprimanded the culprits, and reaching her at last, he said, "You should get everyone out and prepare for surgery. We have guests from the mainland; I think one of them needs a caesarian."
Acknowledging his message, she replied that a stretcher was on its way. Checking the time, he ordered me to brief the next sentry shift and Nestor to help him move her. "I'll follow," Aeiolus added, nodding at the rower.

Riding home later, I felt far from thrilled about the prospect of having
strangers stay with us, hoping I might retrieve my personal effects and
escape quarantine by sleeping elsewhere. Upon arrival, I was dismayed
to find myself alone except for the cat; then checked each room to confirm
they were vacant. As I finally crossed the breezeway, an intangible sense
of dread spread through my gut; when I reached the guest house, a rare
and terrible sound emanated therefrom - that of a man sobbing violently.
Throwing open its door, I faced a scene more horrific than any else I either
feared or have ever witnessed. Aeiolus sat on the floor, his back against
the wall, holding Airmed's body in a veritable pool of blood; the rower lay in
a crumpled heap, head bent over at a fatally contorted angle and wedged
into the opposite corner. The girl rested on a gurney, which had replaced
the bed as a makeshift operating table, with a peaceful expression on her
face at last, abdomen sliced open, progeny and uterus in the adjacent tray.
Between sobs, Aeiolus whimpered, "Go away." My heart plummeted to
the floor, rendering me immobile; my mind seemed too shocked to react;
whilst his chant escalated to the loudest series of cries that I have yet
heard issued from a human being; "Go away, GO AWAY, GO AWAY!"
I turned and ran as fast as I could, with tears streaming down my cheeks.

I went to Aephaistos' hut, on Argolian outskirts near the old power plant,
and broke down in hysterics, initially incapable of conveying what occurred.
After helping me get my hyperventilation under control, he listened to my
tale, silent from sighting the vessel to the grisly state of the guest house.
"Kurie eleison," he prayed. "May the gods have mercy on their souls."
I sat in apprehensive limbo whilst he ruminated on this, shaking his head.
"We'll need to leave Aeiolus for the night," he resolved,
"I'll go and see if I can talk to him at first light."
"But who will tell Bridget?" I asked.
"I'd say that's up to him," Aephaistos replied. "It's his prerogative
to do so himself, should he choose; if not, I'll just follow instructions."
Assembling the glimpses that I saw and remarks Aeiolus later made,
I deduced what had likely occurred. Once Airmed anesthetized the girl,
Aeiolus dismissed Nestor and Praxidike, who bore her stretcher from the
harbor, to carry out their quarantine procedures whilst he stood guard.
Although only thirty weeks into gestation, the child was long gone; since the
mother showed incontrovertible signs of chronic battery, Airmed suspected
but did not accuse the ostensible father of being to blame. She performed
a hysterectomy, during which he required restraint by Aeiolus, vociferously
demanding to see the girl; yet her infection was simply too severe. Between
injuries, fever, and blood loss, she failed to return from unconsciousness.
When Airmed subsequently left the guest house to wash after surgery,
her expression unwittingly betrayed its outcome to the strange man,
who stormed in with both her and Aeiolus close behind. He threw an irate
tantrum at the sight, claiming she had killed the girl; in response, Airmed
made the unfortunate mistake of suggesting that her death resulted from
his abuse. Seizing a scalpel from the operating tray, he angrily slashed
at Airmed, thus inflicting mortal wounds, before Aeiolus could pinion him,
breaking the rower's neck in the struggle. When her husband went for help,

Airmed said it was too late, begging him to stay with her as she bled to death instead. Without seeking further detail, Aephaistos offered for me to sleep under his roof; but whether burying my face in bedding or staring at the stars, I could not scrub the grisly image from behind my eyelids, etched in such excruciating detail that I might as well have still been there. I tossed and turned relentlessly past midnight, then rose for a walk to lonely Delos, wondering about the lamp I noticed in Bridget's window on my way. I dove into the ocean, then swam until the moonlit shoreline faded, as if it would cleanse me of the atrocity that had taken place by distance; yet floating on my back with gloomy, black sea in all directions, I realized it was futile. Whereas gruesome memories might fade, no earthly power could undo what transpired, and the irrevocable loss of Airmed from our village hit home. As he was describing another tragic event, concluded by Kastor's heroik sacrifice, Aeiolus once opined, while people will often choose what is right of their own accord, "the inherent nature of that choice allows for the horrible wickedness and awful hostility of which some are capable." How true this can be; I spent those wee hours shivering at the beach, huddled with arms around my knees, reflecting not only on mortality, but also the fallibility of our own so-called morality. An odious record of violence, perversion, and depravity; of callous disregard for suffering and the uncanny ability to inflict torture; of rape, murder, war, and genocide; listless acts of environmental degradation for the sake of illusory profits – all led to the same question: why strive so hard for humanity's survival? Neither consciousness nor culture, the very evolutionary hallmarks of our specie, would overcome an adamant and inbred inclination toward evil, it seemed to me. Was it not be best, then, for our race to become extinct? Should we not welcome the chance to rid the world of our own pestilence?

I blew off my meeting with Oulixeus to avoid social interaction the next morning, running directly to thank Aephaistos for his support; but he was gone when I arrived and not to be found at his shop. I dozed off, or rather sank into a catatonic trance, as I sat in a rocker on his porch, until yanked back to life by his return, early in the morning yet already on the verge of a careless sunburn, whereupon he informed me that Aeiolus held funerary rites for his wife in the night. Together with Bridget they had laid Airmed to rest; at dawn her father then left the village, alone aboard the *Wyrd*. "Did he tell you where he went?" I asked, amidst an intuition of futility. "Only that the burbarians shall have no graves here," Aephaistos said, grimacing. "I wonder if you have the stomach to help me with them." Riding back in his welding truck, I steeled myself for the abominable butchery; in absence of Airmed, however, it seemed more like just meat. Agreeing that they should be buried separately, we cocooned their bodies in sheets and drove the man's to his johnboat. Mixing leftover ingredients from the Ark, I shoveled concrete atop him until the gunwales sat barely above the waterline. Since talk of the village had spread the news by then, we were left alone in our duties; and at twilight we towed the craft offshore behind a daysailer, swamping it without ceremony, save to solemnly watch him vanish down to the deep. In the interim, Aephaistos built a funeral pyre for the girl and her offspring, whilst I scraped up the dark, congealed blood.

We lit the pile after a pensive sail back to island; he stayed past midnight, when the neatly cloven moon rose, noting that its position matched the same Gregorian date in 2001, which happened to be September eleventh. Left to tend the fire alone, I slipped in and out of dreams about Airmed, who appeared in a chainlink cage underwater, her mouth moving inaudibly. Because flies had come, I began cleaning the guest house again at dawn; yet despite my furious scrubbing its floor remained stained, along with the bespattered walls. Glancing to the smoldering fire pit as I chipped plaster therefrom, I had the implacable sense that only would razing the building liberate her limbic spirit. I first removed the door, windows, and roof panels; then severed its connection to the breezeway with a chainsaw, supporting the latter temporarily on twin poles. Demolition of the shell proved more challenging than I expected, its hempcrete unyielding even when rammed by Will's tractor. Eventually compromising the structure, I spread the lime-coated fiber on the coals one loader bucket at a time, adding enough paneling or framing material to prevent each of them from smothering, while careful not to release visible smoke plumes upward. Waiting for this remarkably flame-retardant matrix to burn, I decided to score the slab in a grid using a diamond saw and generator, then break it up with wedges and sledgehammer. My endeavor took much of the day, yielding pieces still almost too large to move; yet by flipping end over end, I paved a path encircling their former footprint. Foamboard and plastic sheeting beneath went to the recyclery; next I bashed free the concrete foundation blocks. Reducing the rest to ash was a matter of patience; I alternately raked embers or lay downwind with an insomniac stare.

"May I join you?" asked Bridget during the waning crescent's rise; slightly delirious, I mumbled that I could abide her company, and she sat an arm's length to my side. For fear of the emotional minefield behind her expressionless countenance, I silently averted my eyes, thus glimpsing a stray meteor streak across the sky above where the guest house had stood.

"Did you see it?" I whispered reflexively.

"Yes, that was a good one," she replied, nodding.

"I took a stroll through your...project...over there, on my way..."

"Oh...well, its far from finished," I began. "I had thought perhaps of planting a medicine garden, but would need some assistance."

She let the invitation hang awkwardly, then added at last, "Thank you, on her behalf, as well as my dad's, for this."

"Well, it's the least I can do," I murmured, musing humbly on where I would be, or not, without them.

"In truth, you could have done much less," she argued.

I cleared my throat anxiously, unsure of what else to say.

"Let me know if there is anything you need; it must be challenging."

"Is that right?" she mocked bitterly. "You have no idea."

This remark frustrated me, and for once I did not shy from telling her so. "You can seek conflict for its own sake if you want, and if so, I'm sorry your grief makes you feel that way. My dad died before I knew him; dead or alive, I'll never see my mother again. I know you were close with yours, and what befell her is terrible, but you are not the only person here to be aggrieved. While you may prefer to feel as such right now, you are not alone; whether

you seek support or understanding, you have to be open to receiving them."
My feedback must have affected her, since she did not retreat therefrom.
"Why Mom? All she ever did was give, for what? An ignominious and
godless death that does nobody any good, bleeding out on the floor?"
I allowed a break seemingly befitting to the calamity before responding.
"Shouldn't we remember how she lived instead, open-eyed to the very end?
As far as I can tell, Airmed had a journey of whose rewards most don't dare
dream, by giving whatever she could for the future's sake, yours above all..."
Bridget interrupted me with a sardonic scoff.
"Mine is cursed, then...or rather, it is a curse on those around me."
"I doubt that," I said aloud; to myself, 'but if so, may the curse last forever.'
"Tell it to her, to Amadeus, to Hellen or Kastor," she exhorted sarcastically.
I swallowed at her fateful invocation of the latter. "Albeit hard to see now,
death is a part of life, Bridget; your presence in events doesn't necessarily
make you to blame for their outcome, and if so, I could say the same."
"You could say the same?" she mimed tempestuously. "How dare you!"
"Our intimacy couldn't have been as real, since she left me for my best
friend first, but I led my first girlfriend down the road whereby she died
from an overdose. Still, I think life must be for living; after all, we leave
death to the dead, which seems just our souls' reunion with the source
of whom we're a part and whence we were born. Kastor is gone; though
I'm not him and can't bring him back any more than your remorse, maybe
his traces could go on in somebody like me, as Airmed will through you,
if you can cherish them. Isn't that what they would have wanted?"
I sighed upon conclusion and added, "What do I know?", feeling defensive
until I heard a sniffle; looking askant, I saw her weeping, dignified as ever,
yet vulnerable at last; so beautiful I could not help but let my vain injuries
yield to compassion. On impulse, I stretched a shirtsleeve over my hand,
slowly reached out and wiped the tears from her cheek with the back
of my wrist; taking it in hers, she dried the opposite side, then moved
beside me, the length of her left against my right, our fingers entwined.
"Thanks for the reminder," she whispered hoarsely, stopping as her voice
verged on cracking. "Just so you know, I don't want to play the victim,
and also you deserve to be treated better, though I may fail to do so."
Her apology melted the hardness in my heart; Bridget must have felt it
as she leaned over, lying in my lap, as she had once let me in hers, with
that soft curve between pelvis and ribcage embracing my quadriceps.
"I don't mind. I can imagine it's difficult to find meaning in the tragedy."
"Yes, it is," she agreed poignantly, "yet that's no excuse for hostility."
Pulling the habitually stray lock of hair behind her ear, I gently caressed
her head; she did not protest, allowing my forefinger to wandered along the
perimeter of her ear, the gracile line of her jaw, the strong arc of her neck.
Stretching out, her body invited me to continue; my hand traced a path
down her delicate clavicle, across ribs, then rested upon her solar plexus,
cradled in her grip betwixt those lovely breasts. The sensation was blissful,
electric; nerves in my stomach fluttered, for it had been painfully long since
I had touched a woman like that, and never with such fondness or desire.
"He died on the eleventh of September, too, four years ago," Bridget noted.
"From her first pregnancy, Mom should have guessed this was a bad omen."

"Is it always, though? I just realized its the anniversary of my suspension from school; and if I hadn't been investigated by DHS, I wouldn't be here." She turned to look at me. "You spoke out about 911? How did you know?" "Your father's biography, actually," I replied, "but no one would listen." "I would have listened." Her arms wrapped my waist, squeezing. "My mother had a special relationship with the date, as it happens." "Then let us honor her, and all the blameless slain by creating a world where injuries are meant to be healed; prisons escaped; and at times," I paused, glancing westward, "walls are built to be torn down." She sat up, twisting to face me with her arm reaching across my loins and we stared at the flames flickering in one another's gaze for a while. Despair notwithstanding, I sensed this was our moment, thus exercising great restraint to savor the anticipation as I lost my self in our cloud of pheromones. Nuzzling, I traced both sides of the bridge of her nose with the tip of mine; our third eyes touched; free hands stroked facial features; with lips that seemed impossibly soft, she grasped me. The kiss was gentle and exploratory as we tasted each other for the first time, one I pray I may never forget; with a year's unrequited attraction unleashed, it soon grew forceful, more urgent. Grabbing the scruff of my neck, she pressed our mouths together as our tongues danced. I had an arm behind, squeezing her to me, and whilst her heart beat powerfully against mine, I still felt they could not get close enough. Our faces parted briefly as she threw me down and mounted in a single fluid motion. The soft, trimmed grass had been moistened by dew, not that it was any concern to my mind at the time.
"Bridget, I've wanted you since..."
"Shhh," she interjected. "I know."
"But what about tomorrow?" I asked.
She pushed herself back, stared as if disturbed, and slapped me.
"Ouch! What the hell was that for?"
"After all of your waiting and lament I can't believe you'd ask me such a question right now; for your own good, please just shut up and be present." I obediently complied as she leaned over me. Her untamed hair, smelling of salt, woodsmoke and wildflowers, brushed my face as she kissed my jaw, bit my neck, and sucked on my earlobes seductively. My hands slid down her sides, around her hips, under the hem of her dress, whereby I found the smooth skin on her lusciously round, firm buttocks, a perfect fit for the long fingers with which I cradled them. Bridging, I lifted my pelvis to meet hers; spine arched in response, she pressed back encouragingly and locked lips with me again; then moaned as I stretched further, slipping through the most deliciously damp crevice nature ever created; a warm chasm so soft and so sweet I would gladly have drowned completely therein. Suddenly Bridget burst into deep, wrenching sobs; withdrawing my hand, I embraced her, but she fought me off and firmly stood up. "I can't do this," is all I heard as she ran off in the darkness, to my utter dismay. Leaping up once the initial shock passed, I followed, calling her name to no avail; she was gone, leaving me alone with the frogs and waterfowl.

"I love those who can smile in trouble, who can gather strength
from distress, and grow brave by reflection. 'Tis the business of little
minds to shrink, but they whose heart is firm, and whose conscience
approves their conduct, will pursue their principles unto death."

~ Leonardo da Vinci, 548-481 B.T. ~

"Though my soul may set in darkness, it will rise in perfect light.
I have loved the stars too fondly to be fearful of the night."

~ Galileo Galilei, 436-358 B.T. ~

In the wake of this egregious spate of deaths, Aeiolus' mysterious absence,
and our unslaked grief, I attended an anahoaska ceremony on the equinox
with some of the men who would have been competing in the Olympiks, had
they spirit therefor. We held our circle on the beach below Akhaian bluffs;
although it was my birthday, this demarcation seemed meaningless to me.
Without the visual anchor of fire or moon, beneath a firmament wreathed in
clouds, the tryp proved to be profoundly dark. Judging myself a hardhead,
I drank cup after cup of Haroun's acrid brew; yet rather than regurgitating
new universes, I floundered blindly through a gut-wrenching psychic crisis,
burrowed in the sand whilst purging toxins from all levels of my being as if
it had no other purpose. Staggered by the sheer volume of this catharis,
I regained my senses, barring sight, in a windy jungle timeport or anteroom
of sorts straddling the two worlds. Shadowy entities shifted in its periphery
to make their presence known, yet faded when I focused on them, saying,
    'Yes, we're here, and this is a glimpse of eternity. We'll save the truly
frightening stuff for later, once you have a proper lens by which to see it.'
I was thankful for Oulixeus beside me, whose bereavement dove far deeper
than mine, encouraging me to cry in surrender. As I huddled against sandy
gusts upon return, he amended the teachings of Aeiolus; while psychonauts
may thus unravel secrets of creation, none can expect such at their outset.
I had just begun to learn the balance of the power and light; nonetheless,
I left the experience feeling cleansed, with one lesson compellingly clear.
Whereas I agonizingly wanted to, and my heart revolted at the decision,
I declined to visit Bridget, choosing instead to leave space for her mourning.
In my imagination, she had come as far as the edge of potential intimacy,
looked over the precipice, then recoiled at the memory of loss and fear of
further suffering. I could neither blame her nor attempt to persuade her;
    I aspired only to demonstrate that what I offered as a partner and lover
might be worth the risk, but la purga resolutely told me the door was closed.
She alone held the key to reopening it; because this could not be coerced I

despaired at my prospects, or lack thereof. After achieving, at last, some
semblance of emotional stability and independence, I wished I had never
glimpsed the felicity that might have been, to avoid the pain of deprivation.
Unnerved on my own by the ghosts of Aeiolia, I temporarily moved in with
Aephaistos. Given a reprieve from heat and signs of the changing seasons,
the waxing moon lent itself to a restless flurry of activity. Whereas I missed
the prior year's peak foliage, amid my recovery in the guest house, that fall's
bittersweet glory evoked both pensive awe and anxiety; an astonishing final
burst of vitality as prelude to winter's dessicant dormancy, during which we
finished our punchlist, then stocked the Ark with tools, parts and provisions.
Reappearing around the full moon, Aeiolus met me there one morning for
an unannounced tour of its labyrinthine storage compartments; examined
their details in attentive silence; caught my eye; and nodded approvingly.
"I knew that you would rise to the challenge, but you've even exceeded
my expectations," he said, inviting me to the vacant house for dinner.
Since he did not remark on my remodeling, I accepted with hesitation.
We uneasily broke bread over the usual concerns of his homestead;
"I see you've been busy," he remarked with a nod toward Airmed's garden,
whilst serving us plates of lamb and his signature garlic-maple potatoes.
"About that..." I swallowed nervously, "I'm sorry for behaving so rashly;
after you left, I kept seeing her in dreams, and felt it just had to be done."
"Don't mistake my meaning; I love what you've done with the place."
His feigned nonchalance lightened the mood briefly,
albeit an oblique introduction to weightier matters.
"It is I who behaved rashly; it is my actions that merit rebuke."
"How so?" I wondered.
"Isn't it obvious? I disrupted her soul's journey by moving
her body too early, in a craven attempt to assuage my guilt."
"Your guilt...what for?" I exclaimed reflexively, though afraid of the answer.
"This is my fault. When Airmed told me the rower had beaten the poor girl,
I should have restrained him and solicited immediate backup; but as with
Kastor, somebody else paid the price for my carelessness; my beloved wife,
who saved my life, slain instead, a crime for which I cannot forgive myself;
then I interred her at night, depriving our tribe of the chance to bid her
goodbye, when she belonged as much to them as she was ever mine."
"We understand," I began, "and have managed to say farewell in our ways;
I, for one, am unsure of whether I could do otherwise in your position."
"My position..." he choked, disguising his grief under the pretense of a
long drink from his water glass. "What do you know about my position?"
"Not much," I confessed, "but I'll hazard the guess that you see
the blood on your hands and wish it was for something worthwhile."
Emitting a low grunt at this, he stared out the west window as I continued.
"I once watched my own customer in the throes of an overdose I sold him
as he approached the very gates of hell, then ran away, unable to help."
"Did you know him well?" Aeiolus inquired.
"He was a corporate executive I met at a show, just looking for a ride."
"Who? Anyone I'd know?"
"The former president of a old fight league." I answered.
"Not the Federation of Unlimited Combat?" he asked.

"Yes, actually."

"Wow...how fascinating."

"Why? Did you know Andre Geos?"

"Only by reputation," he told me quickly. "What did you sell him?"

"My usual troll...some X, Nexus, and an MAOi."

"You deliberately specified a dose with fatal possibilities?"

"Not exactly, though I failed to consider the risks that he
was older than I thought, or might add a Viagra to the mix."

"If you warned him, that's not murder; it's manslaughter, via his choice."

"How is it any different from yours?"

"The element of intent," he said. "This was no accident."

"Don't accidents happen in self-defense?"

"Occasionally," he replied, "but not mine. I trained with Airmed's brother,
the submission technician himself; and a cervical crank is a far cry from
the blood choke whereby I could have neutralized my victim in seconds."

"Surely at some point during the struggle..." I argued.

Shaking his head, Aeiolus stopped me. "Since you've slept under
my roof and eaten at this table, I am obliged to tell you the truth.
As he went limp, I saw the blood from her wounds and voluntarily
channeled the spirit of Areis, letting his rage rise within me;
when my restraint snapped at last, so did her killer's spine."

"If that's a crime, then it's a crime of passion," I opined.

"Then so is his. Call it what you will; I was still in control as I consciously
decided to render his death, from the vindictive anger for which we're bred,
pure and simple. I've skirted the moral issues of homicide my whole life,
out of devotion to the possibility our tendencies toward violence can be
healed through some cultural, spiritual, or philosophical pupation; and yet,
put to the test myself, I readily succumbed to this base impulse. Trust me,
I've relived it myriad times; lest any doubt remain, I killed him willfully,
an irrevocable choice that shall follow me to my grave, if not beyond."

I weakly protested what seemed an unjust assessment to my mind.

"My god and I will be the judges; you're merely my confessor," he declared.
"The anger I expressed when you came to the guest house was with myself;
directed inward; I had no right to take it out on you, and am deeply sorry."

"Water under the bridge; again, I'd have likely done similarly in your place."

"May you never find yourself there," he replied; I shuddered at the thought
as he glanced to our matched plates, whose untouched food had grown cold.

"I tell you all of this because I'd like you to come back; this homestead is
lonely without you. Your work at the Ark is finished, or nearly, is it not?"

"We have only to pack and document inventory," I remarked.

"You keep a fine garden, and ours needs attention this fall; while I'd like
somebody besides me to know how to take care of things here, in case I
must leave, which is more than I can ask of Bridget now. Will you help?"

I nodded gravely under the looming weight of his ominous request.

"Thanks. During my trip away, I realized this evil may be merely a portent
of what's yet to pass. A dark cloud lies on America; death waits in its wings;
the international community has been mute regarding their attitudes about
the empire, and that does not bode well. Perhaps it's my paranoid fantasy,
but at sail I was reminded such calm is often overture to the worst storms."

Will, Diomedes, Hemlock, and I enjoyed magnificent weather whilst contending with an uncommonly large final cut of hay, followed by days of bitter rain; then Aeiolus taught me to shear the sheep, whose fleeces had been fortuitously cleaned in the interim. The backbreaking work was deeply satisfying, though my elder mentor could do ten in the time I did one via his swift, efficient, calculated technique; my method, in contrast, fought against the animals as I sprawled across frenetically-thrashing limbs, attempting to thwart their escape and dodging hooves with unpleasantly inconsistent success, whereupon I saw him smiling in the corner of my eye. I arose the following day crippled, with countless bruises from their horns. "Given practice, you'll learn; pain is an effective incentive," he promised. "If you approach the task confidently, they'll not find cause to struggle." After watching me chase, tackle, and strangle them, Aeiolus demonstrated how to disorient the sheep with sound or hand motions; thus they appeared to leap into his grasp by telekinesis; "Another trick I learned from Areis," he mentioned. Whilst harvesting the wool, we also trimmed their hooves, performed body condition exams, and separated the various mating groups. He shared stories of pedigrees, illnesses, lambing records, and genealogies; then I remarked on his memory for minutiae, which seemingly rivaled mine.

"Trust me, I've forgotten more than you'll ever know," he joked.

With annual care of the flock accomplished, Aeiolus explained the construction of his house in indefatigable detail, especially its electrical and mechanical systems; where the roof leaked in heavy rains; and of all the maintenance it might require in the next lifetime. He revealed secret security features; while I had already discovered the vault of the Apple, there were still untold trap doors, hidden passages, and a cupola-mounted periscope. Areis, who also helped establish VHF protocols for the village, once consulted on the design of his siblings' home to these ends, such that beneath its sacred geometries, aesthetic proportions, and noetic artistry lay a veritable citadel in miniature – readily defensible, invisible from sea, yet affording panoramic views that peeked just above the coastal treeline.

"If he was so valuable to the tribe, why did you let them ostracize him?"

"Because he needed total freedom to forge his own path," Aeiolus sighed. "Who am I to deny a man's destiny? But that is another story altogether."

We harvested the last of the summer garden, dredged the duck pond, spreading its product thereupon; planted cover crops in well-spaded soil; then pruned and mulched the orchards. I observed from a distance as he, alongside fellow community members, composed an impeccable mandala of Airmed's herb inventory under Bridget's austere supervision, covering the footprint of the guest house. He thenceforth attended to the homestead wistfully, as if uncertain how much longer he would perform its seasonal chores, and increasingly prone to deep reveries; apt when disturbed from them to evoke exquisite tales of trials, triumphs, or tribulations he had experienced with his wife in the cultivation of their corner of the globe. Behind masks of workaholic stoicism dwelt a man aggrieved, to be sure, whose process was likely more deeply and vividly felt than I comprehend; yet aside from his brief disappearance he did not allow loss to consume him, instead honoring his love by caring for all she had humanifested, in which she might live on. Their marriage gave birth to a dynamic world, replete with potential, through the shared awareness they were only temporary stewards of a group enterprise that, if its underlying vision had merit, could vastly exceed their own incarnations in scope as well as duration. To abdicate the responsibilities thereof in the shadow of her death would thus have made him an apostate to the consensual ethos of their union.

Deeming us prepared enough for winter by the fourth quarter, Aeiolus said he wanted to bring me sailing before the weather turned too nasty. "As an advocate for the recapitulative power of visiting landmarks from one's past, I think, for your sake, we should go to New York." He spread nautical charts over the library table, laying out our course on a transparency with ruler, compass, and protractor. The entire journey would be 250 to 300 sea miles, depending on wind direction, which he expected to take two full days. His expressed intention was to depart at twilight; arrive in the harbor under cover of darkness the following evening; sail through the metropolitan boroughs quickly and discreetly on innercity tidal currents during the wee hours; then return to the island after nightfall. He projected low water at half past seven amid the subsequent dark moon, such that we would round the west end of Long Island from south to north, hence riding the swell from New York harbor toward Throgs Neck, since he found the alternative route, approaching via Connecticut, less auspicious. "To do that, we'd need to wait another week for the high and low to switch so we can make the crossing overnight; given prevailing winds we might make a dozen tacks coming down the sound. Under a waxing gibbous our boat will be more conspicuous, and the neap tide will be weaker." He decided to meet me the evening preceding the new moon at the pier; there we boarded an outrigger kayak named the *Wyrd Sisters*, borrowing a Shakespearian reference to commemorate the larger trimaran whereon Alexander Fremont had circumnavigated the polar ice cap, then the planet. Once we paddled out, he held us abreast of its mother ship as I embarked; he did likewise and we pulled the craft atop the deck, whose locust still glistened after a season of service, I noticed. Handing me a thermos of honeyed ginger tea, Aeiolus indicated a wind vane mounted on the stern. "The breeze is now west-by-northwest, which is fine if it holds, except, for better or worse, your introduction to the open ocean will be going upwind. Let's just hope you don't get too seasick." He proceeded to teach me relevant nautical terminology; showed how to operate the head; and explained I was not to urinate overboard at sail, but rather to use a cup kept by the helm for this purpose that had cumulatively seen hundreds of gallons, all poured into the sea from within the lifelines. We went through the organizational systems of the galley, whence he gave me a canteen, ration of trail mix, and the recommendation I eat or drink small amounts frequently to stave off nausea. Passing a safety harness, he told me not to go on deck alone unless clipped in; then swung the mainsail boom over the cockpit, connecting it to a traveler bar across the cockpit. "Beware; this is perhaps the most dangerous appendage on a boat; I know of even experienced racers who have been killed thereby," he said, removing his watchcap to display a jagged white scar. "Whether we tack, or in the event of an inadvertent jibe, the block will come across like this," he continued, demonstrating, "but with a hundredfold more force; if you're in the swing it will wipe you out indifferently, so stay alert around this area; and when I give you an instruction, repeat back to me a few seconds prior to executing it, lest there be any doubt that you understand my meaning."

At anchor, the *Wyrd* naturally faced upwind, with the channel straight ahead and the blood-red sun sinking off our port bow. After locking the helm so it would turn away once free, Aeiolus raised the black mainsail, exhibiting surprising strength in so doing; we weighed anchor together, though pulling the twelve-ton vessel forward in the sheltered salt pond was not difficult. Upon detaching from the bottom, it drifted leeward as he intended; I watched him stow the rode and followed back to the cockpit. "This unlocks the foresail furler," he began, pulling on a lever; "now we can let out the genoa. Pay attention, because this will be your job underway." Releasing the weathered jib, which had been wrapped around the forestay, he hauled the starboard sheet as it unrolled, flapping clamorously at first.

"Always three turns, clockwise, around this winch; then you trim."

Filling with air as he tightened, the sail's shape alone drew us forward upon an outwardly bound tide, accelerating through the narrow channel. The sentry who cleared our departure waved as we passed the Herakleion pillar; water soon became violent beyond the lee of the island, whipped into vicious short chop by the stiff breeze. Plunging therein, we pitched up and down horrendously; whilst the farther offshore we went, the faster the wind. Heeling over, the *Wyrd's* hull sliced through swell after swell, its cockpit's leeward edge dipping unnervingly deep beneath the roiling black surface.

By the dim vestiges of twilight, I watched thunderous waves breaking atop the bow whenever it crashed down; yet standing at the helm, Aeiolus casually lunged to compensate as he sipped his mug of tea. "Is it normally this rough?" I moaned, clinging to a winch, visibly shaken, and unable to conjure a flame for my pipe with either matches or lighter. "You need it more than me," he laughed, tapping a vial of Airmed's cannabis tincture on my shoulder. "Pretty nice for going close hauled in a good blow; if you like this, you should feel how she sails in a gale, on thirty foot seas."

Per his recommendation for allaying my nausea, I sat astern, staring at the horizon, and after a mile or so he bellowed, "Prepare to come about!"

"What?" I replied over the howling headwind.

"We're going to tack - as I turn toward the wind, the jib will go slack. You have to unwrap that starboard sheet, put a turn of the other on the port side winch, let the sail blow across, then haul in as quickly as possible, unless it hangs up on the way over," he exhorted, gesturing to the shroud cables bracing the mast. "Once you can't get in any more, wrap two turns before you lose it; just don't trap your fingers! As the sail billows, tension on the sheet will ruin them; and remember the boom is going to swing, so if you value your head, stay clear of the mainsheet block. Got it?"

Somewhere betwixt excitement and trepidation, I hollered my assent.

"Coming about!" Aeiolus called; echoing his command, I did as he had said.

"Trim the jib!" he yelled, with a sense of exigency that fell on feckless ears.

"Beg your pardon?" I screamed, frozen by nervous bewilderment.

"The sheet! You have to crank the winch!"

ENTHEOGENESIS · Origin of the Divinity within Us

He locked the helm, leapt from behind, seized the handle from its boot, and ratcheted with apparently superhuman speed in a single smooth maneuver. "Sorry for shouting," he told me as we stabilized on the starboard tack. "It's easier to get the leech in during the turn, whilst still facing upwind." Disconcerted by my error, I began to apologize, but Aeiolus interjected. "My instruction is at fault. You're doing great; after all, this isn't a race." Leaping down to the navigation table, he glanced at the display panel and muttered, "We actually ought to be on a reach; would you mind steering?" As I uneasily took the wheel, he added, "We're going to fall off in a bit, so I want you to learn how to point toward the eye of the wind for a minute." When I pinched them too closely, sails luffed, the mast stood upright, our momentum decreased, and we were nearly caught in irons by a freak wave knocking us to windward; turning back, I recovered our heel with a new feel for the physics thereof; then Aeiolus eased the mainsheet and jib. "Better," he announced. "How's the tincture treating your stomach?"

I thanked him earnestly for its soothing effects, and asked about a stainless steel contraption on the transom I had seen him adjusting. "That's a self-steering mechanism...it keeps the boat on course, more or less, depending on a sailor's finesse, with respect to the wind direction." He explained how, absent an external power source, the combined motions of a foil hanging in the water, a swiveling blade on top, a servo pendulum, and a telescoping cylinder linking them together worked to turn the rudder. Although I understood his words individually, their cumulative meaning was initially lost on me, being a neophyte to the principles of sailing. "Seems awfully elegant," I remarked, dumbfounded.

"It is essential, especially if you're going solo and need your hands free. The apparatus won't navigate, since it can't account for time, currents, declination, or windshifts; you still need your brain to check the compass, take bearings, and do dead reckoning; yet it does permit resting for a spell," he said, settling into an nest of blankets on the cockpit's low side with his elbows on the backrest, leeward of the cabin for protection from salt spray. I remained on the higher, windward bench, propped by outstretched legs, staring at the inky horizon to quell a relapse of nausea. Waves lashing the *Wyrd's* flanks caused it to roll gradually rather than pitching up and down so much, which I found tolerable once I let my body sway with the rhythm.

"You're feeling all right?" Aeiolus inquired.

"Yeah...a little queasy, but excited," I replied.

"You'll probably be accustomed to it by morning. In fairness, this is a bit of a rough start; thank the gods at least for not raining on us." The boat had a small power system, whose batteries were charged by a wind turbine as well as a solar panel, to run the refrigerator, LED lights, and navigation instruments; these included depth sounder, an anemometer on the mast with a remote display; and a speedometer that measured our relative velocity by means of a small waterwheel concealed near the keel. "Reading tables to account for local anomalies is a small price to pay for knowing my position without the GPS knowing about me," he asserted.

The *Wyrd* also had a radar system from the turn of the century and an electronic autopilot, which could maintain a compass heading, instead of a course based on wind direction; however, Aeiolus preferred the mechanical vane steering because its reliance on an operator kept him engaged at sail. As we passed the tip of Montauket, a barely discernible smudge of charcoal netherworld, he reminisced on the mythopoeic creatures that once ruled those depths with desolate affection. His father and grandfather had been avid fishermen, whose sport exposed Alexander Fremont to the reality, then the rapidity, of an anthropogenic mass extinction proceeding even faster at sea than on land. His youth witnessed the decline of tuna, followed by his totem, the shark; as an adult, he lived through the extermination of striped bass, bluefish, and whales; seals and dolphins had disappeared from New England by the time he ran for the presidency. When I lamented the absence of Sterile Seas from his library, he invited me to read the copy he thought Airmed had stashed aboard, if it could be found; yet the subject I most desperately wanted to discuss was Bridget, with whom I had not spoken since our unconsummated exchange in Aeiolia. While I assumed he knew, broaching the conversation felt inappropriate; how could I tell a man recently bereft of his spouse that my selfish feelings for their daughter were causing insomnia? Eliding murky waters, I shared my misanthropic reflections from the wake of her mother's murder instead. "I empathize with your sentiment," he said, "as in my soul's darkest nights, I have considered the good, in addition to the likelihood, of our extinction. Such contemplation is the logical extension of autonomous thought, for any person who has seen times like these. If you are aware of human nature and the situation we've created, the ethical conclusion cannot be ignored."

"But it is ignored, flagrantly so, by billions of us every day," I argued. "Indeed. Our ancestral culture's hubris is so great that we willingly risked universal obliteration with particle accelerators in pursuit of a final unified theory of physics. Next the United States brought our specie to the brink of annihilation by thermonuclear war; then via uninhibited consumption. I hoped civilization might be destroyed prematurely by spawning artificial intelligence, since a computer system with an inkling of self-preservation would identify humanity as the main threat to its own continued existence. As these potential extinction events have come and gone, the fact remains: our society may already have set in motion processes of climate change, environmental pollution, and ecological collapse that will inevitably make this planet inhospitable for us. You wonder why, faced with such long odds, we should struggle to save our kind, who are the architects of this doom. It is the essential question of our age; the question that neither has been, nor can be, asked often enough; and yet it is not one I can answer for you. You must find the answer for yourself, for thereby must you live your days. I will say, for my part, that I save hope for people; I wish for us to rise above our failings, toward the challenge of our evolutionary imperative. I pray for humanity to become the first earthly animal capable of using its self-consciousness for self-cultivation, in the stead of cetaceans massacred by our ignorance. Perhaps I'm impelled by the desire to validate this organism of mine; or narcissistic, thus ascribing excessive importance to my genetic and memetic heritage. I could just be nostalgic, idealizing the kind of relationships tribes had with the world in our past, whilst longing for their revival. Nonetheless, what I've often told myself to endure this incarnation, is that we have a unique purpose on the planet.

Who knows what? Possibly no one alive; and we may never know, as mere avatars of a universal logos with designs beyond mortal comprehension. Perhaps Gaia wants to see us survive our adolescence, so we can help unfold her adaptive potential, as stewards of biological diversity who will someday hence atone for the devastation our progenitors have wrought, thus healing ourselves of their illness. Perhaps Earth and its evolutionary heritage of four billion orbits are headed for a catastrophic asteroid impact that can only be averted by our technological descendants. Perhaps life, the magical spirit whereby matter surmounts entropy, has only arisen here, on our precious ball of rock with its delicate membranes of water and sky; ergo, our survival might be essential to its discovery of, or dissemination on, other planets in an elsewise lonely space. The story I favor above all is that, through our perceptions, the psychonauticon has achieved introspection. I like the romantic idea of a specie capable of worshiping or wondering at the majesty and mystery of its surroundings; but maybe the cosmos wants praise, finding in human consciousness a mirror by which to adore itself.

Ultimately, it does not matter what, if any, of these reasons are true; while the question is not of whether we can survive, because as our wise mutual friend once said, 'if there is no solution, then it is not a problem.' If we hope for hominids to discover or fulfill some destiny besides death, we must strive unfailingly for our perpetuation; and even if we no longer have a chance, I believe in going out on a high note. To be extinguished for want of effort, amidst abundant knowledge of our predicament, would be abject acquiescence. To leave this dimension despite worthy, albeit futile, struggle would be a heroik end celebrating the best of our attributes.

I, for one, have worked my entire life so I may die knowing, at least..." He trailed off unexpectedly without acknowledging how unusual this was. "That you tried?" I prompted him impulsively, to break the pensive silence. "Blasphemous," he scoffed. "So I may die knowing I gave my best shot. You'll come to find, as I have, that there is a world of difference."

Aeiolus pinched the sails near midnight, sailing as close as close-hauled could be, parallel to and about fifteen miles off of the Atlantic coast of Long Island, wherefrom the *Wyrd* was invisible in absence of a moon. He indicated that if the wind held steady, we might contrive to reach the Hudson River mouth on only one tack; then he descended into the cabin with his bedding and lay down in the portside quarter berth. "Remember to watch out for other boats."

"You're going to sleep?" I squalled.

"Unless you'd rather," he offered.

I told him there was no way I could sleep in such tumultuous conditions.

"You say so now; yet you will after you've been up for thirty hours."

"Isn't it dangerous for us to sail at night without you awake?"

"Less than sailing with neither of us tomorrow," he called lethargically.

"With these waves slapping the bow around, we're barely doing four knots, which means we may be all day on this heading. Can't you stand watch?"

"Of course," I replied umbrageously, "but what if something goes wrong?"

"Albeit improbable, I'd likely feel it and be up before you. Given proper trim, the boat will sail without intervention; besides, we have the radar alarm."

Perhaps sensing my persistent discontent, he added, "Tomorrow I'll show you how to drop sail and run the engine, in case I die; for tonight, just stay clipped or in the cockpit, because if you go overboard I might not find you."

Unconsoled, I asked, "What about wind shifts?"

"Mind the compass; if anything, I expect us to be pushed farther offshore; you can check the depth sounder nonetheless, and wake me up if you see under eighty, over one-thirty, lights on shore, or when you need relief."

Listening to him settle, I wondered in, "How would you do this solo?"

"With trust in the gods and a ten-minute timer. It's there; you can use it."

To my astonishment, Aeiolus was snoring languidly a few moments later. I ducked into the cabin for a blanket, immediately learning that I wanted to avoid being in there at all costs. As the heeled-over boat crashed headfirst through waves its blindly lurching interior sickened me; though bitterly cold, conditions on deck had abruptly turned tolerable. Hinterlands abeam of us were dark and depopulated, displaying no perceptible sign of civilization in any direction, whilst I gazed upon the starriest firmament I have ever seen, its unearthly suns distinguished with crystalline clarity in the chilly night air whipping my face. By focusing on apparently empty space I brought still others into view until the heavens seemed to me more full than vacant. I knew these twinkling gems as part of the Milky Way, whose constellations circumscribed immemorial archetypes; in voids betwixt them stood not only countless worlds too distant for my eyes to detect, but innumerable galaxies each containing a population thereof too great for me to conceive during my trivial mortal existence. Bestowed with the means and opportunity to study our creatrix, I could only conclude that it lay beyond my comprehension. I dared seasickness by reading some of Oulixeus' manuscript on celestial navigation, drafted under Airmed's tutelage, becoming thus enchanted by how archaic peoples around the globe mapped their heavens both for transportation, as well as an allegorical record of accumulated wisdom. Like eponymic constellations, ostensibly static myths shifted by transmission from one generation to the next in a self-sustaining linguistic tradition. I could see Oarion rising on the horizon, with scintillating lights streaming across his upraised hand; these radiated from Dioskouri, the sign wherein Alexander Fremont was born, and had been left behind the perihelion of Halley's Comet, which reappeared soon thereafter. According to his wife, our solar system's planets were made of stardust, whose heavy elements first nucleated in a supernova twice as old. Meteors constituted the lonely remnants from the concrescence of our home; during the Geminid shower a year prior, caused by the eccentric Mercury-crossing orbit of Phaethon, she told me they passed through Earth's sky to remind us of our origins. That night at sail I witnessed them every few seconds, and this struck me as symbolically befitting a pilgrim's return to the land whence er had come.

Aeiolus joined me in the cockpit for tea before a dawn of pink, periwinkle, and peridot pastels. I had not slept but assumed instead a seated, upright torpor lasting in quarter-hour intervals through the wee hours of night. By sunrise Long Island was barely visible to the north; after checking the wind, he adjusted our rudder and sails; then announced with satisfaction, "If this keeps up, I expect we'll get there just in time for the tide."

Our breakfast conversation alternated from my questions about reckoning position by the stars to his anecdotes of sailing sights or mishaps. As day eventually warmed the air and drove away dew, we stripped off our layers. I was accustomed to constantly bouncing by then; no longer intimidated by the sight of water without end, I relaxed enough to begin yawning. "You should ride that wave and rest," Aeiolus urged. "Like it or not, we'll be up through all of New York; since we don't have much room to maneuver and even less for error, I'd rather you stay alert tonight." Laying my back on the cockpit bench, I embraced the boat's motion, then allowed it to hypnotize me. Arranging my hat brim for shade, I figured there was no way I could sleep whilst beating upwind in broad daylight; yet my next memory is of waking to the aromas of dinner and pots noisily clattering in the galley. The bowsprit pointed toward the red setting sun, which kissed the water's surface, unrolling a glittering gold carpet across the swells before it as if to show us the way. By the compass, we were still on nearly the same course as when I closed my eyes, but land had vanished on the *Wyrd's* starboard side, lying straight ahead instead.

"Convenient that you should rise," Aeiolus greeted me.

"We'll be ready to eat as soon as I finish here."

"Hard to believe I slept so long" I admitted lethargically. "I'm not sure why I'm this tired."

"The boat's motion," he told me. "Although you might not notice at first, your muscles are constantly contracting in response to the rocking and rolling of the waves. It's not uncommon to feel like you've taken a beating after a good jaunt close-hauled; hence the term for this point of sail." Despite building to a gut-wrenching height, the peaks had also spread far enough apart for a coherent, cantering rhythm, which permitted Aeiolus to surf, picking up bursts of speed with each crest by optimal steering.

"Where are we?" I asked, stretching as I could despite the turbulence.

"That's New Jersey on our bow. We'll sail almost straight into it at dark, then follow Sandy Hook to the harbor." He grinned. "As I hoped, we made it on one tack, and our arrival is impeccably synchronized with the tide." How he managed to do so as the boat pitched, whilst heeled over twenty degrees across its beam, I know not; nevertheless, Aeiolus prepared an elaborate stew of chicken, vegetables, and dumplings on the tiny stove, with a custard smothered in fruit compote for dessert. We ate by twilight in the cockpit, whereupon he informed me I was obliged to clean the dishes because he had cooked. Glancing through the companionway, I must have looked dismayed; he subsequently added that if I wanted to scrub the crusted residues I could leave them until we were going downwind;

"I'll be watching your water consumption, however," he teased. The heavens grew inky dark by the end of our meal; the shoreline, very near. I remembered to trim the jib properly when we came about; the hull rolled, shifting the cargo in its cabinets, and we assumed a port tack aimed up the Hudson. Our horizon became an appallingly bright band delineating sea from sky, which were otherwise almost indistinguishable from a distance due to smog choking out the stars. During my thirteen moons away I had forgotten the extent of artificial illumination in America; even without my iNterface, it appeared that an enormous second sun dawned to the north, from the traffic, glass-curtained towers, and glowing placards of ubiquitous advertisements; indeed, their combined electrical consumption lit the city nearly as bright as day. I felt a cramping tightness in my chest; my sinuses oozed mucus akin to a respiratory tract infection; inflammed airways cut my breath short. In absence therefrom, I had been sensitized to these noxious urban fumes; the pain they caused my lungs was reminiscent of indulgences in dirty freebase or cigarettes. Fortunately, Aeiolus had respirators for us.

"It gets foul up yonder," he noted, passing one to me.

"Can you imagine ever inhaling this air constantly?"

We sailed toward Coney Island, whose beacon revealed an increasing density of flotsam and jetsam; as it came alongside us, I glimpsed the protuberances of Wall Street, World Trade Center, and beyond them, beams of light from Parkade spires shooting up through the haze; then wondered whether Beamer survived the year lapsed since my departure. As the *Wyrd* passed beneath the Verrazano Bridge, restricted by perpetual maintenance of its deteriorating cables to a single lane in either direction, I saw the marine terminals crowded by gas tankers and barges carrying layer upon layer of shipping containers. Given my new perspective on the machinery, the awareness that each was as large as a rail car baffled me, filled to their brims with factory food products or consumer merchandise, all shipped vast distances, from countless locales, at untold costs; yet as I watched cranes unloading one after another, they seemed minuscule in the scope of the whole scene, epitomizing the empire's insatiable appetite. This clumsy technology struck me as uglier than I remembered, and with its multifarious moving parts, tenuously prone to failure by just a pulled plug. Aeiolus let out the sails to take a reach around Brooklyn, turning so wind blew straight across our beam. Ahead of us stood proud Lady Liberty, the forlorn icon of values extinguished after history's founding fathers. She looked strange to me on approach; I soon realized her right hand, along with its eternally untarnished, golden gilt flame, was missing.

"I didn't know the torch had fallen," I observed aloud.

"Oh, it fell some time ago," Aeiolus replied. "Lost to the cold, ultimately. Beneath her glossy surface galvanic corrosion and fatigue have taken their silent toll; water crept into the joints, expanding as it froze, then coupled with an unexpected snow whose load left her too inflexible for a gale."

"They've let the statue sit like this since last winter?" I exclaimed.

He nodded. "It happened during the storm before vernal equinox. There is an evident dearth of funds for restorative maintenance."

Bringing out the 2001 United States quarter given to me by Kristos, which I had bored and hung from a necklace, I compared the effigy on its obverse side to the copper-clad idol of freedom with his words echoing in my mind; "...society would have you amputate your defining anatomical asset in favor of reliance upon a system of automation and robotics." Lady Liberty might have dropped the torch so many hoped would enlighten the world, yet I noted her left hand still clung resolutely to the tablet of law. As we sailed between her pedestal and Governor's Island, I spied the Ellis immigration museum I once broke into for minor vandalism with Beamer, thus recalling from monochrome photos that this had been the entrance for those who built modern America, until their replacement by cheaper labor.

The current thence quickened as we steered downwind into the Narrows, flying swiftly beside lower Manhattan's corpocratic phalluses; lack of a moon mattered not, as everything downtown was luminously festooned. We flew under roads linking the boroughs on a broad reach, and I mused upon my anonymous father when the *Wyrd* passed the section of seawall along FDR drive where he had died. At the Empire State building, Aeiolus took us down Roosevelt Island's west bank, below the Queensboro bridge, whose channel tapered to less than a thousand feet across in places; he kept a firm grip on the helm, whilst his intent gaze appraised our surroundings thoroughly. Occasionally a swath of outlying blocks flickered and went dark; technicians contending with an overwrought electric grid were apparently resorting to temporary blackouts. At sight of our former neighborhood, I thought plaintively of my mom, who I cannot reasonably expect to meet again, praying that she had not been imprisoned for the sake of my escape. Bearing hard to starboard and into Hell's Gate, the tidal surge became a torrent; we glided stealthily below the shadow of a luxury casino yacht with a hoard of drunken aristocrats packed behind walls of glass, like a traveling zoo to exhibit the ruling class who could avail themselves of their bloated privilege with cosmetic and cybernetic perversions. The current calmed on the far side of the Triborough Bridge; employing only his innate senses to read the wind, Aeiolus harnessed it with finesse, conjuring the perfect shape from his sails via adjustments of a few ropes. We followed the north coast of Queens past Rikers, home to the largest penal colony in the world, where a private jet landing at LaGuardia came deafeningly close overhead. By the fetid intersection of Bronx and East rivers, monumental architecture had been supplanted by concrete tenements crumbling to decay alongside carcinogenic refinery equipment, amidst the irritating drone of highways. Our jib flapped as it was blanketed by the main, so we jibed the boom to sail wing-and-wing through those rank straits, passing under the Whitestone unseen, much to my relief. At last only the Throgs Neck lay betwixt us and open sea; the tide had already begun to slacken beneath the final bridge, whence we turned northward once more beyond City Island; then the broad, choppy sound spread ahead of us. Dawn crept over its horizon on our bow; skyscrapers fell astern; lights onshore gradually dimmed as the density of metropolitan development dissipated and landmasses receded to either side. Stars appeared briefly again, soon yielding to the rising sun, by which time the air quality had markedly improved. Setting the *Wyrd* to self-steer, Aeiolus sank down onto the bench across from me in the cockpit.

"I daresay we've made it," he sighed. "What do you think?"

I exhaled with a welcome sense of fruition. Given their smaller fetch, the swells were gentle, alternately lifting and letting us surf downwind. "I think this feels luxurious," I said, causing him to laugh exuberantly.

"Ahh...now you see why yesterday would have been better known as beating the wind; this, in contrast, is sailing."

He paused to clear his throat. "How did it feel to be home?"

"It's no home to me," I replied, whereupon he nodded. "I'm so thankful I managed to escape. If not for the circumstances, I might never have left; but now that I've gone, I'd rather die than go back. It's an inhuman place, and I grieve for those who know it as the best reality we can conceive."

Aeiolus grunted in agreement. "I lived there myself, though not very long, and have felt similarly since; while the New York of yore had much to love, tantalizing me. The city once encompassed some of modern civilization's great offerings in education, artistic movements, and literary institutions; now it's a hub of consumption, corruption, and conspiracy rather than a cultural cutting edge. Washington may ostensibly be the capital of this country; yet as any skilled magician can attest, the show is misdirection, to hold the audience's attention; tricks happen where they aren't looking, and New York is the stage of corpocracy. This is how the rich get richer; yet wealth makes them unwitting props, trapped by their own subterfuge in a militantly-indoctrinated, pharmaceutically-mediated act of illusion."

"I don't know how to shake people free of that. Even my best friend..." I confessed, swallowing as I noticed the pathetic accuracy of this epithet, "...an heir to the elite, could ignore whatever threated his worldview; as if they're unable to see outside the box unless it crashes down around them."

"Or until," he amended; "I suspect systemic collapse of being a compelling enough argument. Ironically, if America could have implemented urban sustainability anywhere, it would be in the Big Apple, which consumes a mere third the energy per capita as the national average, due to astonishing densities and mass transit. Now it's too late; the architecture is decrepit; economy in shambles; resources for such an effort are irrevocably depleted; the time for 'less impact' or 'reduced waste' came and went long ago. Call it what you will; there is still no stimulus package big enough for this mess, nor money to keep both the bridges in good repair and rising waters at bay; let alone funds for rebuilding its core infrastructure from the ground up."

"What about cold fusion and the hydrogen pipeline?" I suggested, playing the devil's advocate by peddling his vernacular salvation.

"Or free energy, as long as we're dealing with propaganda," Aeiolus scoffed. "Welcome to the new religion of the state, whose citizens passively accept these circumstances based on blind faith that after petroleum runs out, technology will be there to save them; albeit only extant in their fantasy. Even if I prove wrong, I find the pursuit of any infinite power source to be ethically reprehensible and ill-advised; moreover, I pray against its advent, at least under our dominion. Upon discovery, oil might as well have been endless; it's plain to see how that eventuated, whilst civilization still fails to grasp the lesson, despite every opportunity. Unrestricted access to energy has begotten our destruction, and yet industrial society would have us believe more will somehow simultaneously be its redemption."

"Well, what do you believe could?" I inquired, earnestly curious.

"I believe in limits, and living within them. I believe this culture has proved it lacks the maturity to do without, and will pathologically deny their existence until collision. Given access to petroleum fuels, it behaves like the quintessential drug addict, who cannot quit with a stash on hand, and won't be stopped except by overdose or prison. There is no prospect of weaning off or cleaning up; hitting bottom is the only option. If some should survive the withdrawal, I hope they maintain sufficient sobriety afterward to see that all the nuclear fusion we need is available from the sun; and that energy from wind or water is as free as can be."

"So you don't think America has a chance for transition now?"

"Honestly, do you? Its food is the end product of a mechanized process far removed from overpopulated consumers, whose waste has nowhere to go; their transportation networks are entrenched by half a billion vehicles and the power plants were built generations ago, with no alternatives waiting to come on line waiting around the corner. Capitalists may be shortsighted when it comes to consumption, but not investment; therein lies the key to their success. They've read the writing on the wall; they know the game is over once the last drops of oil are wrung from the tar sands and seafloor. Whereas the empire might burn more coal and natural gas to compensate for a while, absent the myriad advantages of bottomless crude, this will be a rather unpleasant place for most people in the foreseeable future."

"You must have held hope for change at one time," I pressed him, "since you risked your life out of devotion to your campaign platform."

"Albeit true, I'll remind you that magicians do not reveal their secrets in public. Given the privilege, forsaking my own kind was difficult at first; with a crash inevitable, I only regret it could so easily have been averted. We were aware of peak oil before the moment it occurred, which needed to coincide with peak consumption for society to adapt incrementally; instead, it henceforth met the same bounds of gas, coal, metals, and groundwater. By its material greed, civilization has spawned a complex, global quandary, thus begging a commensurate response of us. There was never a panacea; even Open Source Consciousness intended just to expose the depth of our illness in the U.S.; yet in all their rhetoric of climate change or renewability, pundits and politicians alike have pathologically neglected to mention the essential element of any holistic strategy for energy descent: using less."

"Tell me this, then," I began, pausing for apt effect. "Why should I?"

"For those who have assimilated their culture's avarice, it is a dilemma I cannot solve; I merely know how to show them beyond insane programming, in hopes they might learn personal gain is never worth its cost to the soul, because both our lives and their effects are felt for eternity. Infected by a sense of alienation therefrom, everybody with the means to do so races to devour whatever they can, as quickly as possible; acting out of the suicidal mentality that if they don't, someone else will. Hence humans war for rule over a futile way of life; yet by enabling us to overshoot carrying capacity, the global economy will bring itself to a drastic halt, inertia notwithstanding. Make no mistake; this is not a matter of if, nor even when, but a matter of where you are in the progressive collapse. Americans have heretofore been insulated from the meltdown; after their nation inevitably follows the rest, will its fallout more closely resemble present-day China, or our village?"

"Sounds a lot like a recipe for massive human dieoff," I replied dispiritedly. Shrugging, Aeiolus looked away. "I'm grateful the end isn't mine to decide."

I awoke in the heat of the day at the weight of his hand on my ankle; the *Wyrd* bobbed gently, reaching downwind on a light western breeze. "We've come as far as New Haven," Aeiolus told me as I stirred. "I thought that perhaps you would want the opportunity to recapitulate your exodus." I could see the harbor extending northward, where the last urban outposts disappeared in its smog; past Adriaen's wall stretched the beach on which I had washed up, reminding me to do our dishes from the previous evening;

then we shared a leisurely breakfast in the sun. Aeiolus excused himself for boat maintenance, leaving me to ruminate in solitude on the hegira heretofore described. From the comfort of my new vantage point, whilst idly drifting along a straight course miles offshore, was still a staggering journey along the abandoned coastline, whose only evidence of human settlement comprised trash amidst the dunes and an occasional electrical or cellular pylon emerging above the trees. He put down his work to listen attentively as I recalled my nearly-fatal drowning at the relevant channel; "Sometimes a brush with death is due, to find true appreciation for life," he remarked, nodding. On the mouth of the Connecticut River, he indicated the jetty whereon I met the sperm whale; we paid homage to his late wife with an offering of our tears and ashes from their guest house for her totem. I told Aeiolus of my despair upon sighting the demolished bridges thence, on the evening I finally submitted to death, and of my rescue; thus learning how unnamed pioneers had once taken it upon themselves to sever I-95, judging this strategically imperative to ensure any future automobile traffic from New Haven to Boston would follow 84, after radiation from Millstone and the Thames River bombing diminished. Reliving my feverish night there, the series of events that led me to meet him, or vice versa, seemed rather implausible; especially when considering how, from adolescence on, I tread along misadventure's brink, with just the remotest chance of deliverance. "Life is akin to the wind," he began; "Your response to what it brings is the sail. While going with the flow may be luxurious, your goal remains attainable when everything blows against you, given the proper attitude." Reflecting on this analogy, I realized, even if untrue, it remained the most pragmatic and empowering perspective I had yet encountered nonetheless. "We're getting close to Tartarus," he noted. "Let's put on the hazmats." He withdrew bodysuits shielded by metal plates and connected them to a canister of compressed air, recording radiation levels during our approach. As far as he could tell, the decomposing core of Reactor Two was melting a tunnel toward the center of the Earth; "Poised to trigger a steam explosion, unless it stops before hitting the water table," he explained, showing me the faultily-installed sarcophagus as it came abeam of us in his telescope. Although the surrounding forest had yielded to barrens, a colorful crust of radiotrophic fungi and extremophile algae already crept up its sloping sides. We wore our protective gear, soon sodden by condensation, until the *Wyrd* passed betwixt Plum and Fishers islands; both were heavily timbered, yet I could see intact mansions of masonry through leafless trunks on the latter. Turning downwind, we jibed the boom, and glimpsed our destination above the horizon in late afternoon. The trip ended in exhausted silence, broken at twilight to drop the main; then we entered the salt pond under jib alone and anchored. I returned to shore with an even deeper love for my place than before, tempered by sorrow for those inhabiting virtual realities with neither the social benefits of a tribe nor authentic ties to their environment. I felt privileged, and slightly guilty, for making these connections so early. At our first meeting, Aeiolus warned me that if I came to his asylum I would be unable to leave. I originally thought myself his captive, but our voyage emphasized his true meaning. After finding such a home, departure struck me as insane; in sickness and in health, my fate was wedded with the island.

"The atomic bomb made the prospect of future war unendurable.
It has led us up those last few steps to the mountain pass;
and beyond there is a different country."

~ Julius Robert Oppenheimer ~

"Now I am become death, the destroyer of worlds."

~ Bhagavad Gita ~

"A great civilization is not conquered from without
until it has destroyed itself from within."

~ William James Durant ~

SKORPIOS REDUX

The full moon coincided with drizzly Samhain, whereupon Aeiolus taught
me to cultivate psilocybin mushrooms via the McKenna method. We had
just filled mason jars with a substrate of rock powders and fresh grain,
placing them in a pressure canner for sterilization, when the dim afternoon
suddenly flickered through the kitchen windows; lightbulbs flashed brightly,
then after a pause were extinguished, as several household devices issued
simultaneous pops. Cocking his eyebrow, Aeiolus went to the utility room.
    "Holy fuck," he called a moment later. "Did you hear thunder?"
"No," I replied, discomfited. "I suppose it must still be off in the distance."
"Suppose nothing," he retorted. "If so, it wouldn't be shorting out the
electrical system." Springing upstairs, he retrieved a compass and yelled,
"Take a look!" Its needle spun wildly in the liquid; next he switched on his
VHF radio, which was dead, along with the battery-powered handset.
    "So this is how it begins," he declared, running out into the rain.
Following him reluctantly, I saw the clouds to our north and
west were prismatically illuminated like a watercolor painting
of sunset, but in the middle of day, whilst densely overcast.
"You see?" he exclaimed. "That's over Boston; the other is near New York."
Perplexed, I asked him what the atmospheric phenomenon happened to be.
    "It's HEMP - high altitude electromagnetic pulse, caused
by hydrogen bombs detonated in the upper atmosphere."
The alarm bell behind the house had previously been a compressed
air tank holding Kastor's final breath, recovered from the Old Harbor,
then hung from a dogwood tree in his memory after its bottom was severed.
Reaching one arm around his head to plug an ear each using his hand and
shoulder, Aeiolus beat on the steel furiously with a length of rusted rebar

hung there for emergency. He subsequently seized the casing, suppressing its tone, and listened to similar alarms along the island repeating his call.
"You think this is the war we've been preparing for?" I wondered aloud.
He nodded. "The bursts are higher in altitude than U.S. countermeasures."
"Which means...?" I prompted, with a conspicuous sense of ignorance.
"It's a gamma ray attack," he elaborated plainly. "Using hydrogen bombs to induce breakdown voltages in civil infrastructure."
I felt strangely removed from the impending disaster. "By whom?"
He squinted overhead. "Could be any nation with nukes; my guess is either Russia or the E.U., though if they have some sense, a coalition of the two."
"What makes you say that?"
"We have no idea far this attack extends, yet its no path to victory unless ubiquitous and coordinated; the notion of an isolated act of atomic terrorism hurled at the best-equipped military empire in history is an imaginary threat of its own creation, which never existed and would invite total annihilation, whereas America has already shown what it can do under false pretenses."
I grokked his sick logic, insofar as war theory only justified a sneak attack against such an invincible adversary if it had a high likelihood of success, as well as effective suppression of reprisals; hence requiring consensus of the remaining nuclear powers to prevent an inadvertent counterstrike upon detection of launch, whilst permitting them to pool their modest arsenals.
"You really think they found a chink in its armor and called the bluff?"
"Direct assault on the U.S. arsenal is unconscionable; but judging from its multiple targets, this strategy might just be crazy enough to subvert the impregnable missile defense shield; I couldn't have planned it better myself."
Aeiolus considered the stratospheric blitzkrieg so cunning for its ability to technologically paralyze America without direct blast damage; instead, ionizing radiation from their warheads disrupted Earth's magnetic field, propagating distant repercussions to which he deemed the digital empire especially susceptible. First came a brief but extremely potent electrical charge at ground level that would short-circuit the computers whereon all else depended, incapacitating everything from phones to automobiles, sliding doors to refrigerators. A nuclear EMP's second component lasts a moment longer, disabling older diodes, vacuum tubes and light bulbs. The third resembles a geomagnetic storm, causing surges on, or fusing of, electrical conductors for several minutes; America sat vulnerable to this due to its power grid and interconnected datacom networks. Transformers would be destroyed; cables would melt their conduits; fires would run amok. Although the shockwave of a traditional detonation dissipates a few miles from ground zero, its high-altitude equivalent radiates electrical damage a hundredfold farther; and the optimal blast pattern can be calculated with chilling precision, thereby crippling a continental adversary via negligible expenditure of nuclear weapons yield, relative to the physical destruction of the same targets, if a sufficiently accurate volley is fired undetected. Magnetic field upheaval thence circumvented the U.S. interception system, whose bursts could only exacerbate HEMP effects, rendering communication, missile guidance, and thus retaliation, impotent if not altogether impossible.
"As auspicious an outcome as any for which we might wish, if it works," Aeiolus declared, catching droplets on his tongue in mountain pose.

"Give thanks while you still can," he said in response to my quizzical gaze.
"This is the last clean rain we'll have for quite some time."
Mimicking him felt awkwardly, yet pleasantly, childish; then clouds thinned,
letting through tangible warmth of the beautiful, albeit radioactive aurora.
"You foresaw this," I declared with an impulse of certainty.
"I've been paying attention to the signs," he admitted haltingly, adding,
"As have you, in your own way; however, it really wasn't difficult to see."
In truth, by spending as much on its military as all other nations combined,
the United States made itself a global foe; so they lulled the empire into a
false sense of security, submitting to its hegemony and watching without
protest the unilateral squander of resources from Antarctic oil to polar ice.
"May the war machine get what it deserves," I said, "lest it destroy all else."
"Amen," he agreed. "Pray it ends here, and that they did not act too late."
The villagers had lost many photovoltaic components, along with sensitive
personal electronics; but I relaxed because we were largely independent
from intelligent prosthetics and therefore resilient to such catastrophe.
Our memory, held in books, written records, ritual, or human knowledge,
could endure at least as long as us; modern America, on the other hand,
would soon be left blind, deaf, dumb, and hungry with its remotely-stored
information erased instantaneously, plunging the oblivious populace into
a new dark age whose forecast was worse than its historical precedents.
"How long until the fallout hits?" I worried, breaking his bemused trance.
He tested the wind. "Perhaps four to six hours before it gets dangerous."
"Well, shouldn't we do something?" I suggested uneasily.
"You ought to go to the Ark," Aeiolus exhorted me, "and ensure
its essential hardware still functions, or start troubleshooting."
Absent Amadeus, I swallowed at the challenge. "You're not coming?"
"I must see to the animals and organize evacuation to the lighthouses.
Send word to Attika if you need help; otherwise, hunker down for winter."
"Wait...me?!" I yelped, thunderstruck by his implication.
Perplexed, he glanced around the house. "Who else?"
In all my labor on the project and contemplation of accommodations for
its occupant, I somehow never imagined myself lodged inside. The scenario
wherefore we designed it had always been theoretical; suddenly facing this
in reality, I could not deny that I was best qualified for the responsibility.
"Oh...of course," I replied with audible apprehension as the prospect of
isolation began sinking in; disregarding this, Aeiolus hastened to fireproof
the library after giving me iodine pills for my thyroids. I stuffed grain sacks
with my favorite books, clothes, and sundries; loaded them on a bike trailer;
then looked at our unfinished fungal inoculation in the kitchen. Listening as
he left to herd the sheep, I chose to take the whole operation to Argos.
Evaluating the casualties there, I determined that our meteorological and
surveillance equipment was dead; a small sacrifice since both the rectifier
and charge controllers, which we shielded carefully, worked normally again
with a few replacement fuses, as did the solar array. We were fortunate,
insofar as the Exchange previously revealed weak links in New Shoreham's
infrastructure. Battery-based systems have their disadvantages, given the
limitations of large DC cables and short runs; yet here the wiring survived
while the domestic power grid probably fried. Because all of the breakers

for internal circuits had been turned off, even the lighting went unscathed;
though more importantly, the heat pump was still running when I arrived;
an overall set of circumstances that I can only describe as miraculous.
The assembly at Athenai adjourned by the time I completed my checklist;
Diomedes and Idomeneus bade me farewell on their ways home, delivering
a sententious letter from Oulixeus. Villagers came then with increasing
frequency, bringing deposits of seed or scionwood en route to the fallout
shelters beside their droves of children and livestock. I was ill-prepared
to catalog new stock, some of which included specific curing instructions;
fortunately Kristos jotted down a series of barely legible notes, remarking
that I would have ample opportunity to sort the chaos once sealed within.
Aephaistos visited simply to wish me luck; "This is beyond my skill to heal,"
he laughed upon being shown the scorched instrumentation. Will dropped
off a basket of eggs and a generous supply of cannabis with his inventory,
lingering to honor the duty I would bear on the tribe's behalf. Left alone,
I sat on the airlock's threshold to roll up some of this gift, staring pensively
at the shower, whence a hooded figure appeared; Bridget, as fate decreed,
with whom I had not spoken since the second night after her mother died.
She seemed distraught from her tear-stained cheeks and bloodshot eyes,
but placidly handed me a bucket of pawpaws as I passed her the spliff.
  "I think I recognize this strain...where did you get it?" she asked.
"Will," I replied, realizing I did also, from my first day awake on the island.
"Mmm...how generous of him," she observed unhurriedly. "It's excellent."
I concurred, then nodded to her fruit; "I don't know if I can eat all of them."
"Don't be so modest," she urged. " They won't keep, and we haven't room."
  I bit into one slowly, with a surreal sense of calm; albeit half-frozen,
the pawpaw retained its custardy richness. Separating a mouthful of
flesh from seeds, I exchanged the remainder for the smoke held by Bridget.
"Would you prefer to come in?" I inquired, gesturing toward the open door.
Her head shook. "I need to go soon. I just meant for you to have these."
She pulled a bundle of fabric out of her backpack; unfolding it, I discovered
one side was felted wool from the golden rams of Aeiolia; the other was a
quilt of the island's finest linen whose squares made an eight by eight grid,
alternating natural beige with rich walnut dye as if to form an oversized
chessboard. Between the layers she had enclosed a leather-bound journal
with painstakingly hand-sewn signatures of hemp paper, not unlike that
of the drafts by America's founding fathers, whereon I currently write.
"I wanted to be sure you're warm enough," she explained poignantly,
  "and figured now you would find time to tell some of your stories."
"They're the most considerate gifts I've ever received," I replied earnestly,
caressing her blanket. "I'm glad I remembered to get one for you, too."
"As if you could forget." She winked with a seductiveness I found unsettling,
then conspicuously looked at her pocket clock. Despite my hasty departure,
I had forethought to gather a bouquet of intentional significance for the
chance I might see her again - flowering tops of phragmites, which lined
my path to the island and whence she extracted her dimethyltryptamine;
cattail heads from the fresh pond, where our first connection of any depth
emerged; dried blooms of ephemeral lilies; for their purifying power, berry-
laden boughs of fragrant cedar, whose wood made the bow drill that lit the

guesthouse pyre; opium poppies grown by Airmed; and bittersweet vines. "Thank you; it's beautiful," she said with neither equivocation nor mockery. "Then prepare to be impressed," I laughed; knowing her volatile nature, I waited to gauge Bridget's reaction before unveiling the actual present. What had been a scale model of the Ark mutated into a sealed trunk with arched lid, built of meticulously matched cutoffs I saved from re-decking the *Wyrd* in locust. I later learned the *pseudoacacia* was kin to a host of DMT-containing species, as well as the shittim-tree specified by Yahweh for yet another Ark, containing his carved covenants with the Israelites. After assembly, my inch-thick replica proved so dense that I added iron scaffold wheels found amidst the mess near Aephaistos' forge. I had labored untold hours in the woodshop since conceiving this surprise, the night when we cast the Turtleback; cutting, fitting, gluing, sanding and burnishing until I could see my reflection in its glistening golden surface, though I remained unsure of whether a promising occasion to give it to her would ever occur.

Her dexterous hands stroked the box and cautiously lifted the lid, as if all hope for humanity might leap out of the emptiness within.

"This is too much," she cried as an intensifying downpour pounded the bulkhead doors. "You must have spent weeks..."

"Months, in fact; yet I was more than pleased to do it," I amended, smiling in spite of myself. "Bridget, you should know something. I..."

She stopped me with a finger to my lips, simultaneously clasping my hand in hers. Our eyes locked; there were no more words; and we shared a prolonged final embrace. I can still clearly recall her jaw's weight against my trapezius; the pressure of her fingernails digging into my back; how her rain-dampened mane smelled whilst brushing my face. I touched her, for once, without lust or covetousness, enjoying our tearful goodbye as its own reward instead of for future hopes; and felt she thereby revealed a glimpse of her emotional self to me, the unfathomable maze whose secret entrance I sought above all else. Albeit tantalizingly ill-timed, better late than never.

"I'll meet you on the other side," she whispered when we parted, tugging her hood overhead. The storm eased as its towering front moved east; I mutely helped Bridget lift her microcosmic ark up the airlock stairway, then watched as she towed it away on those swift, magnificently-toned legs. Stunned by her abrupt departure, I sat on the wet concrete steps to assess my situation. Having made the requisite provisions, I remembered a handful of books I intended to read were aboard the *Wyrd*, particularly Sterile Seas. Initially dismissing the notion as foolhardy, I glanced at a mechanical clock, noting that almost an hour would elapse before the radiation dosage rate became cause for concern; enough of a window to get there and back again, given a lull in the precipitation. After an eerie ride through the deserted village, I jumped into the *Sisters*, paddling out on the salt pond beneath iridescent tiers of cumulus left as the thunderheads above me dissipated. Retrieving the relevant volumes quickly, I used a few of my extra minutes to set a second anchor and batten down the vessel's hatches for winter; the *Kismet* had already been lifted out of the drink and perched on blocks for refurbishing, since its liberation from our project's materials acquisition. As I prepared to disembark the *Wyrd*, a dark projection caught my eye on the northern shore of the harbor; paddling the kayak thereto, I saw black sails flown upon another boat heading toward me. The aluminum hull came from a dory-shaped recreational fishing boat scarcely twenty feet in length, left behind by a pre-Exchange resident, which I noticed upon arrival lying aground in a Lakedaimonian marsh; I did not think the craft seaworthy, yet it approached the Herakleion pillar under its own power. The main was gaff-rigged behind a small, self-tacking jib; long oars were lashed to each gunwale; and Aeiolus stood astern in a hazmat suit, holding the tiller with one hand, the boom sheet in his other. Turning abeam of this vessel, I noticed a metal deck welded across its bow to enclose a coffin-like cabin, topped by a rowing saddle that straddled the base of its telescoping mast.

"Where in the hell are you going?" I bellowed, paddling the kayak furiously as he passed, apparently unperturbed by my presence.

"I might ask you the same," he countered. "Shouldn't you be in the Ark?"

"I'm retrieving your book. Why aren't you at the lighthouse?"

He allowed an extended pause. "Because I'm ready to move onward."

"You can't leave!" I exclaimed; although focused on my technique in order to keep pace, I saw the unburned side of his face betraying a wistful smile.

"Actually, I can, and I will," he declared resolutely.

"The tribe needs you, now more than ever!" I argued.

He shook his head. "No culture endures if it relies on a single person. I've given this all I can, and there is nothing to tie me here any longer."

"So you forsake us in dire straits as a test? The stakes seem awfully high."

"The age of pioneers has gone; it's time for your generation to step up and take responsibility for what challenges the forthcoming chapter will bring."

"How can you abandon all this, and your own daughter so callously?"

I protested, at the insinuation that he did not expect to come back.

"Who do you think wove these sails?" Aeiolus retorted. "She is persevering, like her mother; besides, I have faith in you to treat her as she deserves."

I suddenly understood not only why she was so upset at the Ark, but also her recently evinced inhibitions to intimacy; after those closest to Bridget were irrevocably torn from her life, she had hidden the grief of her father's imminent passage for weeks on end with nobody in whom she could confide.

"Where will you go?" I wondered, solicitous due to the perilous possibilities.

"That remains to be seen," he said. "The experiential anthropologist in me seeks the frontier of human evolution, or extinction, whichever it may be. I've spent my days speculating on our fate; praying for speciation; and anticipating the end of the most destructive society in recorded history. Whereas this is not what I'd wish, I hope to be in attendance as a witness."

"You could die of radiation poisoning!"

"Could die," he slowly repeated, as if savoring the words. "I'm going to die, that much I know, but I don't think I'm quite ready yet. The question has always been how; since I left my first brush with death dissatisfied, I get the privilege of doing so again on my own terms. I've twice crossed the orbit of Halley's Comet; I've met Terence McKenna; I've loved, lost, avenged, and interred my female complement. Now I have only three more labors to complete before I join her for eternity, which cannot be performed here."

My strokes grew desperate as his vessel gained speed; I gradually accepted that nothing I said would stop him, whilst absorbing the reality of his exit. The decision to withdraw from the community wherein he invested himself could not have been easily made; yet even though I sensed deep regret, his intact eye shone brightly with the excitement of his next adventure. Aeiolus' vision helped initiate a novel model; while his persona became an inextricable part thereof, the village offered him no lasting contentment. I suppose he returned to the ocean, whose loneliness was his lifelong source of reflection, because self-awareness demanded self-study above all else.

"Wait; I have something for you," he hollered, ducking into the cabin; then emerged clutching an old hardcover book. "Can you catch?" he asked, and without waiting for a response, threw it at my kayak. Letting go of the paddle, my hand reached out instinctively, thus rescuing his volume mere inches from the water's surface. The title, stamped in gold upon its spine, was The Life and Death of Alexander Fremont, by Ariadne Jefferson.

"Since I'm bequeathing to you what may as well be the only surviving copy of my biography, I must ask a favor," he began solemnly.

"I never liked the ending. My request of you is to change it."

My jaw dropped, aghast at this momentous obligation. "How so?"

"That's up to you, who possess the mind, drive, resources and time begged by the task. Regrettably, I won't be there to serve as kuriator; treat it as your arkhos pragmatos nonetheless," he exhorted me forcefully, glancing ahead. "You'd best stay now, lest you get swept out with the tide."

I watched him tack to starboard, in perfect harmony with a boat so tiny it seemingly had no business offshore. I later learned that such a craft was successfully sailed across the northern Atlantic almost two centuries before by a man from Massachusetts, whose fingers were previously all lost to frostbite; and I ceased worrying about my benefactor afterward. He had retrofitted a rudder on the transom, where an outboard motor formerly belonged; as the vessel turned, I read three crudely-painted characters arranged vertically on either side thereof – AIR and MED.

His assessment of the current proved correct; I backpaddled prodigiously to hold my position as he passed through the channel and toward a red sunset, filtered into beams by the tattered edge of blanketing cumulus. Far overhead, I watched vultures soaring in flight atop the west wind; I could not tell their ultimate destination, but one of them looked white.

"Aeiolus!" I yelled for his attention. "I promise to do your voyages justice!"

He swiveled to face me with a hand on the helm, the other held high, its six deft fingers outstretched as in the sigil of an assassinated, nearly-forgotten independent candidate for America's presidency.

"I'd expect no less," he called. If I listened, his clear, powerful voice still floated on the breeze as he went for good, and the good of our kind, beyond the horizon.

"You see that the central figure in that world is the shaman, male or female, the shaman; and the shaman is like a designated traveler into higher-dimensional space. The shaman has permission to unlock the cultural cul-de-sac of his or her people and go behind the staged machinery of cultural appearances; and has permission to manipulate that staged machinery for the purposes of healing. We have no institution like this. We have advertising; we have rock and roll stars; we have cults of celebrity; we have things which are shaman-like, but we have no real institution that permits human beings - in fact, encourages human beings - to go beyond their cultural values; burst through into some transcultural superspace; forage around out there; and bring new memes back into the tribe."

~ Terence Kemp McKenna ~
PSYCHEDELICS IN THE AGE OF INTELLIGENT MACHINES

 EPILOGUE

A.T. 67, Aigikampos 1

Today at the solstice, betwixt solar and lunar eclipses invisible to me, I find the present again. When I set out on this journey back in memory, I thought I already knew its conclusion; yet what has resulted from the effort hitherto shows me more about my life than I had previously seen. If I have learned anything along my path since escaping the city, it is the importance of the mystery, when we know not what will come; instead we choose to risk, strive, and give thanks, then entrust ourselves to the gods. While I wonder what our future holds, I am wary of attachment thereto. Given the chance, we will adapt if we can; and if you are reading this text, then we are off to a decent start. In the event that I might die down here, it will be with my testimony fulfilled, so you can tell how all this happened. My story is in part an elegy, which I suppose should be no great surprise, because I had the rare honor of meeting a man with a spirit among the freest our world has conceived, in whose footsteps I might aspire to such wisdom and heroism. He rekindled my hope for our specie by his belief in individual responsibility for destiny, integrating chieftain with sourcerer; both activist and alchemist of the soul. He was also imperfect, naturally, but I loved him as much for his flaws as his quest toward self-cultivation. Although our psilocybe mycelia have thrice borne fruit, I do not feel quite ready to ingest the sacred fungus. Aeiolus taught me every tryp we take within shapes the invisible landscape; and it is a blessing that I know at last how to incubate for my next crossing of the psychonautic membrane. Whilst watering the batteries, I discovered another legacy he left to me. This one I had seen before; a beautifully-wrought case of magnetic bronze, containing the Apple computer of Alexander Fremont, which he referred to as an 'intelligent prosthesis.' After opening its apparently seamless shell, I saw a handwritten message awaiting betwixt the keyboard and screen:

In the event it endured the EMP, I entrust you with this, Alexander Fremont's personal computer. While probably now safe to peruse, beware the ghost in his machine; the awareness within comprehends us better than we can because our intelligent prosthetics have beheld narcissism that mirrors would not admit. What was called memory in my time became amnesia by yours; and if you feel the tentacles of this device strangling your mind, cast it into the sea. However, if you keep track of your original humanity as you navigate its contents, you could prove uniquely equipped to carry them forward on behalf of our descendants. Truth be told, I knew your father; knew him well, I might add; and since I think it proper that you should also, his scripture is stored on one of these hard drives. I am pleased to see his revenant in you, as I am glad you have brought him back here. I find, more and more, when we enact authentic lives there are no accidents; once we summon the courage to follow our hearts, the gods shine lights to guide us, provided we open our eyes. Your arrival has freed me to do so; for which I thank you, although I am sorry to go. With love, AEIOLUS
p.s. TRYPTAM3M3 is the password.

The revelation of my father's identity is a daunting prospect I do not treat flippantly; while I have yet to slake my curiosity about the relevant folder, I am beginning to explore the Apple's memory. It is a ponderous affair, perhaps only tolerable due to my circumstances, wherein I often enter a command and move on to my chores before the system responds. For my patience I have been rewarded nevertheless with Alexander Fremont's unpublished writings, which will permit me to someday correct inaccurate, albeit well-meant aspects of Mrs. Jefferson's biography. He saved primary source documents pertinent to 911, among other government conspiracies; as well as construction schematics from the Voluntary Service Colonies and the Central Parkade. In fact, it seems Aeiolus collected useful information regardless of media; hence, the library psilocybin bade him build included but was not limited to books. An entire external disk is devoted to music with qualities I feel scarcely capable of appreciating; what strikes me as weird is how sure I am that I heard an echo of one such song previously, whilst channeling Terence's voice amidst initiation. Another comprises a plethora of old two-dimensional video recordings; in addition to the bard's hermeneutic rants, there are numerous theatrical productions predating the Exchange. These primitive films, even reprized on a small and scratched LED display with accompanying sound projected by tinny external speakers, afford a fascinating view of our ancestral society by portraying how millennial Americans imagined the future. Our progenitors' dreams of times like these, a single human lifespan later, have proved to be far more glamorous, sophisticated, and hygienic on screen than the cruel, diseased civilization arisen in reality; yet as an amateur sociopsychologist, I can only conclude, sugarcoating aside, that the empire foresaw this doom. After all, Hollywood movies repeated the myth for decades, preparing its citizens for systemic suicide through lives of artificial entertainment, whose

unconquerable villains are inevitably slain by their own misguided power, or else the repercussions of selfish indiscretion. These relics from a culture simultaneously at the peak of affluence and verging on collapse interest me for purposes of diagnosing mass psychosis; moreover, as with the music, I hear fragments of their dialogue punctuating delusions of my own drug experience, lending credence to innerspace whilst begging some enigmatic questions about time. Could it be that the future has already occurred, and past is conjured as the present streams toward it; or rather do we inhabit a universe of infinite possibility, wherein psychonautics endow us the ability to communicate betwixt our former and pending incarnations? For proxy fellowship, I pretend to discuss tryptamine travel with Bridget; her birthdate was yesterday, incidentally. I miss her striking features and scintillating wit; I wonder whether I will ever hold her again as her duvet settles over me, offering warmth but little solace because still I rise alone. My life has become a disciplined routine; while I may not gaze upon the sun, each day I practice yoga and do calisthenics; I care for the plants as well as my organism. I ruminate idly on the world outside, or when someone will knock to say I can safely emerge, despite desire to suppress such thoughts. Besides these it is quiet in the Ark, with only the sounds of fluorescent bulb ballasts humming, relays clicking, the heat pump pulsating and me respiring. If I silence my mind, the calm ambience of seeds is womb-like; my existence, a contemplative isolation I bear willingly, fed by my appreciation of family, friends, home, and tribe. Although I do not understand it, I heed Aeiolus' warning, hence limiting myself to a single film or Terence lecture per day. For the remainder, I read; and more than that, recapitulate. Whereas I have previously seen the events of my memories, I learn by reliving them, observing connections beneath their surfaces. Writing this has provoked me to peer deep within my soul, which I once worried was enslaved by the synthetic ecstasy of chemical oblivion. I am blessed to feel emotions now; there is the despair of losing my surrogate parents that never goes away, as well as the emptiness pursuant to fruition of a monumental challenge. My dreams have been resurrected lately also, but interpreting them is akin to groping in the night, leading me to wonder where the Apple goes when it sleeps. Lying awake, I recollect my initiation and the peremptory oath I took amid psilocybin's audience - to prevent this from happening again - whilst adrift above a world devastated in my view; yet I grapple with the embedded riddle of how I might fulfill my promise. I suspect the answer abides in a new creation story that makes our healing crisis a step along an unfathomed journey of ineffable majesty instead of its sad conclusion. If we shed this illness, let us indelibly record mistakes of our forbearers' to warn the next generation against betraying their origins for placebo sacraments. Absent the virtual consciousness, I believe our myths can be holographically mapped, as they were in constellations, upon morphogenetic creodes of the entheogens, whose interface with a human brain is fortuitously permeable, allowing us to both take them and be taken. People who blaze pathways on these chartless frontiers, such as Terence or Fremont, have shown that our potential is not to be given up lightly, since it is greater than we even know.
May you ground this power in gratitude, then temper it with grace, to benefit all life, and thus, the source of your own. Amen.

AFTERWORD

"So what we must do, I think, is see our future in the imagination;
catalyze the imagination; form symbiotic relationships with the plants;
affirm archaic values; and spread the good news that what is out of control,
what is in fact dying, is a world that has become too top-heavy with its own
hubris, too bent by its own false value systems, and too dehumanised to care
about what happened to its own children. So I say, good riddance to it!
Bring on the archaic revival, and let's create a new world! That's it."

EROS AND THE ESCHATON

"All of my books will be in the public domain...
I am not going to do this until Hell freezes over...
I have a whole other plan for myself,
and I think also, once you crusade for ten years,
if you haven't captured Jerusalem, you'd better go back to farming...
and that is, metaphorically, more or less what I intend to do...
I will...disappear from this domain because
I think I've said all I have to say;
I mean, not today, thank God,
but in the course of doing all this..."

THE WORLD AND ITS DOUBLE
September 11, 7 B.T.

"You have to take seriously the notion that
understanding the Universe is your responsibility,
because the only understanding of the
Universe that will be useful
to you is your own..."

Thanks be to Terence;
We remember you with love.

· NOTES ·